Mathematics for Engineering

An Active-Learning Approach

D A Clarke

B Eng (Hons), PGCE

David Clarke worked as a Design Engineer developing components for nuclear reactors from testing to installation. He has been involved in a number of projects writing open learning materials. With a wide range of teaching experience behind him, he makes a significant contribution to BTEC courses in Engineering; in addition he is an examiner for GCSE Mathematics and continues to be active in mathematics assessment. He is now responsible for the co-ordination and delivery of all mathematics courses at North Oxfordshire College.

DP Publications Ltd
Aldine Place
142/144 Uxbridge Road
London W12 8AW
1994

Acknowledgements

Many thanks to Linda and the boys for their patience and understanding while this book was being written.

A CIP record for this book is available from the British Library

ISBN 1 85805 043 X
Copyright D A Clarke © 1994

Pageset by
    Kai, 21 Sycamore Rise,
    Cinderhill, Nottingham

Printed in Great Britain by
    Ashford Colour Press, Gosport, Hampshire

Aim

The main aim of this book is to provide an activity-based approach to the learning of mathematics for students on a BTEC National course (Diploma and Certificate) in Engineering. The book covers all the NII and NIII objectives.

Need

Changes in teaching methods and reduced resources in many institutions have resulted in a need for a new type of text book, one that can allow the lecturer to delegate a proportion of the teaching process to students themselves, enabling the lecturer to concentrate on managing students' self-learning. To achieve this, the text has to be *interesting, motivating* and *practical*.

This text is flexible enough, however, to be used in any one of the following ways:

a)   as a support text for fully taught courses;

b)   as a self-learning package with minimum (if any) lecture support;

c)   as a combination of a) and b) according to individual circumstances.

Structure of the book

There are three main sections in the book:

Section 1 – Discovering mathematics *(projects following through the design of a car)*

Section 2 – The information bank *(all the mathematical techniques for this level)*

Section 3 – Developing knowledge and skills *(further projects in other engineering fields)*

Section 1 is made up of eleven projects that require students to recognise the mathematical problems involved in the design of a motor car, and find the appropriate solutions to those problems. The projects can be tackled in any sequence, and lecturers wanting to plan their course can use the Project/skills analysis tables on pages vi-ix to identify exactly which techniques are covered in which project.

Each project begins with a case study relating to a particular element in the design of a car, followed by tasks that require students to solve the mathematical problems of that design element. In order to solve the problems, students can use the 'help lines' that follow each task to refer to that unit of Section 2 which deals with the relevant skill. All tasks in this Section have answers in Appendix 3 so that students can confirm their understanding before proceeding.

Section 2 gives clear explanations and examples of all the necessary mathematical techniques for an engineering course at this level. The section is organised into 'skill areas' (for example, Formulae), which are subdivided into specific 'skills' (in this case, Evaluating Formulae, Rearranging Formulae, Extended Formulae). The section progresses from *primary* skills required for the early part of a course, to *secondary* skills that are needed for more advanced applications.

Students read this section only as directed from the project tasks in Section 1. In other words, they acquire the necessary mathematical skills as a result of recognising the mathematical problem in context.

Section 3 develops students' knowledge and skills by providing a further 13 projects based on other fields of engineering (power generation, electricity distribution and manufacturing). These projects require a combination of skills and are ideal for use as assignments (answers are provided only in the Lecturers Supplement – see below for availability). They can be tackled in any order, but clearly those projects requiring primary skills only could be set in the earlier part of the course (see Project/skill tables pages vi-x for details).

Lecturers' Supplement

This contains outline answers to the projects in Section 3 and guidance regarding the relationship between tasks and projects and the BTEC NII and NIII requirements. It is available free of charge to lecturers using the book as a recommended course text.

How to use the book

Lecturers can plan their courses using the Project/skills analysis tables on pages vi-ix. Students can also use these table to help plan revision.

Students studying alone are advised to work through the Section 1 projects in sequence as the help lines will refer to basic mathematical requirements of *all* projects (eg use of calculators and computers). More advanced mathematical topics are introduced progressively.

D.A. Clarke

Table of contents

Section 1 Projects A to E Primary skills

Section 2 reference	Skills	Body shape A	Fuel system B	Brakes C	Cooling system D	Gearbox E
1.1	Accuracy	●	●	●		
1.2	Calculations	●	●	●		
1.3	Spreadsheets	●	●	●	●	
2.1	Evaluating Formulae	●	●	●	●	
2.2	Rearranging Formulae	●	●	●	●	●
2.3	Extended Formulae			●	●	
3	Radians			●		●
4.1	Data Display			●		
4.2	Interpretation of Results			●		
5.1	Trigonometrical Curves	●	●			●
5.2	Sin, Cos and Tan Formulae	●				●
5.3	Sine and Cosine Rule	●				●
6	Straight Line Graphs	●	●		●	●
7.1	Logarithms				●	●
7.2	Laws of Logarithms				●	●
8.1	Linear Equations	●	●			
8.2	Simultaneous Linear Equations		●		●	●
8.3	Quadratic Graphs	●	●	●	●	●
9.1	Volumes	●	●	●	●	
9.2	Estimating Volumes	●				
9.3	Surface Area				●	
10.1	Exponential Relationships				●	●
10.2	Gradients of Exponential Curves				●	●
11.1	Simultaneous Equations		●		●	●
11.2	Matrices				●	●
12.1	Quadratic Curves		●			
12.2	Quadratic Formula				●	●
13.1	Differentiation					●
13.2	Differentiating Functions				●	●
14.1	Reversing Differentiation					●
14.2	Area Under a Curve					●

Section 1 Projects F to K Secondary skills

Section 2 reference	Skills	Cylinder design F	Electrics G	Suspension H	Windows I	Transmission J	Performance Testing K
15.1	Imaginary Numbers		●				
15.2	Complex Calculations		●				
15.3	Polar Coordinates		●				
16	Series			●			
17.1	Binomial Theorem		●			●	
17.2	Error		●				
18.1	Vectors			●			●
18.2	Vector Calculations			●			●
18.3	Scalar Product			●			●
18.4	Vector Product					●	
18.5	Determinants					●	
19	Maximum and Minimum	●					●
20.1	Trigonometrical Waveforms	●	●				●
20.2	Addition of Sine Curves	●	●				
20.3	Combining Trig Equations	●					
21.1	Function of a Function	●	●			●	●
21.2	Product Rule	●					
21.3	Quotient Rule	●					●
22.1	Integration by Substitution	●	●	●		●	●
22.2	Partial Fractions						●
22.3	Integration by Parts			●			●
23	Numerical Methods		●				
24.1	Differential Equations					●	●
24.2	Separating Variables						●
25.1	Centroids			●	●	●	●
25.2	Volumes of Revolution					●	
26.1	Second Moments of Area			●		●	
26.2	Composite Areas			●			
26.3	Polar Second Moment of Area					●	

Cross reference table

Project		Task		Skills*
A. Body Shape	1.	Approach Area	1	1.1, 1.2, 1.3, 2.1, 8.1, 8.3
	2.	Profile	2.1	1.1, 1.2, 2.1, 2.2, 6
			2.2	8.3
			2.3	1.2, 5.2, 8.3
	3.	Capacity	3.1	1.1, 1.2, 2.1, 8.3, 9.1
			3.2	1.2, 5.1, 5.3, 9.1
			3.3	1.1, 1.2, 9.2
B. Fuel System	1.	Petrol	1.1	6, 8.1, 8.2, 11.1
			1.2	2.1, 2.2, 9.1
			1.3	2.2, 8.3, 9.1, 17.1
			1.4	2.1, 8.3
	2.	Electric Power	2.1	5.1
			2.2	2.2, 12.1
			2.3	2.2, 6
C. Brakes	1.	Drums	1.1	2.2, 3, 9.1
			1.2	6
			1.3	2.2, 3, 9.1
	2.	Discs	2.1	2.2, 3, 8.3, 9.1
			2.2	2.1, 2.2, 2.3, 3, 9.1
	3.	Drum/Disc Comparisons	3.1	4.1
			3.2	1.3, 4.2
D. Cooling System	1.	Radiator Design	1.1	9.3, 12.2
			1.2	8.2, 9.1, 11.1
			1.3	8.3, 9.3
	2.	Water Pump	2.1	2.2, 9.1
			2.2	6, 8.3
			2.3	2.1, 6, 8.3
			2.4	6, 8.3
			2.5	11.2
			2.6	8.3, 9.1, 11.2
	3.	Heat Transfer	3.1	1.2, 1.3, 2.1, 2.2, 2.3
			3.2	2.2, 6
			3.3	7.1, 7.2, 10.1
			3.4	10.2, 13.2
E. Gearbox	1.	Gear and Shaft Speeds	1.1	3, 8.2, 11.1
			1.2	11.2
			1.3	8.3, 14.1
			1.4	2.2, 8.3, 12.2, 14.1
			1.5	2.2, 6, 13.1
	2.	Bearings	2.1	7.1, 7.2, 10.1
			2.2	7.1, 7.2, 10.1
			2.3	7.2, 10.2, 13.2
	3.	Gearbox Housing	3.1	5.1, 5.2, 5.3
			3.2	5.2, 5.3, 9.1, 13.2

Project		Task		Skills*
F. Cylinder Design	1.	Piston Motion	1.1	20.1
			1.2	21.1
			1.3	21.1, 21.2
	2.	Cylinder Size	2.1	19, 21.1
			2.2	19, 21.2, 21.3
	3.	Power	3.1	20.1, 22.1
			3.2	20.1, 20.2, 20.3, 22.1
G. Electrics	1.	Battery	1.1	10.1, 10.2, 21.1
			1.2	10.1, 21.1, 22.1
	2.	Alternating Current	2.1	17.1, 17.2, 22.1, 23
			2.2	15.1, 15.2
			2.3	15.2, 15.3
			2.4	15.2, 15.3
			2.5	20.2, 22.1
H. Suspension	1.	Suspension	1.1	5.3, 18.1, 18.2
			1.2	18.3
			1.3	25.1, 26.1, 26.2
	2.	Damping	2.1	16
			2.2	22.1, 22.3
I. Windows	1.	Windows	1.1	25.1
			1.2	25.1
			1.3	25.1
			1.4	22.3 25.1
J. Transmission	1.	Propeller Shaft	1.1	26.3
			1.2	9.2, 17.1, 25.2
			1.3	25.1
	2.	Final Drive	2.1	18.4,
			2.2	18.4, 18.5
	3.	Circular Motion	3.1	21.1
			3.2	22.1, 26.1
			3.3	24.1, 24.2
K. Performance Testing	1.	Straight and Level	1.1	21.1, 22.1
			1.2	22.1, 24.1, 24.2
			1.3	21.3, 22.2, 22.3
	2.	Cornering	2.1	18.1
			2.2	18.1, 20.1
			2.3	25.1, 22.3
	3.	Hills and Inclines	3.1	18.1, 18.2
			3.2	18.3, 20.1
			3.3	18.1, 19, 21.1

* *References as per project/skills analysis page vi-vii*

Progress to Section 3 projects can be made according to the following table.

Section 3 project	Pre-requisite Section 1 projects
A. Hydroelectrics	A, B
B. Coal and oil	A, B
C. Nuclear power	E
D. Gas turbines	I
E. Generators	F, G
F. Cables	D, G, H
G. Transformers	D, E, G
H. Safety	C
I. Metal forming	D, E
J. Metal cutting	J
K. Strength of materials	H
L. Computer control	J
M. Robotics	H

Section 1 – Discovering Mathematics

Introduction

The main thrust of learning comes through this section of the book. It consists of 11 projects that follow through the design of a motor car. Each of the projects covers one or some of the car's components, giving students a realistic and interesting context in which to learn their mathematical skills.

Projects A–E involve only 'Primary Skills' (see Section 2 Introduction, page 89), while Projects F–K use 'Secondary Skills' and assume that primary skills have already been acquired by students.

The projects are designed as independent units, which can be tackled in any sequence. This gives great flexibility for lecturers to tailor the book to their own course plan. However, tasks within a project should be dealt with in sequence.

Each task is preceded by 'Pilot Questions', which can be used to promote class discussion and to involve the students in the formation of the tasks themselves. (Answers to pilot questions are given at the end of the project.)

The tasks, which provide the main basis for learning, are divided into steps. Students should use the detailed answers provided in Appendix 3 (page 288) to monitor their progress through each step of a task. This means that difficulty with one step does not prevent the whole task from being completed. Help references to Section 2 are very specific and encourage the students to maintain an independent approach.

After successfully completing a project or group of projects in Section 1, the skills and techniques acquired can be consolidated by working through the relevant Section 3 projects. See table on page x.

Contents – Section 1

Introduction

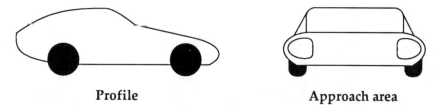

Profile   Approach area

The body shape of a motor car is an important factor in its design as it affects *performance*, *capacity* and not least its *appearance*. The project focuses on;

Task 1 *Approach* Shows how suitable dimensions can be found to limit the approach area.	Skills Used:	Accuracy Calculations Spreadsheets Evaluating Formulae Linear equations Quadratic Graphs
Task 2 *Profile* Examines the effects of changing the leading angle.	Skills Used:	Accuracy Calculations Spreadsheets Evaluating Formulae Rearranging Formulae Sin, Cos and Tan Formulae Straight line graphs Quadratic Graphs
Task 3 *Capacity* Estimates the capacity of common and irregular shapes.	Skills Used:	Accuracy Calculations Spreadsheets Evaluating Formulae Trigonometrical Curves Sine and Cosine Rule Quadratic Graphs Volumes Estimating Volumes

Tasks follow on from one another and should be attempted in *sequence*. Each task is introduced with a brief explanation of how components work. Specific details are given about the application; these are required throughout the task. For answers to tasks in this section, see Appendix C, page 288.

'Pilot questions' lead students into the task by stimulating thoughts about different aspects of the problem. Appropriate mathematics can then follow. Suggested answers to these pilot questions are given at the end of this project (page 9).

Task 1 *Approach area*

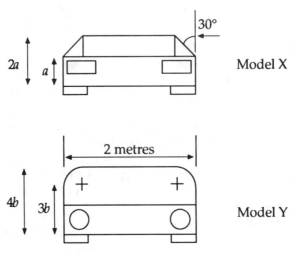

☐Pilot question 1

What would you expect to be the benefits of limiting the area of approach of a vehicle?

☐Task 1.1

Note: for answers to tasks see page 288

Find suitable dimensions that will satisfy a suggested area limitation of 2.5 square metres.

STEP 1   Write down a formula for each of the given areas (wheels may be ignored)

$$\text{Area of model X} = \ldots\ldots\ldots$$

$$\text{Area of model Y} = \ldots\ldots\ldots$$

STEP 2   Using a realistic range of values for *a* and *b* construct tables of corresponding areas. (Use a programmable calculator or computer spreadsheet if possible).

a									
area									

b									
area									

STEP 3   Plot these points on appropriate graphs. (A graphical calculator or computer graphics program is recommended).

STEP 4   What values of *a* and *b* are required to give an area in each case of 2.5 square metres.

Information Bank Section 2   Unit 1.1 Accuracy *page 91*
Unit 1.2 Calculations *page 93*
Unit 1.3 Spreadsheets *page 95*
Unit 2.1 Evaluating formulae *page 96*
Unit 8.1 Linear equations *page 132*
Unit 8.3 Quadratic graphs *page 134*

☐ Extension task

Find the front view of a production model from car leaflets or magazines.

Measure any unknown angles and lengths and use the scale to estimate actual values.

Calculate an approximation to the approach area.

Task 2 *Profile*

The height of a vehicle and the angle that the front makes with the air stream are important factors in its design. This task uses the results from wind tunnel experiments, together with flow distance calculations, to suggest suitable dimensions.

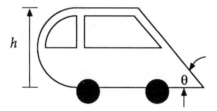

☐ Pilot question 2

How do you think the results of wind tunnel tests using small models relate to a full size vehicle performance?

☐ Task 2.1

Wind tunnel tests were carried out on wedge shapes as shown to establish a relationship between the height and the retaining force required to hold the model stationary.

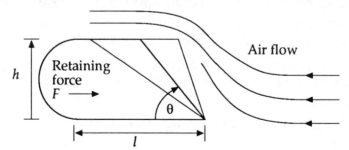

The height of models was varied whilst all other factors remained constant and the force measurements were:

Height h (cm)	5	6	7	8	9	10	11	12
Force F(N)	1.3	2.6	4.0	5.3	6.8	7.9	9.5	10.5

From these results develop an approximate relationship between the retaining force F and the model height h.

Using this relationship, calculate the retaining force required for a life size model of $h = 120$ cm.

If the greatest retaining force that can be applied is 45N, what is the tallest model that can be tested?

STEP 1   Plot a graph of force F against a height h and draw a line through the points (do not join the points together, these are experimental values)

STEP 2   Form an equation to represent the line.

STEP 3   Use the equation to give F when $h = 120$ cm, and to calculate h when $F = 45N$

Information Bank Section 2   Unit 1.1 Accuracy *page 91*
Unit 1.2 Calculations *page 93*
Unit 2.1 Evaluating formulae *page 96*
Unit 2.2 Rearranging formulae *page 97*
Unit 6.0 Straight line graphs *page 125*

☐Task 2.2

In a similar way to the tests of task 2.1, wind tunnel results can be used to give a relationship between the retaining force F and the angle θ. These results are:

Angle $\theta°$	30	40	50	60	70	80	90
Force $F(N)$	3.2	4.3	5.4	6.6	7.8	9.0	10.4

What is the smallest angle that can be used if the length 1 (shown in the diagram) is 15 cm and the height of the model is 8 cm.

What angle θ requires the maximum retaining force?

Estimate the angle that requires a retaining force of 6 N.

STEP 1   Use trigonometry to calculate the smallest angle possible.

STEP 2   considering the flow of air, what angle is likely to give a maximum value for F, and what will happen beyond this angle?

STEP 3   Plot a graph of the test results showing the retaining force F required for different angles θ. Draw a curve through the points.

STEP 4   What type of equation does the curve represent

STEP 5   Estimate from the graph the angle when $F = 6$ N.

Information Bank Section 2   Unit 8.3 Quadratic graphs *page 134*

□Task 2.3

The distance that air has to flow around the body shape affects the retaining force due to skin friction. It also influences pressure changes above and below the vehicle causing lift (as with an aircraft wing). Consider the distance of the flow of air over the top surface only (slope plus horizontal length). Calculate these distances for the range of angles used in the tests. What angle gives a distance of 20 cm?

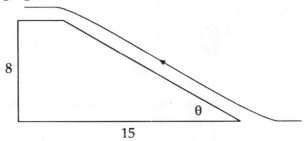

STEP 1   What is the minimum possible angle that can be used here? Calculate the corresponding flow distance.

STEP 2   Calculate flow distances for each angle and complete the table.

Angle θ°	30	40	50	60	70	80	90
Flow distance (cm)							

STEP 3   Plot a graph of flow distance against angle θ for this range.

STEP 4   Estimate the angle that gives a flow distance of 20 cm.

Information Bank Section 2   Unit 1.2 Calculations *page 93*
                                         Unit 5.2 Sin, Cos and Tan formulae *page 120*
                                         Unit 8.3 Quadratic graphs *page 134*

□Extension task

Obtain scale drawings or pictures showing the profile of a sports car and a car with poor streamlining. Assume that any curves are a series of straight lines and estimate the flow distance for each.

Compare these distances and comment on the results. Are they as you would expect?

Task 3 *Capacity*

Design calculations for capacity have to be carried out for the body shell of a vehicle. The precise volume is not always very meaningful because some space may be awkward to use in practice. However, it should give us an idea of the sort of shape to aim at in the design if other things are equal. Initially, simplified common shapes are considered. For irregular shapes where volumes are difficult to define, numerical methods need to be employed to obtain estimates.

□Pilot question 3

What practical methods can you suggest that could be used to determine the volume of a car (assuming it was available as an empty shell).

□Task 3.1

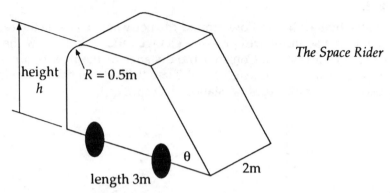

The Space Rider

Calculate the volume of this simplified vehicle shape using the measurements given, a height of 1.2 metres and a leading angle of 60°.

If the angle θ is 45° determine the height that will produce a volume of 5.5m³

STEP 1   Calculate the side area using $h = 1.2$ and $θ = 60°$ and multiply this by the vehicle width

STEP 2   Write down a formula for the volume V in terms of h if $θ = 45°$.

STEP 3   Draw a graph of this relationship.

STEP 4   Using the graph, read off the height that gives a volume of 5.5m³.

Information Bank Section 2   Unit 1.1 Accuracy *page 91*
Unit 2.1 Evaluating formulae *page 96*
Unit 8.3 Quadratic graphs *page 134*
Unit 9.1 Estimating volumes *page 140*

□Task 3.2

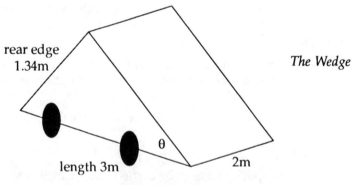

The Wedge

Calculate the available space in the wedge if the angle θ is 26°.

What angle is required to give a capacity of 4 m³

STEP 1   Use appropriate trigonometry to calculate the side area when $θ = 26°$

STEP 2   Complete the table of volumes for each angle θ.

Angle θ	10	12	14	16	18	20	22	24
Volume V								

STEP 3   Construct a graph to show the relationship between volume V and the angle θ.

STEP 4   Use this graph to estimate the angle that gives a capacity of 3 m³

Information Bank Section 2   Unit 1.2 Calculations *page 93*
Unit 5.1 Trigonometrical curves *page 116*
Unit 5.3 Sine and cosine rule *page 121*
Unit 9.1 Volumes *page 140*

☐Task 3.3

The areas of cross section are found at eight regular intervals through the length of a car.

Use these areas to estimate the volume if the length is 2.65 metres.

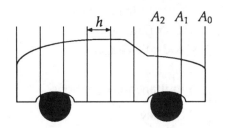
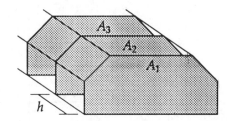

The areas are presented in a table:

Position	0	1	2	3	4	5	6	7	8
Area (m²)	0.86	1.12	1.27	1.41	1.84	1.75	1.63	1.34	0.91

STEP 1   Use 'Simpsons Rule' to give an estimate of the volume of the car.

STEP 2   How could the accuracy of this result be improved.

Information Bank Section 2   Unit 1.1 Accuracy *page 91*
Unit 1.2 Calculations *page 93*
Unit 9.2 Estimating volumes *page 144*

☐Extension task

Produce a small car shape from modelling clay (or similar).

Make measurements along the length at regular intervals. Calculate the approximate area at each position(slice through the clay). List these in a table. Estimate the capacity of the vehicle using either 'Simpsons Rule' or the Trapezium Rule.

Suggested answers to pilot questions
1. Save petrol, better performance and faster.
2. Fluids, such as air, are effectively thicker with a model producing less critical results.
3. The shape could be filled with fluid and then emptied into a measuring container.

Introduction

The supply of fuel to petrol engines is analysed in detail and a comparison is made with an electrically powered alternative. The project focuses on;

Task 1 *Petrol*	Skills Used:	Accuracy
		Calculations
		Spreadsheets
		Evaluating Formulae
		Rearranging Formulae
		Straight Line Graphs
		Linear Equations
		Quadratic Graphs
		Volumes
		Simultaneous Equations
Task 2 *Electric Power*	Skills Used:	Accuracy
		Calculations
		Spreadsheets
		Rearranging Formulae
		Trigonometrical Curves
		Straight Line Graphs
		Quadratic Curves

Tasks follow on from one another and should be attempted in sequence. Each task is introduced with a brief explanation of how components work. Specific details are given about the application, these are required throughout the task.

'Pilot questions' lead students into the task by stimulating thoughts about different aspects of the problem. Appropriate mathematics can then follow. Suggested answers to these are given at the end of this project (page 18).

Task 1 *Petrol*

Petrol engines are supplied with fuel from the petrol tank via a carburettor. The carburettor mixes petrol with air to enhance combustion when it enters the cylinders.

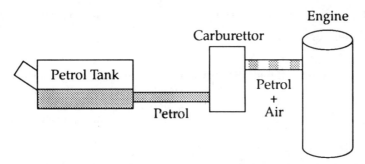

It is required to design a petrol fuel system that provides efficient operation and meets the practical requirements of the motorist.

☐ Pilot question 1

Suggest possible reasons why petrol is the most common form of fuel for cars. What are the advantages and disadvantages of the petrol engine over the other types?

☐ Task 1.1

To design a petrol tank we must think about the requirements. The type of car and driving conditions will have an effect on the volume that is necessary. This volume will of course determine how far a vehicle can travel before refuelling.

Table showing petrol consumption (mpg) under different driving conditions.

	Urban driving	Steady 56 mph
Small saloon	46	60
Family Saloon	32	53
Van	27	46
Sports	14	33

In order to establish what would be a suitable size it is necessary to consider practical situations. Here, we need to examine how much of each type of driving is likely to be experienced by motorists. use the road test results and determine mileage that can be achieved under different conditions. Verify whether the suggested tank sizes are suitable.

Road tests reveal

A family saloon car travels for 400 miles. The journey can be considered to be made up of town driving and open roads where a steady speed is achieved. If an 11 gallon full tank of petrol is used, calculate the distance travelled on each type of road.

A sports car travels 510 miles. Again the journey is made up of town driving and open roads. A fuel tank of petrol is used the capacity of which is 18 gallons. Calculate the distances travelled on each type of road.

STEP 1   For the saloon car, write down two simultaneous equations in terms of the petrol used in town driving and petrol used at steady 56 mph driving.

STEP 2   Solve these equations and give the number of gallons used for each type.

STEP 3   Calculate how many miles was completed in and out of town.

STEP 4   Draw a graph of distances for urban driving against open roads for the tank volume of 11 gallons.

STEP 5   Follow a similar procedure for the sports car and draw another graph.

STEP 6   Comment on the results.

Information Bank Section 2   Unit 6.0 Straight line graphs *page 125*
Unit 8.1 Linear equations *page 132*
Unit 8.2 Simultaneous linear equations *page 133*
Unit 11.1 Simultaneous equations *page 151*

□Task 1.2

The volume of the petrol tank can be achieved in various ways, but there are limitations due to the shape of the space available under the vehicle. Here, a maximum depth is used of 15 cm and other dimensions are examined.

Investigate these shapes for their suitability for a tank with capacity 11 gallons.

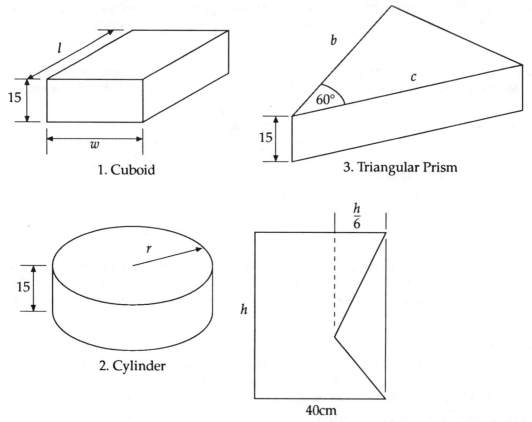

1. Cuboid

3. Triangular Prism

2. Cylinder

4. Maximum Area (fitted around structure
of car, with depth 15cm)

STEP 1   Write down formulae for the volume of each shape in terms of the dimensions.

STEP 2   Let each of these formulae be equal to 11 gallons (convert to cm³).

STEP 3   Rearrange equations appropriately.

STEP 4   Draw a graph for each shape (where necessary) showing the relationships between dimensions.

STEP 5   Eliminate any unreasonable sections of the graph based on the practical
situation

Information Bank Section 2   Unit 2.1 Evaluating formulae *page 96*
Unit 2.2 Rearranging formulae *page 97*
Unit 9.2 Estimating volumes *page 144*

☐Task 1.3

The supply of fuel to the engine is controlled by the carburettor. Petrol is held in a float
chamber that regulates the flow (using a similar principle to the ball'cock in a toilet
cistern). Air drawn into the cylinder sucks petrol into the airstream producing a fuel/air
mixture which is delivered to the engine.

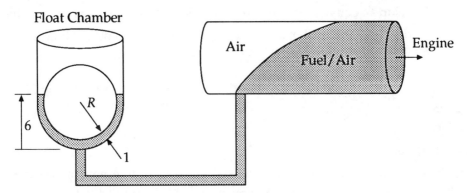

A spherical float of radius R is partly above the surface and the fuel level is maintained so
that the depth is 6 cm. The float chamber dome has a radius which is 1cm greater than the
float. What would be a suitable radius for the float chamber so that 150 cm³ of petrol
could be held.

STEP 1   Write down an equation for the volume of petrol in the float chamber.

STEP 2   Produce a graph for volume against a practical range of radii.

STEP 3   Read off the radius that corresponds to a volume of 150 cm³.

Information Bank Section 2   Unit 2.2 Rearranging formulae *page 97*
Unit 8.3 Quadratic graphs *page 134*
Unit 9.1 Volumes *page 140*
Unit 17.1 Binomial theorem *page 182*

☐Task 1.4

Regulation of the fuel, naturally, controls the power of the engine. The energy available
from 1kg of fuel is obtained from a table of calorific values (heat of combustion, joules/kg)
for fuels (reference section).

The power produced will therefore depend on the flow rate F of the fuel (kg/second). In
practise some energy is always lost to the environment (heat, noise etc).

Power (joules/second) = supply rate (kg/second) × calorific value (joules/kg)

In a test, fuel is supplied to two similar engines at different rates following these relationships;

Engine 1: $F = 30t$ (where t is time)

Engine 2: $F = 5t^2$

At what times are the engines delivering the same power if petrol is used. How is this affected if the second engine is fuelled with alcohol.

STEP 1   Form equations for the power of each engine using the calorific value of petrol.

STEP 2   Draw a graph with curves to represent the power of each engine related to time t.

STEP 3   Read off times when the engines produce the same power.

STEP 4   Develop an equation for engine 2 with alcohol (reference section) as the fuel.

STEP 5   Add a curve for alcohol power to the graph and read off the time at the intersection with engine 1 power curve.

Information Bank Section 2   Unit 2.1 Evaluating formulae *page 96*
Unit 8.3 Quadratic graphs *page 134*

☐ Extension task

Investigate alternative fuels that could be used to drive an internal combustion engine. Calculate flow rates that would be required to deliver power at the constant rate of 50 kwatts in each case. Comment on the practical implication of using alternative energy sources.

Task 2 *Electric power*

An electric motor can be used to drive a vehicle as an alternative to a petrol engine. The design has to ensure that both the battery and the motor are fit for the job.

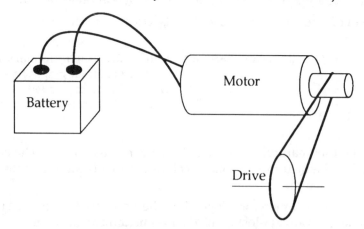

☐ Pilot question 2

What would you say are the advantages and disadvantages of electric power.

☐Task 2.1 *Motor design*

An electric motor consists of coils wound on an armature rotating between the poles of a magnet (in practice a number of magnets and far more coils would be used). Forces acting on each conductor are dependent on its position within the magnetic field.

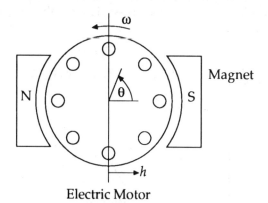

Electric Motor

If the radius of each coil is 5 cm, investigate the change in the position of a conductor as it rotates in the magnetic field.

The turning effect T is thought to be directly related to the distance of the conductor from the centre line of any formula;

$$T = 260h \text{ (where } h \text{ is in metres and } T \text{ is Newton metres).}$$

Negative distances (to the left of centre) also produce a positive turning effect since brushes reverse the direction of current in the coils.

1. At what position is the maximum turning effect achieved and when is it zero?
2. Determine all the angles that give a turning effect of 8Nm.
3. Calculate the total turning effect of eight conductors (4 coil windings) in the positions shown above.
4. How many coil windings are required to produce an overall effect of at least 200Nm?

STEP 1   Draw a graph of $h = 5 \cos \theta$ from 0 to 360°

STEP 2   Convert the radius into metres and draw a graph for the turning effect.

STEP 3   Observe the angles that give maximum values (consider only the magnitudes) and zero.

STEP 4   Read all the angles from the graph that give 8Nm (positive and negative).

STEP 5   Determine the turning effect of each of the eight conductors and calculate the sum.

STEP 6   Produce a table giving the turning effect for numbers of coils n until 200Nm is exceeded.

Information Bank Section 2   Unit 5.1 Trigonometrical curves *page 116*

☐Task 2.2

The battery has to provide sufficient power to accelerate the vehicle to road speeds at an acceptable rate. This is of course dependent on the voltage.

In a series of tests the power output of 5 batteries was recorded after using them to supply a load. The current flowing in each case was noted. The results are presented in a graph;

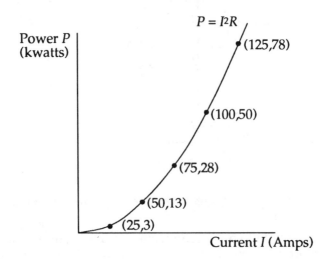

From the test results establish the resistance of the circuit, the voltage of each battery used and the current requirement for a 58 kwatt load. How would these results differ if an 8ohm circuit had been used, Suggest suitable battery capacities for a 58 kwatt motor.

STEP 1   Using the relationship for power calculate the electrical resistance of the circuit used in the tests.

STEP 2   From the application of 'Ohms Law' determine the voltages of the 5 batteries.

STEP 3   What current has to flow to produce a power output of 58 kwatts.

STEP 4   For a different circuit of resistance 8 ohms draw a graph to represent the power output against the current.

STEP 5   What current has to flow in an 8ohm circuit for a power output of 58kwatts.

STEP 6   What would be suitable battery capacities (current I and voltage V) to supply a 58 kwatt motor if the electrical resistance was between 3 and 9ohms.

Information Bank Section 2   Unit 2.2 Rearranging formulae *page 97*
Unit 12.1 Quadratic curves *page 156*

☐Task 2.3 *Battery size*

There is a requirement for the battery to store enough energy to give the car a reasonable range before recharging is necessary. A conventional car battery has the dimensions 25 cm × 16 cm × 11 cm as shown and a capacity of 33 ampere hours (Ah). If the capacity (Ah) of a battery is directly related to its volume, complete the table for each of the requirements;

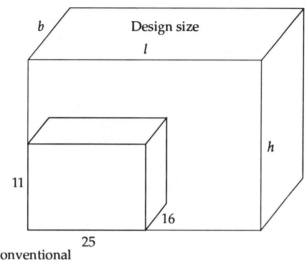

Conventional size

Capacity	Length l	Breadth b	Height h	Volume (cm³)
33	25	16	11	4400
2000		100	11	
5000	Length = breadth		30	
	$l = 3b$		25	5.3×10^7
12000	$l = b = h$			

How long will each of these batteries last if the power requirement is 52 kwatts at 12 volts.

STEP 1   Draw a straight line graph to give the relationship between capacity and volume. Determine the gradient of the line.

STEP 2   Write down an equation that represents this relationship.

STEP 3   Calculate each volume and the unknown capacity.

STEP 4   Form equations relating the dimensions to the volume, and solve them.

STEP 5   Calculate the current drawn for a power rating of 52 kwatts.

STEP 6   Comment on the practical problems associated with each result.

Information Bank Section 2   Unit 2.2 Rearranging formulae *page 97*
Unit 6.0 Straight line graphs *page 125*

☐ **Extension task**

For a battery shape with a semi-circular end as shown, investigate practical dimensions that would give a volume of 800 litres.

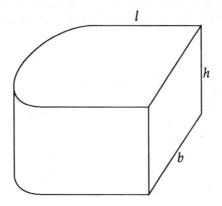

Introduction

The brake types considered operate by, shoes rubbing against drums, or pads rubbing against discs, in each case it is therefore friction that provides the resistance to motion. The materials used, together with the areas that are in contact, are important design factors. The detail design for each type is carried out and comparisons are made.

The project focuses on the following.

Task 1 *Drums* Suitable dimensions are required for brake shoes to fit inside a drum of a given size. The thickness is particularly important as this will affect the frequency at which they have to be replaced.	Skills Used:	Accuracy Calculations Rearranging Formulae Radians Volumes
Task 2 *Discs* Dimensions calculated for disc pads to fit within set limits. Graphs used to find the most suitable angles and radii.	Skills Used:	Accuracy Calculations Evaluating Formulae Rearranging Formulae Radians Quadratic Graphs Volumes
Task 3 *Drum/Disc comparisons* Realistic brake test data is given and used to compare the performance of disc brakes with drum brakes. Graphs and statistical calculations are used to quantify the differences.	Skills Used:	Spreadsheets Data Display Interpretation of Results

Tasks follow on from one another and should be attempted in sequence. Each task is introduced with a brief explanation of how components work. Specific details are given about the application, these are required throughout the task.

'Pilot questions' lead students into the task by stimulating thoughts about different aspects of the problem. Appropriate mathematics can then follow. Suggested answers to these are given at the end of this project (page 26).

Task 1 *Drums*

Brake shoes are pressed against the inside of the brake drum creating friction and a braking effect.

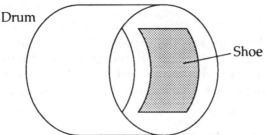

The task is to determine suitable dimensions for each of two shoes, inside a drum of internal radius 10 cm and width 7cm. The area in contact with the drum should be as large as possible in order to reduce wear and to minimise the risk of overheating. Different rates of wear need to be considered, and shoes need to be sufficiently thick so that frequent replacement is not necessary.

☐Pilot question 1

Suggest ways in which the friction between any two surfaces can be increased.

☐Task 1.1

To allow space for the brake mechanism the largest value for θ is $\frac{2\pi}{3}$ rads. It is thought that the contact area needs to be at least 50 cm² to prevent overheating. With these limitations what angles are acceptable.

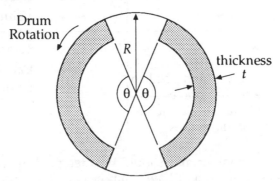

STEP 1   Write down a formula for the area that is in contact with the drum, of each shoe, in terms of the radius (R), the angle (θ measured in radians) and the width (w) of the shoe.

Use $\theta = \frac{2\pi}{3}$ rads and the formula to calculate the largest area for each brake shoe.

STEP 2   Rearrange the formula and make θ the subject.

Calculate the minimum angle that can be used giving an area greater than 50 cm².

Information Bank Section 2   Unit 2.2 Rearranging formulae *page 97*
Unit 3.0 Radians *page 102*
Unit 9.1 Volumes *page 140*

☐Task 1.2

Develop a relationship between area A and θ with a maximum shoe width. How is this relationship affected if the width $w = 5$cm.

STEP 1   The maximum value for the width of a shoe (w) is 7cm. Draw a graph of area (A) against angle (θ) for an acceptable range of angles.

STEP 2   Recalculate the minimum angle for a width of 5 cm and draw a new graph on the same axes to show how area is affected.

Information Bank Section 2   Unit 6.0 Straight line graphs *page 125*

☐Task 1.3

As brakes are used, material from the surface of the shoes is worn away. In order to decide on a suitable thickness t the rate of wear needs to be assessed.

Develop a relationship for the depth of wear t when $R = 10$, $w = 7$, and $\theta = \dfrac{2\pi}{3}$

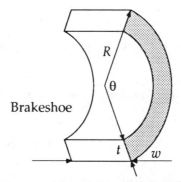

Brakeshoe

STEP 1   Use two methods to calculate the volume of material used in making a brake shoe of thickness (t) 0.5 cm;

a)   an approximation; by assuming it is a thin strip.

b)   accurately; by considering sectors

Compare the answers and comment on the possible reasons for any error.

STEP 2   Write down a formula for the volume V of material lost if a shoe is worn down by t cm.

Give V in terms of R, w, θ, and t.
Rearrange this formula to produce a quadratic equation.

☐ Extension task

Find out the actual dimensions of some brake shoes.

Calculate the volume of material used in their production.

What differences are there between the shape of shoes in use and the shape that was assumed in Task 1.

Task 2 *Discs*

Brake pads are mounted either side of a disc and a calliper squeezes them (similar to brake blocks on a bicycle) so that friction between pads and the disc provides the braking force.

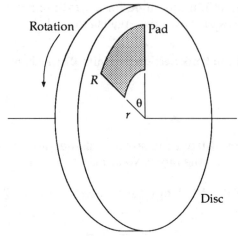

Determine suitable dimensions for brake pads for a disc of radius 17cm as shown.

☐ Pilot question 2

How do you think the reliability of braking systems can be measured?

☐ Task 2.1

Using the maximum possible outside radius R, consider how an area of 80 cm² can be achieved with two brake pads.

What angle θ is required to produce this area if the smallest acceptable radius r is 3 cm.

The largest angle that is practical is $\theta = \frac{\pi}{3}$ rads calculate the required radius r that gives the same area.

Suggest suitable values for angle θ and the inner radius r, within the range indicated. Comment on the most suitable combination for efficient braking.

STEP 1   Write down a formula for the area A of the pads in terms of the radii (r and R) and the angle (θ in radians). Substitute the maximum possible radius R.

STEP 2   With inner radius $r = 3$ cm, draw a graph to show how the area is related to the angle θ. Find the angle that gives a total area in contact with the disc of 80 cm². Rearrange the formula to make θ the subject and verify the result.

STEP 3   With angle $\theta = \frac{\pi}{3}$ rads, draw a graph to show how the area A is related to the radius r. Again find a value (this time for r) that produces the same area.

STEP 4   Draw a graph for a suitable range of values, relating the angle q to the radius *r* that satisfy the area requirement.

STEP 5   Use the graphs to suggest dimensions of a brake pad.

Information Bank Section 2   Unit 2.2 Rearranging formulae *page 97*
Unit 3.0 Radians *page 102*
Unit 8.3 Quadratic graphs *page 134*
Unit 9.1 Volumes *page 140*

☐ Task 2.2

The thickness *t* of a pad has to be designed to last sufficiently with normal use. Therefore the rate of wear needs to be assessed. Dimensions of a brake pad are as shown;

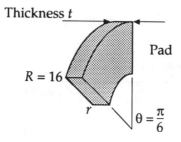

The inner radius *r* is decreased by 1 cm ($r - 1$) to reduce the rate of wear. This increases the contact area with the disc by 5 cm². Calculate the improved radius ($r - 1$).

When brakes are applied with the improved radius ($r - 1$) pads wear at the rate of 3×10^{-3} cm³ per minute. With 15 seconds for each application, what thickness *t* is required so that the brakes can be used 4000 times before they are 90% worn.

STEP 1   Write down a formula for the area A_1 (before improvement) in terms of *r*.

STEP 2   Write down a formula for the area A_2 (after improvement) in terms of ($r - 1$).

STEP 3   Combine these formulae and solve the resulting equation ($A_2 - A_1 = 5$ cm²).

STEP 4   Using this value for the inner radius ($r - 1$) determine the disc contact area.

STEP 5   Calculate the volume of material that can be worn away.

STEP 6   What is the required thickness *t*.

Information Bank Section 2   Unit 2.1 Evaluating formulae *page 96*
Unit 2.2 Rearranging formulae *page 97*
Unit 2.3 Extended formulae *page 99*
Unit 3.0 Radians *page 102*
Unit 9.1 Volumes *page 140*

☐ Extension task

Find out the contact area and thickness of some brake pads that are used in vehicles.

How long would it take to wear these pads out (continuous braking) at the rate of 3×10^{-3} cm³.

Why is this an unrealistic value. What other considerations are there.

Task 3 *Drum/disc comparisons*

There are advantages and disadvantages to each of these types of brakes. It is required to obtain detailed data that can be used to select the most suitable braking system for given specifications. The differences can be quantified using statistical techniques, but we must ensure that results are not misinterpreted.

Brake shoes and pads have to be replaced at regular intervals due to wear. It is therefore an important factor in the design to investigate the availability of different types. A survey of stockists will allow decisions to be made on this basis.

The efficiency of each type of brake should be a major consideration. We therefore need to carry out and analyse the results of controlled tests modelling a host of road conditions.

Braking distances in a number of trials can be recorded.

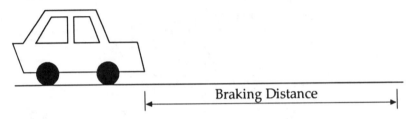

Braking Distance

☐ Pilot question 3

What different road conditions need to be considered in the testing of brakes? How do you think these factors are likely to affect the performance? Make some hypotheses about the behaviour of drum and disc brakes.

☐ Task 3.1

A survey of the availability of different diameter shoes and pad sizes was carried out with the following results:

Drums

Diameter	Shoes
5"	2
6"	15
7"	8
8"	1

Discs

Size	Pads
2.5"	3
2.75"	24
3"	5
3.5"	12
3.75"	2

Use the data to produce appropriate charts and diagrams. Comment on the distribution.

Suggest which is the most useful middle value for this application with an explanation.

Information Bank Section 2   Unit 4.1 Data display *page 104*

□Task 3.2

Using the data from the series of brake tests evaluate the differences between drum brakes and disc brakes and produce a report discussing these. Suggest possible explanations for any tendencies that are indicated. How could this be investigated further.

Test Results
The tables give braking distances (in feet) for each type of brake system to bring a vehicle to rest, from the same speed in each case of 50 mph.

Drum Brakes
Road Test

86	174	112	115	116	119	111	123	136	139
89	106	103	172	178	186	121	128	133	131
91	103	102	181	179	156	124	128	149	143
98	97	162	169	165	186	126	127	157	141

Disc Brakes
Road Test

88	91	93	97	108	108	106	102	109	112
115	115	118	117	111	123	124	128	171	113
146	146	156	158	159	167	162	127	128	125
132	133	136	139	136	134	135	144	143	142

STEP 1   Construct a frequency table for each set of data.

STEP 2   Produce columns of cumulative frequencies.

STEP 3   Draw cumulative frequency curves and use them to determine median and the interquartile range.

STEP 4   Make comparisons of the two types of brake.

STEP 5   By considering the operation of each braking system try to assess why the differences might have occurred. What other data could be collected to verify our conclusions.

Information Bank Section 2   Unit 1.3 Spreadsheets *page 95*
Unit 4.2 Interpretation of results *page 108*

□Task 3.3

Use alternative statistical techniques to calculate 'middle values' and the 'spread of the distribution' from the test results of task 3.2. Compare the two braking systems. Comment on the suitability of each statistical analysis.

STEP 1   Construct a frequency table for each set of data.

STEP 2   Determine the mean braking distance for each system.

STEP 3   Use mean values to calculate standard deviation and double check the results (spreadsheet listings allow formulae to be checked).

STEP 1   Construct a frequency table for each set of data.

STEP 2   Determine the mean braking distance for each system.

STEP 3   Use mean values to calculate standard deviation and double check the results (spreadsheet listings allow formulae to be checked).

STEP 4   How do the comparisons of these results measure up with inferences made previously.

STEP 5   With reference to the methods of calculation used here and in task 3.2, what are the limitations of each.

Information Bank Section 2   Unit 4.0 Statistics *page 104*

☐ Extension task

Conduct a series of reflex tests on samples of people under the age of 40 years and over 40 years. Record the measurement when a ruler is dropped through someones hand as shown. The height of fall is directly related to the persons reflexes.

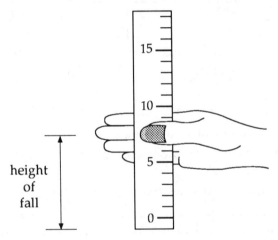

Using the data from the tests evaluate the differences between the young and not so young results. Produce a report discussing these. Suggest possible explanations for any tendencies shown.

Suggested answers to pilot questions

1. Roughen the surfaces. Increase the pressure.
2. Road tests under different conditions.
3. Heat will cause faster wearing of shoes or pads. Discs will cool faster than drums. Wet conditions will make brakes less efficient. Discs will dry out easier.

Introduction

Water is pumped through a system of pipes in the engine and returns to a radiator where it is cooled. The project focuses on;

Task 1 *Radiator design*	Skills Used:	Quadratic graphs Volumes Surface area Simultaneous equations Quadratic Formula
Task 2 *Water pump*	Skills Used:	Evaluating Formulae Rearranging Formulae Straight line graphs Quadratic Graphs Volumes Matrices
Task 3 *Heat transfer*	Skills Used:	Spreadsheets Evaluating Formulae Rearranging Formulae Straight line graphs Logarithms Surface area Exponential relationships Gradients of exponential curves Differentiating functions

Tasks follow on from one another and should be attempted in sequence. Each task is introduced with a brief explanation of how components work. Specific details are given about the application, these are required throughout the task.

'Pilot questions' lead students into the task by stimulating thoughts about different aspects of the problem. Appropriate mathematics can then follow. Suggested answers to these are given at the end of this project (page 36).

Task 1 *Radiator design*

A car radiator has to fit within a confined space, yet a large surface area is required to allow the water to cool inside. Fins are used to increase the area. The diagram shows a typical radiator shape and gives dimensions for a particular vehicle (cm).

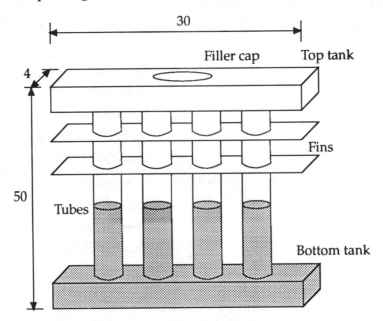

The number of tubes and fins can be varied and alternative systems need to be considered.

☐ Pilot question 1

What do you think are the factors that affect the efficiency of a radiator?

☐ Task 1.1

Calculate suitable sizes for the components of a radiator that is required to fit within the dimensions shown. The surface area has to be 4000 cm² to facilitate effective cooling.

Seven circular tubes are to be used, with length 42 cm.

STEP 1   Calculate the maximum surface area, of 7 circular tubes, that can be achieved without fins if the distance between the tanks is 42 cm.

STEP 2   Write down an equation for the top surface area of one fin if the tubes have radius *r*.

STEP 3   Write down an equation for the total surface area of the tubes and fins if 5 fins are fitted (the fins can be considered to have negligible thickness). Let this be equal to 4000 cm².

STEP 4   Solve the equation.

STEP 5   Write down an equation for the total surface area of the tubes and fins if 10 fins are fitted (the fins can be considered to have negligible thickness) Let this be equal to 4000 cm², and solve the equation.

STEP 6   What are the advantages of fitting 5 fins.

STEP 7   What are the advantages of fitting 10 fins.

 Information Bank Section 2   Unit 9.3 Surface area *page 145*
                                                        Unit 12.2 Quadratic formula *page 160*

☐ Task 1.2

The total water capacity is 2.4 litres. Seven circular tubes are to be used as before. When 1 litre of water is contained in a radiator with 7 tubes of radius 0.8 cm the overall depth is to be 20 cm. Calculate the heights of the top and bottom tanks.

STEP 1   Write down an equation for the volume of the bottom tank and the water in the tubes in terms of the tank height and the tube depth.

STEP 2   Write down a second equation in terms of these heights.

STEP 3   Solve the resulting simultaneous equations.

STEP 4   What is the volume of the top tank (here, tubes are not 42cm).

 Information Bank Section 2   Unit 8.2 Simultaneous linear equations *page 133*
                                                        Unit 9.1 Volumes *page 140*
                                                        Unit 11.1 Simultaneous equations *page 151*

☐ Task 1.3

With the number of tubes t of radius of 0.8 cm and length 42 cm and f fins of negligible thickness, suggest suitable combinations f and t.

STEP 1   Write down a formula for the surface area of tubes and fins together in terms of t and f.

STEP 2   Let this formula equal 4000 cm².

STEP 3   Rearrange the equation to give f in terms of t.

STEP 4   Draw a graph of this relationship.

STEP 5   List the combinations of values for t and f that satisfy the equation.

 Information Bank Section 2   Unit 8.3 Quadratic graphs *page 134*
                                                        Unit 9.3 Surface area *page 145*

☐ Extension task

Take all the necessary measurements of a car radiator, estimate the number of tubes and fins, and obtain an approximation of the surface area.

What alternative arrangements of tubes and fins could be used giving the same surface area.

Task 2 *Water pump*

The water pump is responsible for pumping cooling water round the engine and back to the radiator to be cooled.

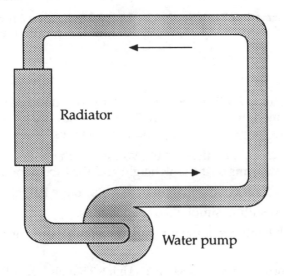

The flow rate is of importance, because the faster hot water can be replaced by cold the more efficient will be the cooling. So that cooling can be analysed in detail the velocity of water through the system must be studied.

☐ Pilot question 2

Why is it necessary to cool an engine? What advantages can be gained by introducing a cooling system to an engine?

☐ Task 2.1

Water leaves the pump and travels along a straight pipe with constant radius of 1.2 cm.

Determine a suitable water velocity that will give a flow rate of 0.3 litres per second.

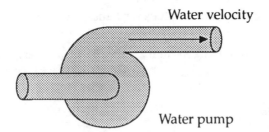

STEP 1   Convert 0.3 litres into cubic centimetres.

STEP 2   What length of pipe will contain this number of cubic centimetres.

STEP 3   Convert velocity into metres per second.

   Information Bank Section 2   Unit 2.2 Rearranging formulae *page 97*
Unit 9.1 Volumes *page 140*

☐ Task 2.2

A water pump starts from rest and increases the flow rate from 0 to 0.4 litres per second steadily over a period of 10 seconds. Determine the time after which 2.4 litres has been pumped.

STEP 1   Write down an equation that relates flow rate to time.

STEP 2   Draw a graph showing the change in flow rate over the 10 seconds.

STEP 3   Develop a formula for the area (pumped water) under the graph in terms of time t.

STEP 4   Express this formula as a relationship for the volume of water pumped. Let this be equal to 2.4 litres (converted as appropriate).

STEP 5   Solve the resulting quadratic equation.

Information Bank Section 2   Unit 6.0 Straight line graphs *page 125*
Unit 8.3 Quadratic graphs *page 134*

☐ Task 2.3

A pipe system includes a section where the diameter increases from 2.4 cm to 3.8 cm, continuously over a length of 7 cm, through a conical shape. How is the velocity of the water in a pipe related to its diameter, if the flow rate is 0.3 litres per second.

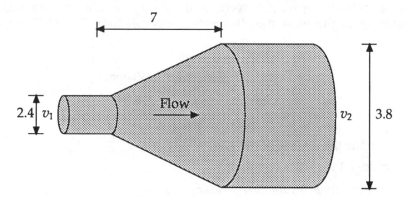

STEP 1   Calculate the velocity of the water before the transition piece in the 2.4 diameter pipe and also in the 3.8 diameter pipe after the flow change.

STEP 2   Form an equation that relates the velocity of the flow, to the radius of a pipe, using a flow rate of 0.3 litres per second.

STEP 3   Draw a graph to represent the change in velocity for the change in radius over the 7 cm transition piece.

STEP 4   Draw a straight line graph for the velocity against $\frac{1}{r^2}$ and state the gradient of this graph.

Information Bank Section 2   Unit 2.1 Evaluating formulae *page 96*
Unit 6.0 Straight line graphs *page 125*
Unit 8.2 Quadratic graphs *page 133*

☐Task 2.4

A test carried out with an alternative pipe system has a diameter change from 2 cm to 4.8 cm, continuously over a length of 12 cm through a conical shape. The velocity of water in the pipe was measured at intervals along the pipe system.

Radius	1	1.2	1.4	1.6	1.8	2	2.2	2.4
Velocity	118	82	60	46	36	29	24	21

STEP 1 Write down an equation that relates the flow velocity to the pipe radius.

STEP 2 Draw a graph showing the relationship between the velocity and the radius of the pipe.

STEP 3 Draw a straight line graph for the velocity against $\frac{1}{r^2}$ and state the gradient of this graph.

STEP 4 Use this value and the equation to estimate the flow rate.

Information Bank Section 2   Unit 6.0 Straight line graphs *page 125*
Unit 8.3 Quadratic graphs *page 134*

☐Task 2.5

During tests to consider the cooling effect of a system of pipes through an engine, two constant flow rates (litres per second) were used for varying time periods (seconds). The volume of water passing through the pipe system was measured (litres). The results were recorded in matrix form.

Test results

$$\overset{Times}{\begin{pmatrix} 2 & 6 \\ 5 & 3 \end{pmatrix}} \cdot \overset{Flow\ rates}{\begin{pmatrix} F_1 \\ F_2 \end{pmatrix}} = \overset{Volumes}{\begin{pmatrix} 4.6 \\ 3.1 \end{pmatrix}}$$

STEP 1 Determine the inverse of the matrix for times.

STEP 2 Rearrange the matrix equation.

STEP 3 Calculate values for the flow rates F_1 and F_2.

Information Bank Section 2   Unit 11.2 Matrices *page 152*

☐Task 2.6

Constant flow rates F_1 and F_2 were used in testing the cooling effect of a pipe system. These flow rates applied for different time intervals, and produced volumes given by the matrix equation;

Test results

$$\overset{Times}{\begin{pmatrix} 3 & 6 \\ 4 & 1 \end{pmatrix}} \cdot \overset{Flow\ rates}{\begin{pmatrix} F_1 \\ F_2 \end{pmatrix}} = \overset{Volumes}{\begin{pmatrix} 6.15 \\ 2.6 \end{pmatrix}}$$

With flow rates F_1 and F_2 show how the velocity changes along the length of pipe section shown;

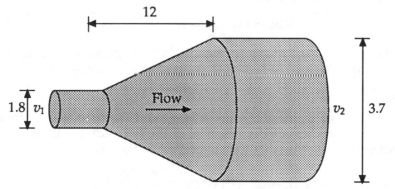

STEP 1   Solve the matrix equation and determine values for the flow rates F_1 and F_2.

STEP 2   Calculate velocities before and after the junction

STEP 3   Develop an equation for the velocity at distances along the connecting piece.

STEP 4   Draw a graph to represent this relationship.

Information Bank Section 2   Unit 8.3 Quadratic graphs *page 134*
Unit 9.1 Volumes *page 140*
Unit 11.2 Matrices *page 152*

Task 3 *Heat transfer*

When cold water flows through a hot engine, heat is transferred from the engine to water in the cooling system. The engine loses heat while the water gains this same quantity of heat (heat is a type of energy and therefore measured in joules).

In order to design a cooling system that reduces the engine temperature sufficiently, we need to be able to calculate how much heat flows from the engine.

Heat transfer depends on;

     1   Temperature difference $(T_2 - T_1)$
     2   Materials used
     3   Area of the interface

Mathematically, the flow of heat can be treated in a similar way to the flow of electricity. The rate of flow of heat is comparable with current in an electrical circuit.

Using this analogy 'Ohm's Law' allows us to write down a similar relationship for heat.

$$\text{Rate of heat transfer } = \frac{T_2 - T_1}{\text{Thermal Resistance}} \quad \left(I = \frac{V}{R} \right)$$

The thermal resistance is itself dependent on a number of factors;

$$\text{Thermal Resistance} = \frac{L}{kA}$$

L = length of flow
k = conductivity of material
A = area

☐ Pilot question 3

Consider the equation for the flow of heat:

$$\text{Rate of heat transfer} = \frac{kA(T_2 - T_1)}{L}$$

Why does the rate of heat transfer increase if water is pumped through a pipe system, rather than having zero flow? Which of the values from the formula changes?

☐ Task 3.1

It is required to cool an engine at the rate of 5kw (5000 joules/second), through a cast iron pipe with effective thickness of 10 cm. Calculate the area required for each of the temperature differences given in the table and suggest a suitable area.

ENGINE (T_2)

		50°C	60°C	70°C	80°C	90°C	100°C
	15°C						
	25°C						
WATER (T_1)	35°C						
	45°C						
	55°C	×					
	65°C	×	×				

STEP 1   Rearrange the equation for rate of heat transfer $\dfrac{dQ}{dt}$ to give an expression for area.

STEP 2   Look up a value for the conductivity of cast iron (reference section).

STEP 3   Calculate areas in a spread sheet or using a programmable calculator.

STEP 4   Find out the actual operating temperatures of some cars and suggest a suitable value for the heat flow area.

Information Bank Section 2   Unit 1.2 Calculations *page 93*
Unit 1.3 Spreadsheets *page 95*
Unit 2.1 Evaluating formulae *page 96*
Unit 2.2 Rearranging formulae *page 97*
Unit 2.3 Extended formulae *page 99*

☐ Task 3.2

Using the suggested area from task 3.1, consider the use of other materials. Again for a heat transfer rate of 5kw and 10cm thickness, determine which materials are suitable and for what range of temperature differences. Materials to be investigated are:

Cast Iron, Copper, Mild Steel, Lead, Aluminium

STEP 1   Look up the conductivity for each material.

STEP 2   Use the heat transfer equation to calculate values.

STEP 3   On the same graph draw lines to represent the rate of heat flow, against a range of temperature gradients for each material.

STEP 4   The heat flow rate of 5kw allows suitable materials to be found. Find materials that give this heat transfer rate at practical temperature differences.

Information Bank Section 2   Unit 2.2 Rearranging formulae *page 97*
Unit 6.0 Straight line graphs *page 125*

☐ Task 3.3

The temperature of the water is of course changing as it flows through the pipe system. This complicates the heat flow analysis and makes further investigations necessary.

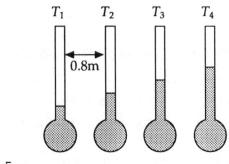

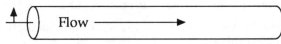

In a test on a cooling system the temperature was measured along the length of a pipe at intervals of 0.8 metres. The engine temperature may be assumed to be constant at 70°C. A table of values was obtained for different water flow rates.

Flow rate	T_1	T_2	T_3	T_4	T_5	T_6	T_7
0.3 (l/s)	15	33	45	53	59	63	65
0.5 (l/s)	15	30	41	49	55	59	62

It is thought that the relationship for temperature T is given by;

$$T = 70 - 55e^{m}$$

(where n is a constant for a particular flow rate and x is the distance that water has travelled along the pipe)

Show how the temperature rises along the length of the cooling system.

STEP 1   Draw a graph with a curve for each of the water flow rates representing temperature changes along the pipe.

STEP 2   Use logs to calculate the value of n for each flow rate.

STEP 3   Draw a graph for a flow rate of $0.8 \frac{l}{s}$ if $T = 70 - 55e^{-0.1x}$

STEP 4   Use this graph to find the distance at which the water temperature is 50°C.

STEP 5   Calculate the time it takes to increase the water temperature from 15°C to 50°C as it flows through the system.

Information Bank Section 2   Unit 7.1 Logarithms *page 128*
Unit 7.2 Laws of logarithms *page 130*
Unit 10.1 Experimental relationships *pages 148*

☐ Task 3.4

A pipe system has diameter 3cm. The water temperature increases along the length of the pipe, but the rate of heat transfer is decreasing because the temperature difference reduces.

Determine the rate of change of temperature with the distance at the point when $x = 2.4$ metres if temperature T is given by;

$$T = 70 - 55e^{-0.3x}$$

(for a flow rate of $0.4 \frac{l}{s}$)

Also, find the relationship for the rate of temperature change with time $t\left(\dfrac{dT}{dt}\right)$ and calculate the rate when $t = 5$ seconds.

STEP 1   Differentiate the expression with respect to x.

STEP 2   Substitute the value 2.4 metres for x and calculate the temperature change per metre at this point.

STEP 3   Replace x with a relationship in terms of t.

STEP 4   Differentiate the expression with respect to t.

STEP 5   Substitute the value $t = 5$ seconds for t and calculate the temperature change per second at this time.

Information Bank Section 2   Unit 10.2 Gradients of exponential curves
page 150
Unit 13.2 Differentiating functions *page 167*

☐ Extension task

Assuming that the temperature of water flowing through an engine is related to the distance travelled by an equation similar to that used previously;

Original equation:

$$T = 70 - 55e^{-0.3x}$$

Values can be replaced with more general symbols for engine temperature T_2 and water temperature T_1:

$$T = T_2 - (T_2 - T_1)e^{nx}$$

Carry out some research into engine running temperatures, and lengths of cooling systems. Using these known values draw appropriate graphs for the water temperature if it reaches 80% of the engine temperature at the end of the cycle. Calculate corresponding values of n from the equation.

Suggested answers to pilot questions

1. Surface area, temperature difference.

2. Overheating will deform the engine. More power can be delivered without causing a temperature rise.

3. The temperature difference is maintained because heated water is continually replaced. $T_2 - T_1$ is larger.

Project E *Gearbox*

Introduction
A simplified gearbox is considered, with first and second gear identified. Bearings and gearbox housing design is related to the gearshafts. The project focuses on;

Task 1 *Gear and Shaft Speeds*	Skills Used:	Rearranging Formulae
		Radians
		Straight Line Graphs
		Quadratic Graphs
		Simultaneous Equations
		Matrices
		Quadratic Formula
		Differentiation
		Reversing Differentiation
Task 2 *Bearings*	Skills Used:	Logarithms
		Laws of Logarithms
		Exponential Relationships
		Gradients of Exponential Relationships
		Differentiating Functions
Task 3 *Gearbox Housing Design*	Skills Used:	Trigonometrical Curves
		Sin, Cos and Tan Formulae
		Sine and Cosine Rule
		Volumes
		Differentiating Functions

Tasks follow on from one another and should be attempted in sequence. Each task is introduced with a brief explanation of how components work. Specific details are given about the application, these are required throughout the task.

'Pilot questions' lead students into the task by stimulating thoughts about different aspects of the problem. Appropriate mathematics can then follow. Suggested answers to these are given at the end of this project (page 45).

Task 1 *Gear and shaft speeds*

Gearwheels are mounted on parallel shafts A and B. These are slid along the shaft by gear selectors and various ratios are achieved. Rotation (α and β) is measured in radians ($2\pi = 1$ revolution) and angular speed (ω) in radians per second.

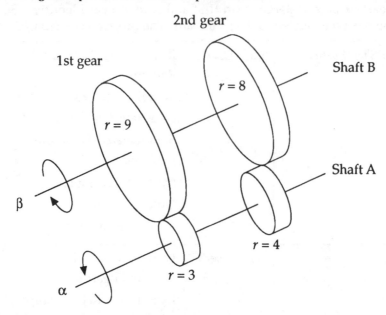

Gear arrangement for first and second gears (shown with 1st gear engaged)

The two shafts rotate at varying speeds and gearwheels are engaged at different times. Consequently the wear on components is complex, and the motion has to be analysed in order to use suitable materials and dimensions.

☐Pilot question 1

Why does a car need a selection of gear ratios? Which is the lowest gear of the following:

a)   A large wheel driving a small wheel or

b)   A small wheel driving a large wheel?

☐Task 1.1

In a test, shaft B is driven so that it rotates 25 times, partly in first gear and partly in second. Determine the angles of rotation in each gear (α_1 and α_2) of shaft if A it rotates 63 times in total.

STEP 1   Calculate the angle (β_1) of rotation of shaft B if the driving shaft A rotates once in first gear.

STEP 2   Write down a formula that relates the angle (β_1) of rotation of shaft B to the rotation of driving shaft A (α_1), again in first gear.

STEP 3   Calculate the angle (β_2) of rotation of shaft B if the driving shaft A rotates once in second gear.

STEP 4   Write down a formula that relates the angle (β_2) of rotation of shaft B to the rotation of driving shaft A (α_2), in second gear.

STEP 5   Combine formulae from STEP 2 and 4 to form an equation giving the rotation of shaft B.

STEP 6   Use two simultaneous equations to calculate the values of α_1 and α_2.

   Information Bank Section 2 Unit 3.0 Radians *page 102*
Unit 8.2 Simultaneous linear equations *page 133*
Unit 11.1 Simultaneous equations *page 151*

☐Task 1.2

Driving shaft A rotates 77 times producing 32 revolutions of shaft B through the gearbox, both first and second gear are used. Determine the angles of rotation in each gear (α_1 and α_2) of shaft A.

STEP 1   Write down two simultaneous equations for α_1 and α_2.

STEP 2   Combine these equations into one matrix equation.

STEP 3   Solve the matrix equation using the inverse matrix.

STEP 4   What are the values of α_1 and α_2.

   Information Bank Section 2   Unit 11.2 Matrices *page 152*

☐Task 1.3

Second gear can be engaged at the shaft velocity of 3000 rpm (revolutions per minute). If the driving shaft A is initially at rest and accelerates at a constant rate of 2 rev/s^2, find:

a)   the numbers of times that the shaft has rotated before gear can be changed
b)   the time when the shaft has rotated 1000 times.

a)   STEP 1   Write down an equation that relates the angular velocity (ω) to the time t, using the constant value for acceleration.

STEP 2   Rearrange this equation and determine the time when the shaft velocity reaches 3000 rpm (conversion is required to rads/sec).

STEP 3   Integrate the original equation to give the angle of rotation (α). The rate of change of the angle $\dfrac{d\alpha}{dt}$ is the angular velocity of the shaft.

STEP 4   Use the condition that when $t = 0$ then $a = 0$, to calculate the constant of integration C.

STEP 5   Calculate the angle α when the angular velocity is 3000 rpm. Convert this angle into number of revolutions.

b)   STEP 6   Draw the graph of the relationship between angle α and time t from $t = 0$ to $t = 200$. Estimate the time after which the shaft has rotated 1000 times.

STEP 7   Rearrange the equation and calculate a more accurate value for this time.

   Information Bank Section 2   Unit 8.3 Quadratic graphs *page 134*
Unit 14.1 Reversing differentiation *page 168*

☐Task 1.4

Second gear is engaged at the shaft velocity of 3000 rpm (revolutions per minute). If, after the gear change, shaft A accelerates at a constant rate of 1.5 revolutions/s², find:

a) the number of times that the shaft has rotated before the angular velocity reaches 3100 rpm.

b) the time when the shaft has rotated 1000 times.

a) STEP 1   Write down an equation that relates the angular velocity (ω) to the time t, using the constant value for acceleration and the initial velocity.

STEP 2   Rearrange this equation and find the time after the gear change when the shaft velocity reaches 3100 rpm (conversion is required to rads/sec).

STEP 3   Integrate the original equation to give the angle of rotation (α). The rate of change of the angle $\dfrac{d\alpha}{dt}$ is the angular velocity of the shaft.

STEP 4   Use the condition that when $t = 0$ to calculate the constant of integration C.

STEP 5   Calculate the angle α when the angular velocity is 3100 rpm. Convert this angle into number of revolutions.

b) STEP 6   Draw the graph of the relationship between angle α and time t from $t = 0$ to $t = 200$. Estimate the time after which the shaft has rotated 1000 times.

STEP 7   Solve the quadratic equation and calculate a more accurate value for this time.

Information Bank Section 2   Unit 2.2 Rearranging formulae *page 97*
Unit 8.2 Quadratic graphs *page 134*
Unit 12.2 Quadratic formulae *page 160*
Unit 14.1 Reversing differentiation *page 168*
Unit 14.2 Area under a curve *page 169*

☐Task 1.5

A relationship for the angle of rotation a is given by :

$$\alpha = 0.7t^2 + 2000\,\pi t$$

Determine a relationship for the angular velocity and estimate how long it takes to reach a shaft speed of 1000 rpm.

STEP 1   Differentiate the equation to give an expression for angular velocity ω $\left(\dfrac{d\alpha}{dt}\right)$ in terms of time t.

STEP 2   Draw a graph for the change in angular velocity with time.

STEP 3   From the graph estimate a value for the time when the shaft speed is 1000 rpm.

STEP 4   Rearrange the equation and calculate a more accurate value for time t.

Information Bank Section 2   Unit 2.2 Rearranging formulae *page 97*
Unit 6.0 Straight line graphs *page 125*
Unit 13.1 Differentiation *page 164*

☐ Extension Task

Find out the first and second gear ratios used in some production model cars and comment on the reasons for any differences.

Use these ratios to calculate the speeds of the driving shaft, when the output shaft rotates at 3000 rpm in first, and second, gear.

For a constant acceleration of 1.3 rads/s² determine the driving shaft velocity after 1 minute if it is initially at rest. What are the corresponding output shaft speeds in each gear.

Task 2 *Bearings*

The bearings support the shaft and allow smooth rotation. The rate of wear needs to be considered so that a design life can be calculated based on average mileage.

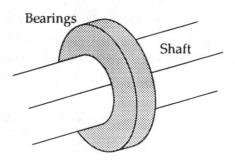

As shafts rotate the clearance between balls and sleeves increases (wear w in millimetres). With greater clearance the rate of wear also increases. The relationship for clearance depends on the type of bearings employed. The table gives equations for three types that are available.

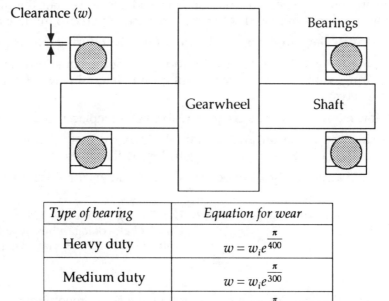

Type of bearing	Equation for wear
Heavy duty	$w = w_i e^{\frac{\pi}{400}}$
Medium duty	$w = w_i e^{\frac{\pi}{300}}$
Light duty	$w = w_i e^{\frac{\pi}{200}}$

where: n is the number of turns of the shaft in millions
w_i is the initial clearance

☐ Pilot question 2

Why do you think bearings should be designed to last a particular length of time?

☐ Task 2.1

Bearings need to be replaced when the clearance exceeds 0.5 millimetres. Select suitable bearings for driving shaft A if the design life is to be 8 years, based on the average running time of 400 hours per year at 3000 rpm.

STEP 1   Calculate the number of revolutions of the shaft during the design life.

STEP 2   Draw graphs to represent the equations for each type of bearing assuming an initial clearance of 0.1 mm.

STEP 3   Ascertain from the graphs which type of bearings are necessary. What will be the clearance after this time.

STEP 4   How many revolutions are permissible before replacement is necessary.

STEP 5   Using the equation and an initial clearance of 0.07 mm determine the clearance after 8 years of use. Logarithms will be needed.

STEP 6   Would any other types of bearings be acceptable with this initial clearance.

   Information Bank Section 2   Unit 7.1 Logarithms *page 128*
Unit 7.2 Laws of logarithms *page 130*
Unit 10.1 Exponential relationships *page 148*

☐ Task 2.2

Shaft B rotates at slower speeds than shaft A depending on the use of the gears. Consequently lighter bearings may be sufficiently hard wearing. The design life should be 8 years as before, but the speed of rotation is considered to be half the rate of shaft A. Again, bearings need to be replaced when the clearance exceeds 0.5 millimetres.

STEP 1   Calculate the number of revolutions of the shaft during the design life.

STEP 2   Using the graphs drawn earlier to represent the equations for each type of bearing, with an initial clearance of 0.1mm determine which type of bearings are necessary.

STEP 3   How many revolutions are permissible before replacement is necessary.

STEP 4   Using the equation and an initial clearance of 0.07 mm determine the clearance after 8 years of use. Logarithms will be needed.

STEP 5   Would any other types of bearings be acceptable with this initial clearance.

   Information Bank Section 2   Unit 7.1 Logarithms *page 128*
Unit 7.2 Laws of logarithms *page 130*
Unit 10.1 Exponential relationships *page 148*

☐ Task 2.3

The rate of wear of the bearings with respect to the number of revolutions, is an important value to consider, because it is representative of how smooth running the bearings are. If the rate of wear is high then the resistance to motion is also high.

With an initial clearance of 0.1 mm calculate the rate of wear for each type of bearings after 600 million revolutions. Also find the number of revolutions that each can withstand before the rate of wear reaches 1.2×10^{-3}

STEP 1   Differentiate the equation for wear w of each type of bearings $\left(\dfrac{dw}{dn}\right)$

STEP 2   Calculate the rates of wear when $n = 600$ from the equations.

STEP 3   Rearrange the equations and calculate corresponding values of n for the rate of wear of 1.2×10^{-3} in each case.

Information Bank Section 2   Unit 7.2 Laws of logarithms *page 130*
Unit 10.2 Gradients of exponential curves *page 150*
Unit 13.2 Differentiating functions *pages 167*

☐ Extension Task

How, in practice, can the clearance of bearings be measured.

The clearance w of medium duty bearings after n (million) revolutions is given in the table.

Revolutions n	200	300	400
Clearance w	0.0974	0.1359	0.1897

With the equation:

$$w = w_i e^{\frac{n}{300}}$$

find w_i and calculate the rate of wear when $n = 400$.

Task 3 *Gearbox housing design*

Calculations are required in the design of the case in which the gearbox is housed. Clearance between the mechanism in this case is necessary to avoid interference, but if the case is larger than is needed, then materials and space are wasted.

☐ Pilot question 3

Why do you think a gearbox should be enclosed in a case?

☐ Task 3.1

The housing is required to be as shown in the diagram, with a minimum clearance of 1cm from all parts. The distance between the gearwheel shaft centres is 12 cm and the centre of the gearchange shaft needs to be 9 cm from the centre of shaft A. The radius of the gearchange shaft is 2.5 cm and the largest gearwheels on shafts A and B are 4 cm and 9 cm respectively. Calculate all the lengths and radii for the profile of the case and consider options that are acceptable within these specifications.

Gearchange shaft

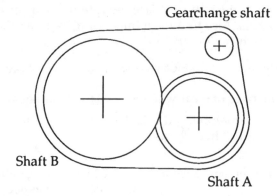

Shaft B

Shaft A

STEP 1   If the shafts are as close together as possible. Sketch a triangle showing the three shaft centres and calculate all the interior angles.

STEP 2   Use these centres to draw arcs representing the required radii for the case.

STEP 3   Calculate the lengths between the arcs using appropriate trigonometry.

STEP 4   Determine the distance between the centres of shaft B and the gearchange shaft (BG) if the angle BAG is 80°.

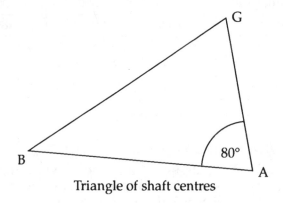

Triangle of shaft centres

STEP 5   Develop an equation that relates the length BG to the angle BAG.

STEP 6   Use this equation to draw a graph of the length BG against angle BAG. A practical range of angles should be used.

STEP 7   What length BG allows the housing to have perpendicular sides.

STEP 8   What angle BAG and length BG allow the housing to have parallel sides.

 Information Bank Section 2   Unit 5.1 Trigonomical curves *page 116*
Unit 5.2 Sin, Cos, and Tan formulae *page 120*
Unit 5.3 Sine and Cosine rule *page 121*

☐ Task 3.2

The housing is to contain gearbox oil for lubrication. It is therefore necessary to establish the volume of the case for different positions of the gearchange shaft.

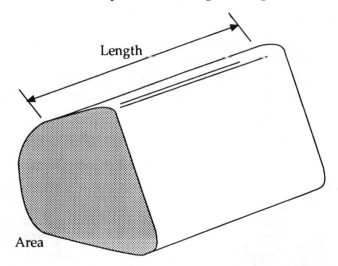

Length

Area

The shape of the housing has a continuous cross section as shown. The area relates to the dimensions investigated in task 3.1 and the length is 50 cm.

STEP 1   Sketch the area of the cross section with dimensions.

STEP 2   Write down an equation for the area of the triangle of shaft centres in terms of the angle *BAG*.

STEP 3   Differentiate this equation and find the angle that gives the largest area.

STEP 4   The corresponding volume can now be calculated.

Information Bank Section 2   Unit 5.2 Sin, Cos, and Tan formulae *page 120*
Unit 5.3 Sine and Cosine rule *page 121*
Unit 9.1 Volumes *page 140*
Unit 13.2 Differentiating functions *page 167*

☐ Extension task

Find out the diameter of some gears that are used in a gearbox and design a case that could contain these with a minimum clearance of 1 cm. Produce a scale drawing.

Suggested answers to pilot questions

1. a) To travel at different speeds.
    b) A small wheel driving a large wheel.
2. So that they last sufficiently long without being unnecessarily large.
3. To contain oil.

Introduction

The cylinders are at the heart of an engine and it is here that the fuel is ignited to produce power. The cylinder design is therefore most important.

An explosion takes place within the cylinders and drives pistons. The capacity of these cylinders will obviously affect the power output. In addition the relative dimensions of the radius to height need to be considered.

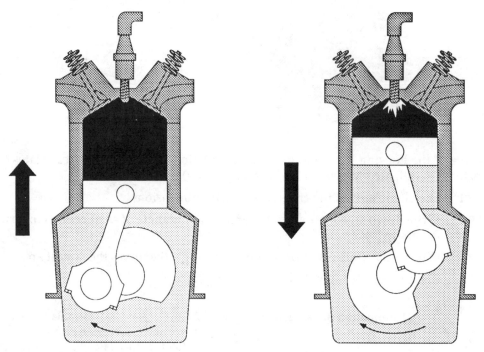

This project encourages a trial and error approach to optimise the system. This is followed by detailed calculations. The design is carried out through tasks.
The project focuses on;

Task 1 *Piston motion*	Skills Used:	Trigonomical Curves
		Volumes
		Trigonomical Waveforms
		Function of a Function
		Product Rule
Task 2 *Cylinder size*	Skills Used:	Volumes
		Surface Area
		Maximum and Minimum
		Product Rule
		Quotient Rule

Task 3 *Power*	Skills Used:	Trigonomical Waveforms
		Addition of Sine Curves
		Combining Trig Equations
		Integration by Substitution

Tasks follow on from one another and should be attempted in sequence. Each task is introduced with a brief explanation of how components work. Specific details are given about the application, these are required throughout the task.

'Pilot questions' lead students into the task by stimulating thoughts about different aspects of the problem. Appropriate mathematics can then follow. Suggested answers to these are given at the end of this project (page 53).

Task 1 *Piston motion*

The motion of a piston is determined by the vertical height of the 'big end' above the centre-line of the crankshaft as shown;

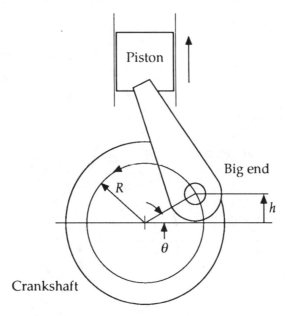

It is important to develop an understanding of this motion, since this is where the explosion of the fuel is converted into the rotary motion of the engine. Clever design here can result in efficient transmission and economic fuel consumption.

☐ Pilot question 1

Assuming constant angular velocity of the crankshaft, when do you think the piston will be moving at its maximum speed?

☐ Task 1.1

The radius of the crankshaft $R = 4.5$ cm. If a piston has a radius of 3 cm, what volume of fuel will be drawn into the cylinder when the piston completes a full stroke.

The fuel is ignited when the angle of rotation is 84° what is the height h at this point.

Determine a relationship between height h and the angle θ. Use this to give all the angles when the swept cylinder is 50 cc (cubic centimetres).

STEP 1 Calculate the volume for one stroke (180°)

STEP 2 Calculate the height h when $\theta = 84°$ using appropriate trigonometry.

STEP 3 Write down an equation giving height h in terms of the angle of rotation θ.

STEP 4 Draw a graph to represent this relationship over one complete revolution.

STEP 5 Rearrange a formula for swept cylinder volume to calculate the height when $V = 50$ cm³.

STEP 6 Read the angles of rotation that correspond to this height from the graph.

 Information Bank Section 2   Unit 20.1 Trigonometrical wave forms *page 199*

☐Task 1.2

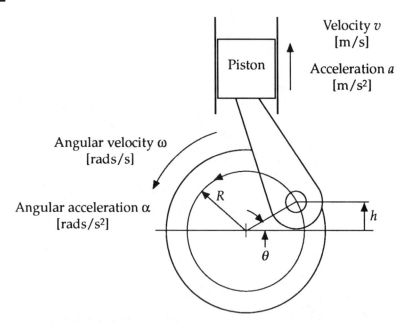

The angle of rotation θ is dependent on the angular velocity ω of the crankshaft. If the shaft is rotating at a constant rate of 1500 rpm, develop a relationship for the velocity of the piston in terms of time t. Also obtain a relationship for linear acceleration.

Calculate both the velocity and the acceleration when $t = 0.015$ seconds

How are these affected if the shaft rotates at a constant angular velocity of 2000 rpm.

STEP 1 Convert 1500 rpm into rad/second. Use this as angular velocity ω.

STEP 2 Write down the angle θ in terms of time t.

STEP 3 Using the relationship for h from task 1.1, make a substitution for θ.

STEP 4   Differentiate this function to obtain the velocity $v = \dfrac{dh}{dt}$, simplify as far as possible. calculate the velocity when $t = 0.015$ seconds.

STEP 5   Differentiate again to produce a relationship for acceleration $a = \dfrac{dv}{dt}$. Calculate the acceleration when $t = 0.015$ seconds.

STEP 6   Repeat the procedure using 2000 rpm.

    Information Bank Section 2   Unit 21.1 Function of a function *page 207*

☐Task 1.3

If the angular velocity of the crankshaft changes with the formula;

$\omega = \omega_1 + \alpha t$ where ω_1 is the initial angular velocity and α is angular acceleration

Determine the velocity of the piston 2 seconds after the shaft has started to accelerate from 1500 rpm to 2000 rpm, if angular acceleration is constant. The increase in angular velocity takes 9 seconds. What is the acceleration of the piston at this point.

STEP 1   Convert ω angular velocities into rads/second

STEP 2   Calculate the angular acceleration α (constant value in rads/sec²).

STEP 3   Rewrite the formula for ω using these values.

STEP 4   Substitute this function of time t into the relationship for h.

STEP 5   Differentiate with respect to t giving the velocity $v = \dfrac{dh}{dt}$

STEP 6   Calculate the velocity when $t = 2$ seconds.

STEP 7   Differentiate the expression for velocity to give acceleration $a = \dfrac{dv}{dt}$.

STEP 8   Calculate the acceleration when $t = 2$ seconds.

    Information Bank Section 2   Unit 21.1 Function of a function *page 207*
　　　　　　　　　　　　　　　　　　　　　Unit 21.2 Product rule *page 209*

☐Extension task

Obtain the radius of a crankshaft from a vehicle. Draw a graph to represent the height of a piston as this crankshaft rotates.

Write down an equation for the motion.

For constant rotation of 300 rpm, find the maximum speed of the piston.

Task 2 *Cylinder size*

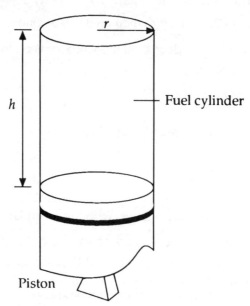

Fuel cylinder

h

r

Piston

☐Pilot question 2

Why would you say it is desirable for the surface area of the fuel cylinder to be as small as possible?

☐Task 2.1

Find values for the radius and height that give us the minimum surface area. Of course the volume has still got to satisfy requirements where $V = 250$cc.

STEP 1   Experiment with different values for the radius and calculate corresponding heights and surface areas.

STEP 2   Draw an appropriate graph.

STEP 3   Using the known volume write down a formula for h in terms of r.

           Write down a formula for the surface area in terms of r only.

STEP 4   Differentiate the formula and find the radius where a turning point occurs. Determine whether this radius produces a maximum or minimum surface area.

STEP 5   What is the minimum surface area.

Information Bank Section 2   Unit 19.0 Maximum and minimum *page 196*

                                                Unit 21.1 Function of a function *page 207*

☐ Task 2.2

Alternative cylinder shapes ought to be considered from the point of view of minimising the surface area.

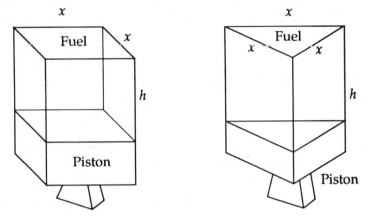

Alternative 'cylinder' shapes

In each of these unconventional shapes calculate values for h and x that produce the minimum surface area, whilst still giving a volume of 250 cc.

STEP 1   Develop formulae for volumes and surface area of each 'fuel cylinder'. Let the volumes be equal to 250 cm³.

STEP 2   Substitute expressions for h into surface area formulae giving equations in terms of x only.

STEP 3   Differentiate each surface area and find values of x where turning points occur.

STEP 4   Establish the nature (max or min) of any turning points.

STEP 5   Use appropriate values to determine corresponding heights h.

STEP 6   Which of the three 'cylinder' shapes is most suitable.

Information Bank Section 2   Unit 19.0 Maximum and minimum *page 196*
Unit 21.2 Product rule *page 209*
Unit 21.3 Quotient rule *page 212*

☐ Extension task

Find out from car manuals actual piston radii and cylinder heights. Determine whether the surface area is a minimum value.

Comment on other possible considerations in cylinder design.

Task 3 *Power*

Cylinder design would not be complete without considering the power that is produced therein. Initially a single cylinder has to be analysed.

A car engine often consists of a number of cylinders rotating out of phase with each other. Let us investigate the combined effects of multiples of pistons delivering forces to the crankshaft.

☐ Pilot question 3

How many cylinders are there in car engines? Why do you imagine they rotate out of phase with each other?

☐ Task 3.1

A cylinder has a radius of 2.6 cm. The fuel is a petrol/air mixture of 1 part petrol to 15 parts air. Calculate the energy released at each combustion stroke, if the velocity of the piston is related to time t by the equation;

$$v = 150 \, \pi \cos 30\pi \, t$$

Fuel is drawn into the cylinder for a period when a valve is open. The valve is held open from $\theta = \dfrac{\pi}{2}$ until $\theta = \dfrac{3\pi}{2}$

STEP 1   Draw a graph of velocity v against time t for one revolution of the crankshaft.

STEP 2   Between what values of time t are the values open.

STEP 3   Integrate the expression for v with respect to time between these limits and obtain the height through which the piston travels.

STEP 4   Calculate the volume of fuel drawn into the cylinder.

STEP 5   Using the petrol/air ratio and the calorific value of petrol, determine the energy released if the fuel is completely burned.

Information Bank Section 2   Unit 20.1 Trigonomical waveforms *page 199*
Unit 22.1 Integration by substitution *page 214*

☐ Task 3.2

A twelve cylinder engine has a phase angle between cylinders of 60° $\left(\dfrac{\pi}{3}\text{rads}\right)$. The torque T (force × perpendicular distance) applied by each of two cylinders to the crankshaft is related to the angle of rotation by;

Cylinder 1 $T = 4 \sin \theta$;   Cylinder 2 $T = 4 \sin (\theta + 60)$

These equations in graphical form are shown with a 60° phase angle.

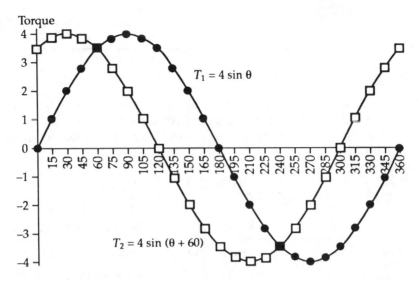

In practise force is only applied during the combustion stroke (the positive section of the graph). Obtain a relationship for the total torque acting on the shaft during the over-lapping period when both cylinders are producing power. Calculate the work done during this time if;

$$\text{Work} = \int T\, d\theta$$

STEP 1   Find the resultant waveform by plotting points that represent the sum of torque values at a series of angles. Consider only the range where torque is positive for both cylinders.

STEP 2   Combine the equations to give a single expression for the total torque $T_1 + T_2$, representing the resultant waveform.

STEP 3   Integrate this total torque with respect to θ over the appropriate range to find the work done (energy transferred).

   Information Bank Section 2   Unit 20.1 Trigonomical waveforms *page 199*
Unit 20.2 Addition of sine curves *pages 202*
Unit 20.3 Combining trig equations *pages 203*
Unit 22.1 Integration by substitution *page 214*

Extension task

Investigate the torque acting on crankshafts and energy transferred, in both four cylinder (phase angle 180°) and six cylinder (phase angle 120°) engines, if torque is given by;

Cylinder 1 $T = 3 \sin \theta$
Cylinder 2 $T = 3 \sin (\theta + \alpha)$ where α = phase angle.

Suggested answers to pilot questions

1.   Maximum speed upwards is achieved at 0° and maximum speed downwards is at 180°.
2.   To minimise the heat loss.
3.   Usually 4, 6, 8 or 12. So that power is delivered continuously and motion is smooth.

Introduction

The change in the flow of current during the charging of a car battery is analysed graphically. A vehicle alternator provides power to recharge the battery. Alternating current generated (from a rotating armature) in this way is considered in depth. The project focuses on;

Task 1 *Battery*	Skills Used:	Exponential Relationships
		Function of a Function
		Integration by Substitution
Task 2 *Alternating Current*	Skills Used:	Imaginary Numbers
		Complex Calculations
		Polar Coordinates
		Binomial Theorem
		Error
		Trigonometrical Waveforms
		Addition of Sine Curves
		Integration by Substitution
		Numerical Methods

Tasks follow on from one another and should be attempted in sequence. Each task is introduced with a brief explanation of how components work. Specific details are given about the application, these are required throughout the task.

'Pilot questions' lead students into the task by stimulating thoughts about different aspects of the problem. Appropriate mathematics can then follow. Suggested answers to these are given at the end of this project (page 60).

Task 1 *Battery*

In order to charge a battery there must be a potential difference between the charger and the battery itself (charging voltage). As a battery is charged this potential difference becomes less and since the charging current is related to this voltage the rate of charging also reduces.

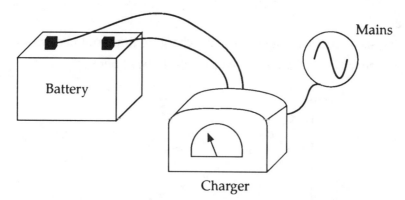

Battery

Mains

Charger

A test on the charging process is carried out, and from the results a relationship is developed and alternative specification looked at. Practical design limitations are observed.

☐ Pilot question 1

When charging a battery, why do you think the charging current would be likely to follow an exponential decay relationship?

☐ Task 1.1

A battery was put on charge for a period of six hours and the charging current recorded every 30 minutes. The results are given in a table:

t	0	1	2	3	4	5	6	7	8	9	10	11	12
i	3.00	2.71	2.46	2.22	2.01	1.82	1.65	1.49	1.35	1.22	1.10	1.00	0.90

Obtain an equation for the relationship if it is assumed that the current follows an exponential decay over the time period.

After what time will the current fall to 10% of its initial value.

What is the rate of change of the current after 3 hours and 15 minutes. When does the rate of change of the current become –0.004 amperes/minute.

STEP 1   Draw a graph to represent the charging current over the six hour period (working in minutes).

STEP 2   Develop an equation for this relationship if it is of the form $i = Ie^{-at}$. Evaluate the constants I and a.

STEP 3   Use the equation to calculate the time when the current has fallen to 10% of its initial value.

STEP 4   Differentiate the function to find rate of change of the charging current $\dfrac{di}{dt}$

STEP 5   Calculate the rate of change of current after 3 hours and 15 minutes.

STEP 6   Calculate the time when the rate of change of current is –0.004 amps/minutes.

Information Bank Section 2   Unit 10.1 Exponential relationships *page 148*
Unit 10.2 Gradients of exponential curves
page 150
Unit 21.1 Function of a function *page 207*

□Task 1.2

From the analysis of task 1.1 suggest how the charging time could be reduced.

If the charging curve for the current is considered to be as before;

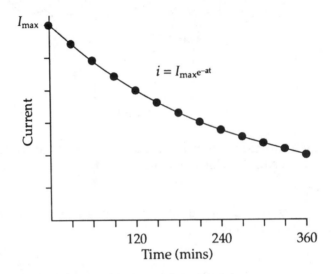

Consider alternative requirements for the charging pattern;

1. After what time will the current fall to 0.3 amps with an initial current of 5 amps, and when does the rate of change of the current becomes −0.004 amperes/minute.

2. If the rate of change is given by the expression; $\frac{di}{dt} = -0.02e^{-\frac{i}{200}}$ and the charging current is 2.96 amps after 1 hour of charging, find the current after 2 hours.

   STEP 1 Suggest two different ways of reducing the charging time.

   STEP 2 Write down the equation for current i in terms of time t.

   STEP 3 Calculate the time when $i = 0.3$ amps.

   STEP 4 Differentiate the function and calculate the time when the rate of change is −0.004 amps/minute.

   STEP 5 Integrate the alternative expression for $\frac{di}{dt}$ and using the current after 1 hour develop an equation for current i.

   STEP 6 Calculate the current after 2 hours.

   Information Bank Section 2   Unit 10.1 Exponential relationships *page 148*
Unit 21.1 Function of a function *page 207*
Unit 22.1 Integration by substitution *page 214*

□Extension task

Monitor the charging current when a car battery is put on charge. Record the current initially and at regular intervals over a period of six hours. Develop a relationship for this current and predict the time after which it will be 90% charged (the charging current will be 10% of its initial value).

Task 2 *Alternating current*

Alternators in vehicles are driven mechanically by pulleys and generate alternating current (a.c.). This is however converted into direct current (d.c.) by a rectifier so that the battery can be charged.

In this task the effects of a.c. supply are examined across different loads so that an understanding of its application can be gained.

Two circuits representing electrical devices are to be used for the analysis. The inductive circuit consists of a coil with inductive reactance $X_L = 7$ ohms and a resistance of 3 ohms.

The capacitive circuit consists of a capacitor with capacitive reactance $X_c = 6$ ohms and a resistance of 20 ohms.

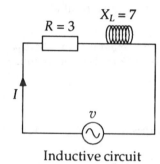
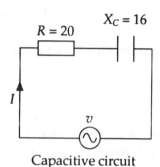

| Inductive circuit | Capacitive circuit |

☐ Pilot question 2

Suggest some applications for coils and capacitors. Where might we find such systems operating in a car (albeit with direct current)?

☐ Task 2.1

Instantaneous values of current i in a particular circuit can be obtained by using the equation; $i = 25 \sin \omega t$ where $\omega = 2 \pi f$ (f = frequency). The frequency of the supply is 40 cycles per second (Hz). Determine the root mean square (r.m.s.) value of this current.

STEP 1   Construct a graph of i^2 over a complete cycle.

STEP 2   Use the 'Mid-ordinate Rule' with 12 intervals to estimate the area under the curve over half of one cycle.

STEP 3   Calculate an approximation for the r.m.s. with this estimate.

STEP 4   Use integration to find the same area.

STEP 5   Calculate the r.m.s. value for the current.

STEP 6   What is the percentage error when the area is calculated using mid-ordinates.

STEP 7   Anticipate the percentage error in the calculation of i^2 using the binomial theorem, where $\sin \omega t$ is accurate to 0.1%.

Information Bank Section 2   Unit 17.1 Binomial theorem *page 182*
Unit 17.2 Error *page 184*
Unit 22.2 Integration by substitution *page 219*
Unit 23.0 Numerical methods *page 222*

☐ Task 2.2

Consider both the inductive and the capacitive circuits and determine in each case the current that will flow if a 40 V a.c. supply is connected.

STEP 1   Represent the impedance Z_L and Z_c of the circuits on an argand diagram.

STEP 2   Calculate the phase angles between the voltage and current. Are they lagging or leading.

STEP 3   Determine the current in the circuits using 'Ohms Law'.

STEP 4   What is the real power dissipated in each of the circuits.

 Information Bank Section 2   Unit 15.1 Imaginary numbers *page 171*
Unit 15.2 Complex calculations *page 175*

☐ Task 2.3

If the loads are connected in series and there is a current of 13/35° amperes in the circuit, what is the volt drop across the system.

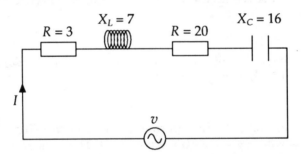

STEP 1   Find the sum of the impedance's $Z_L + Z_c$ for the series circuit.

STEP 2   Calculate the voltage and phase angle.

 Information Bank Section 2   Unit 15.2 Complex calculations *page 175*
Unit 15.3 Polar coordinates *page 176*

☐ Task 2.4

If the loads are alternatively connected in parallel and it is required that the same current as before $I = 13/35°$ amperes flows through the common section of the circuit, what voltage needs to be connected. What current will flow through the coil.

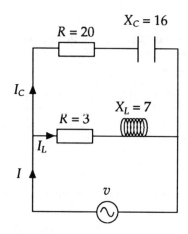

STEP 1   Convert the impedance's from each section of the circuit into polar co-ordinates.

STEP 2   Determine the combined impedance Z of the circuit; $\dfrac{1}{Z} = \dfrac{1}{Z_L} + \dfrac{1}{Z_C}$

STEP 3   Calculate the required voltage and phase angle.

STEP 4   Use this voltage to find the current in the coil.

    Information Bank Section 2   Unit 15.2 Complex calculations *page 175*
                                                          Unit 15.3 Polar coordinates *page 176*

☐ Task 2.5

Find the resultant wave form from the addition of two voltages v_1 and v_2. Determine the r.m.s.value for this sum.

$$v_1 = 24 \sin\theta$$

$$v_2 = 15 \sin(\theta + 50°)$$

STEP 1   Draw a graph representing the two waveforms v_1 and v_2.

STEP 2   Calculate the sum of voltages at a series of points to enable the combined curve to be drawn.

STEP 3   Develop a single expression for this curve $v_1 + v_2$ and simplify as far as possible.

STEP 4   Calculate the r.m.s value using integration.

    Information Bank Section 2   Unit 15.2 Complex calculations *page 175*
                                                          Unit 15.3 Polar coordinates *page 176*
                                                          Unit 20.2 Addition of sine curves *page 202*
                                                          Unit 22.1 Integration by substitution *page 214*

☐ Extension task

Find out details of some resistors, coils and capacitors that are in use and construct a table with columns as shown;

Application	Size (Ohms, Henrys or Farads)	Resistance or reactance at 50 Hz

Use these values to draw circuits and calculate the current flow if a 240 V a.c. supply were to be connected.

Introduction

If the suspension on a vehicle is too soft, continual movement will be experienced by passengers, whereas if suspension is too firm then road bumps will be felt inside. A balance needs to be found in the design. The project focuses on;

Task 1 *Suspension*	Skills Used:	Vectors
		Vector calculations
		Scalar product
		Centroids
		Second moments of area
		Composite shapes
Task 2 *Damping*	Skills Used:	Series
		Integration by substitution
		Integration by parts

Tasks follow on from one another and should be attempted in sequence. Each task is introduced with a brief explanation of how components work. Specific details are given about the application, these are required throughout the task.

'Pilot questions' lead students into the task by stimulating thoughts about different aspects of the problem. Appropriate mathematics can then follow. Suggested answers to these are given at the end of this project (page 67).

Task 1 *Suspension*

There are a number of types of suspension. Here it is intended to assess the merits and structure of a strut suspension system. A telescopic arm together with a spring absorb forces from the road, while a link holds it in place.

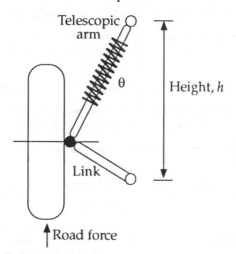

Design a suitable arrangement for this strut suspension system. Consider the angle θ, practical heights *h* and an appropriate cross section for the link piece.

☐ Pilot question 1

Why do you think it is desirable for a suspension strut to be as upright as possible? What restricts the strut from being vertical?

☐ Task 1.1

The body shape requires that the suspension height is 0.7 metres. and the width of the system must be 0.2 metres. Struts are available from suppliers in the lengths as shown.

Xtra Bounce	0.7 m
Comfy Spring	0.6 m
Absorbalot	0.5 m
Techparts	0.65 m

Calculate the length of link required for each of the struts. Determine all of the internal angles for the system.

The vector sum of forces applied by the arm and link must be equal and in the opposite direction to the road force.

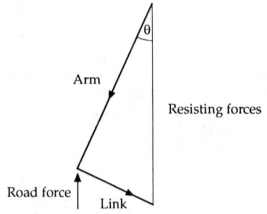

Determine the forces in the arm and the link for all makes of strut when subjected to a force of 10 Newtons. Suggest which strut is the most suitable.

If the maximum permitted forces acting through the strut is 10.5 N, what is the shortest strut length that can be used with a 10 Newton road force and what angle θ would be required?

STEP 1   Produce a table of lengths and angles for each supplier.

STEP 2   Draw a force triangle for each strut and, by resolving forces, calculate the magnitude of each resisting force with 10 N road force.

STEP 3   Sketch a force triangle and use appropriate trigonometry to calculate angles for 10.5 N arm force.

STEP 4   Using these angles, together with body shape limitations, determine the strut and link lengths.

    Information Bank Section 2   Unit 5.3 Sine and cosine rule *page 121*
Unit 18.1 Vectors *page 187*
Unit 18.2 Vector calculations *page 189*

□Task 1.2

As a vehicle travels along roads, it will encounter bumps. The wheel will be lifted by a road force (reaction to gravity) thereby producing energy. The energy needs to be absorbed by the suspension system. Calculations are required to assess the transfer of this energy.

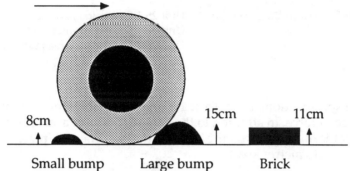

8cm	15cm	11cm
Small bump	Large bump	Brick

If a 12 N road force acts in each case, calculate the energy absorbed by both the strut and the link as the wheel travels along this hazardous road. Use the strut lengths and angles from Task 1.1, assuming there is no change in the angle θ.

What is the largest bump that can be traversed, if the maximum energy that the strut arm can absorb without failure is 2.4 Newton metres?

STEP 1 Calculate the displacement of the struts for each obstacle.

STEP 2 Use the scalar product to determine the work done in the direction of the strut by the road force.

STEP 3 Rearrange the scalar product to find the maximum displacement permitted for an energy limit of 2.4 Nm in the strut.

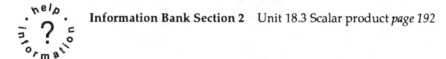

? **help information** **Information Bank Section 2** Unit 18.3 Scalar product *page 192*

□Task 1.3

The link piece in the suspension system only experiences limited bending under ideal operating conditions. However, these are rarely found, so the design of the cross section of this component should be considered.

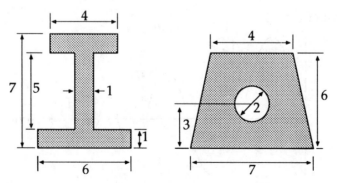

Find the second moment of area for each of these available cross sections (they may be used upside down if this is beneficial).

Design a cross-section that would improve on both of these examples by using only the same area.

Information Bank Section 2   Unit 25.1 Centroids *page 229*
Unit 26.1 Second moments of area *page 239*
Unit 26.2 Composite areas *page 241*

☐ Extension task

Using body shape specifications from Task 1.1 and an Absorbalot strut, reconsider the forces with a 10 N road force. In addition to the angle θ, the strut arm is also at an angle of 20° with the vertical leaning towards the front of the car. The link piece consists of two limbs with their base 0.15 metres apart.

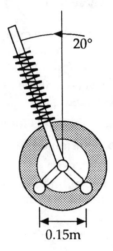

20°

0.15m

Task 2 *Damping*

Dampers in car suspension systems are used to stop the vehicle bouncing up and down for long periods after driving over bumps. The speed at which the car becomes steady can be controlled. Heavy damping returns the vehicle to a steady state quickly, whereas light damping takes longer.

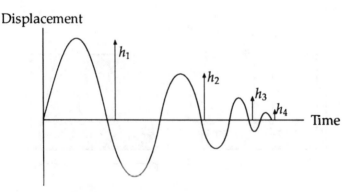

Displacement

h_1

h_2

h_3

h_4

Time

It is important to assess the amount of damping required and to design a suitable device.

☐Pilot question 2

Why do you think damping is required in a suspension system? What would you expect to happen without it or with too much?

☐Task 2.1

The height, h, of each bounce in a system reduces by a percentage of the height of the previous bounce. The table gives some values for different systems.

Without damping	Light damping	Heavy damping
10% reduction	20% reduction	40% reduction

For each type find:

1. How many bounces it will take before the amplitude reduces to one quarter of its original displacement.
2. What will be the sum of all the displacements (assuming the displacement below the normal position is the same as above) if 12 terms are included and the initial displacement is 3cm.

STEP 1   What type of series does this pattern of displacements follow?

STEP 2   Use appropriate formulae for the general term and let this equal $\frac{1}{4}$ of the first term for each system.

STEP 3   Rearrange and solve the resulting equations.

STEP 4   Use the formula for the sum of terms and evaluate for 12 terms.

 Information Bank Section 2   Unit 16 Series *page 80*

☐Task 2.2

The damping effect is achieved by using a piston inside a cylinder full of oil. The oil leaks round the piston and a resistance to motion is created. The rate of flow depends on the difference between the diameters. The smaller the flow area, the heavier the damping that is achieved.

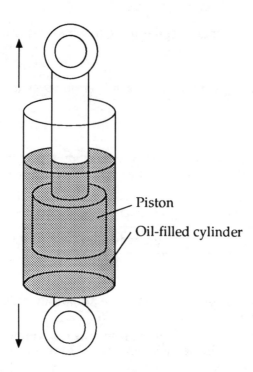

Piston

Oil-filled cylinder

A cylinder of diameter 5 cm is used with a range of piston sizes to create the level of damping required. The results of a test, using a range of different pistons, show how the velocity is affected. Measurements are in cm and cm/second.

Diameter	4.0	4.1	4.2	4.3	4.4	4.5	4.6	4.7	4.8
Velocity	2.2	2.0	1.7	1.5	1.3	1.1	0.8	0.6	0.4

What will the flow rate of the oil be for a piston of diameter 4.5 cm?

It is required to achieve heavier damping than has been recorded in the test. Obtain the flow rate for a diameter of 4.9 cm.

The velocity v is related to the diameter d by the equation:

$$v = 10(\ln 5 - \ln d)$$

Use this equation to develop an expression for the flow rate in terms of piston diameter. Calculate the area under the resulting graph (this area is related to the properties of the fluid).

STEP 1   Write down a formula for the flow rate f in terms of the diameter d and the velocity v.

STEP 2   Using a piston diameter of 4.5 cm, calculate the flow rate.

STEP 3   Draw a graph to represent the velocity change with diameter.

STEP 4   Estimate the velocity when the diameter is 4.9 cm and calculate the corresponding flow rate.

STEP 5   Develop an equation relating flow rate to diameter. Use this to check the flow rate with a diameter of 4.9 cm.

STEP 6   Sketch a graph of this relationship and decide on meaningful limits between which to integrate.

STEP 7   Integrate the equation between these limits and evaluate the area.

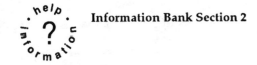   **Information Bank Section 2**   Unit 22.1 Integration by substitution *page 214*
                                                    Unit 22.2 Partial fractions *page 219*

☐ Extension task

If a piston diameter of 4.2 gives light damping (as defined in Task 2.1) and a diameter of 4.8 heavy damping, calculate in each case the number of bounces over a period of 10 seconds. The first bounce height is 2 cm.

Suggested answers to pilot questions

1. So that the spring absorbs most of any impact. A streamlined body shape.

2. Without damping, a vehicle would bounce up and down for a period after travelling over a bump. With too much, a car would be jolted back to its original position.

Introduction

Window areas are treated as flat surfaces and centroids of a host of shapes are required. The project focuses on;

Task *Windows*	Skills Used:	Centroids
		Integration by substitution

Tasks follow on from one another and should be attempted in sequence. Each task is introduced with a brief explanation of how components work. Specific details are given about the application, these are required throughout the task.

'Pilot questions' lead students into the task by stimulating thoughts about different aspects of the problem. Appropriate mathematics can then follow. Suggested answers to these are given at the end of this project (page 71).

☐ Pilot question

Describe a mechanism that could be used inside a door to allow a car window to be wound up and down.

Task *Windows*

Wind-up windows need to be raised by a force applied underneath. To prevent the pane from tilting and jamming between the runners, this force must act through the centroid. Determine the position of the centroid from the left hand edge of each of the four given window designs.

Van design

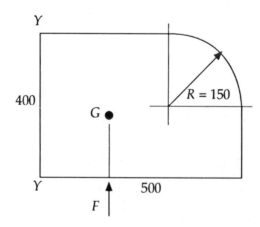

STEP 1   Sketch out the window shape and, with a pencil, divide it into numbered sections that are familiar shapes (rectangles, triangles, sectors of circles etc).

STEP 2   Calculate all these areas $A_1, A_2, A_3, \cdots$

STEP 3   Calculate the position of the centroid for each area from a known vertical axis. Hence, determine the distance that it lies from the edge YY, $(x_1, x_2, x_3, \cdots)$

STEP 4   Use a table to calculate the sum of all areas and the sum of all moments of area.

Shape	Area	Distance of centroid from YY
1	A_1	x_1
2	:	:
:		
Total		

STEP 5   Create an equation involving the distance of the centroid for the whole shape, and solve it.

 Information Bank Section 2   Unit 25.1 Centroids *page 229*

Saloon design

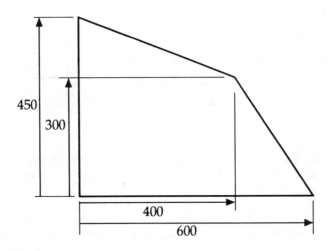

STEP 1   Sketch out the window shape and, with a pencil, divide it into numbered sections that are familiar shapes.

STEP 2   Calculate areas $A_1, A_2, A_3, \cdots$

STEP 3   Calculate the position of the centroid for each area from the edge $(x_1, x_2, x_3, \cdots)$

STEP 4 Use a table to calculate the sum of all areas and the sum of all moments of area.

Shape	Area	Distance of centroid from YY
1	A_1	x_1
2	:	:
:		
Total		

STEP 5 Create an equation involving the distance of the centroid for the whole shape, and solve it.

Sports design

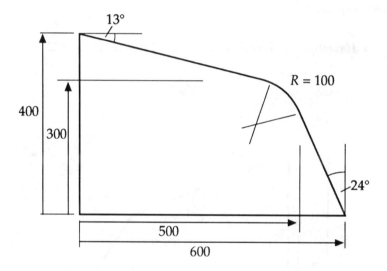

STEP 1 Sketch out the window shape and, with a pencil, divide it into numbered sections that are familiar shapes. Trigonometry is required here for the calculation of angles.

STEP 2 Calculate areas $A_1, A_2, A_3, \cdots$ and distances $x_1, x_2, x_3, \cdots$ and using a table as before, determine the sum of areas and moments.

STEP 3 Create an equation involving the distance of the centroid for the whole shape and solve it.

Model X (next generation)

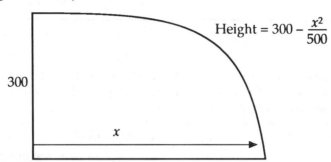

$$\text{Height} = 300 - \frac{x^2}{500}$$

STEP 1   Consider the area and moment of area about the edge of a thin strip.

STEP 2   Find the sum of these areas and the sum of moments by using integration.

STEP 3   Write down an equation involving the distance of the centroid and solve it.

Information Bank Section 2   Unit 25.1 Centroids *page 229*

Extension task

Design a window shape that would be suitable for your own new car model made up from known shapes. Include all necessary dimensions. Calculate the position of the centroid from one edge.

Suggested answer to pilot question

A gearwheel driving a vertical rod.

Project J *Transmission*

Introduction

Energy in the form of rotary motion has to be transferred to the road wheels of a vehicle. A propeller shaft via a series of joints delivers this energy and propels the car along. This motion is looked at in detail: The project focuses on;

Task 1 *Propeller shaft*	Skills Used:	Centroids
		Volumes of revolution
		Polar second moments of area
Task 2 *Final drive*	Skills Used:	Vector products
		Determinants
Task 3 *Circular motion*	Skills Used:	Function of a function
		Integration by substitution
		Differential equations
		Separating variables
		Second moments of area

Tasks follow on from one another and should be attempted in sequence. Each task is introduced with a brief explanation of how components work. Specific details are given about the application, these are required throughout the task.

'Pilot questions' lead students into the task by stimulating thoughts about different aspects of the problem. Appropriate mathematics can then follow. Suggested answers to these are given at the end of this project (page 79).

Task 1 *Propeller shaft*

The propeller shaft connects the gearbox to the final drive on the rear axle. It has to transmit the engine power to the wheels through a system of joints. The design of this shaft must ensure that it is capable of carry the stresses, and that it is supported in such a way as to minimise vibrations.

☐ Pilot question 1

What type of stresses do you think a propeller shaft is subjected to?

☐ Task 1.1

If the shaft is a solid circular section calculate the polar second moment of area J for a diameter of 6 cm. Investigate how this could be replaced with a tubular section having the same area (hence the same weight) but with a much higher value for polar second moment of area J.

With a limit on the outside diameter of 8 cm what dimensions will give the best result for the same weight.

What equivalent value could be obtained for a solid square section shaft.

STEP 1 Use the formula for polar second moment of area with a radius of 3 cm.

STEP 2 Calculate the area of the solid shaft. Determine inside and outside diameters that give this area, and use these to calculate J values.

STEP 3 With an outside diameter of 8 cm obtain the corresponding inside value that produces the required area. Again calculate the J value.

STEP 4 Using the perpendicular axis theorem and dimensions that satisfy the area requirement, calculate I_{ZZ} for a square section.

Information Bank Section 2 Unit 26.3 Polar second moment of area *page 246*

☐Task 1.2

Three types of joint are available that can be used with the shaft. They may be treated as solid steel shapes. Calculate the weight of each of these joints.

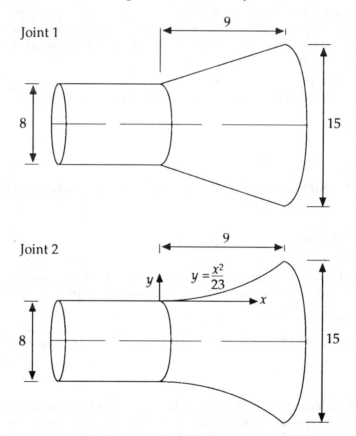

Joint 1

Joint 2

$y = \dfrac{x^2}{23}$

Joint 3 is an irregular shape, the diameters at regular intervals are given in the table;

x	0	0.75	1.5	2.25	3	3.75	4.5	5.25	6	6.75	7.5	8.25	9
d	8.0	8.3	9.4	10.6	11	12.6	13	14.2	14.8	15.1	15.2	15	15.3

STEP 1   Calculate the volume of joint 1 using appropriate formulae. Look up the density of steel and determine the weight.

STEP 2   Form an equation for the surface of joint 2 and use definite integration between limits to calculate the volume. Again use density to find the weight.

STEP 3   Calculate a series of areas (assuming a circular section) from the table of diameters. Apply 'Simpsons Rule' and find an estimate for the volume. Hence calculate the weight.

    Information Bank Section 2   Unit 9.2 Estimating volumes *page 144*
Unit 17.1 Binomial theorem *page 182*
Unit 25.2 Volumes of revolution *page 236*

☐Task 1.3

Find the distance of the centre of mass along the length of each joint from task 1.2.

STEP 1   Use integration to find the sum of moments of volume Vx for joints 1 and 2.

STEP 2   For joint 3, calculate mid-ordinates for the diameters (assuming a straight line relationship between points). Construct a table for the moments of volume for each section assuming it to be a series of cylinders. Determine the distance of the centroid.

    Information Bank Section 2   Unit 25.1 Centroids *page 229*

☐Extension task

Carry out research into the size and shape of some propeller shafts. Determine the polar second moment of area *J* in each case.

Task 2 *Final drive*

The angular motion of the propeller shaft has to be converted into movement of the vehicle, the final drive is where this happens. An understanding of the relationship between angular motion and linear velocity is therefore required.

☐Pilot question 2

If a vehicle has large wheels, how do you think this affects the torque on the shaft driving them?

☐Task 2.1

The speed at which a car is travelling needs to be monitored accurately. The change in the deformation of the tyres at different speeds makes this difficult to ascertain. A device fitted on the axle to record distances *R* could provide a solution. If the device tracks the point where the tyre meets the road, calculations can be carried out with angular velocity to find the precise speed of the vehicle.

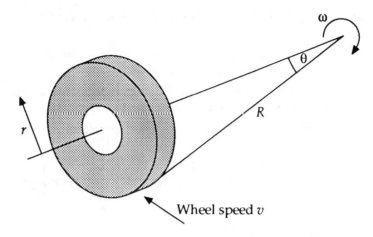

Wheel speed v

Calculate the speed of the wheel if measurements are taken giving:

$$R = 1.2 \text{ m}; \quad \omega = 25 \text{ revs/second}; \quad \theta = 20°$$

What angular velocity would be required to produce a wheel speed of 30 mph, with the same measurements for R and θ.

STEP 1   Convert ω into rads/second.

STEP 2   Use the vector product to determine both the magnitude and direction of the wheel velocity.

STEP 3   With appropriate units (SI) use the vector product to calculate the required angular velocity.

 Information Bank Section 2   Unit 18.4 Vector product *page 193*

☐Task 2.2

Since the speed of a vehicle is continually changing, numerous calculations are required even for a short journey. A systematic procedure is therefore necessary. With vectors represented in component form, calculate the wheel velocity for each set of recorded measurements;

ω	$2k$	$-3.5k$	$7i$
R	$0.4j + 0.8k$	$0.25j + 1.2k$	$0.3i + 1j$

Other results are represented in matrix form, again determine the wheel velocity in each case.

$$\begin{pmatrix} i & j & k \\ 0 & 0 & -3 \\ 0 & 0.5 & 0.3 \end{pmatrix} \qquad \begin{pmatrix} i & j & k \\ -4 & 0 & 0 \\ 0.2 & 0 & -0.3 \end{pmatrix} \qquad \begin{pmatrix} i & j & k \\ 0 & 6 & 0 \\ 0 & 1.5 & -0.5 \end{pmatrix}$$

STEP 1   Draw a sketch of the wheel and axle, and indicate the vectors and unit vectors.

STEP 2   Use the vector product to calculate the velocities, paying particular attention to the positive and negative directions.

STEP 3   Set up a spreadsheet to evaluate determinants and use it to check some previously calculated velocities, then use it with confidence.

STEP 4   What is the meaning of the negative values given for each vector.

Information Bank Section 2   Unit 18.4 Vector product *page 193*
Unit 18.5 Determinants *page 195*

☐ Extension task

Estimate the percentage error that is likely when the radius of a car wheel is assumed to be a constant value (how much variation is there). If there is an additional error of 1% in the measurement of angular velocity, use the binomial theorem to calculate the error in calculating the vehicle speed.

Task 3 *Circular motion*

The wheels and tyres of a vehicle are the most noticeable moving part of the mechanical system of a car. It is therefore easy to appreciate that the circular motion here, is converted to linear motion at this final stage of the energy transfer.

The design is required to consider the effects of realistic road conditions so that appropriate wheel sizes may be employed.

☐ Pilot question 3

How many miles can be driven on a set of road tyres before the depth of tread falls below the legal limit. What conditions will reduce this mileage.

☐ Task 3.1

A car wheel is driven so that it rotates at an angular velocity ω and produces forward motion of the vehicle. The velocity of a point on the surface of the tyre, initially on the centre line as shown, is examined.

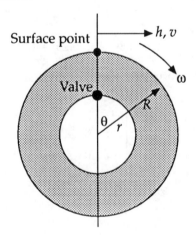

If a wheel of radius $R = 0.3$ metres rotates at the constant rate of 500 revs/min obtain a relationship between the linear velocity v of a point on the surface of the tyre and the time t. Find the total distance that this point will have travelled after 10 minutes driving.

The vehicle applies its brakes and slows down at the rate of 4 m/s². What will the height of the air valve be when the vehicle stops? At the start of braking the air valve is vertically above the centre and the radius $r = 0.22$ metres.

STEP 1   Write down an equation for the distance h of a point on the surface of the tyre from the centre line.

STEP 2   Differentiate this expression to give linear velocity $v = \dfrac{dh}{dt}$.

STEP 3   Add this velocity to the velocity of the centre line itself.

STEP 4   Draw a graph to represent this motion.

STEP 5   How far will the point travel in 10 minutes?

STEP 6   Calculate the time before the vehicle stops with a deceleration of 4m/s² from the initial velocity.

STEP 7   Use this value to determine h (ω also changes with time), and calculate the height of the valve with $r = 0.22$ m.

Information Bank Section 2   Unit 21.1 Function of a function *page 207*

☐ Task 3.2

Two wheel shapes are to be considered for use. Each design is to be made from mild steel.

Design 1

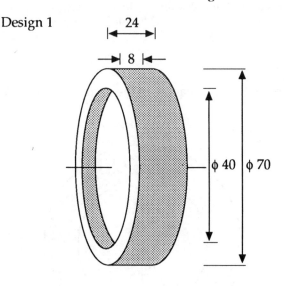

Design 2

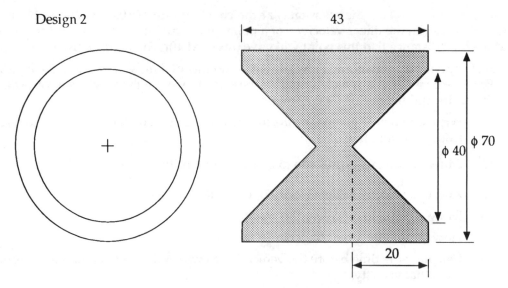

Calculate the moment of inertia of each wheel design about the centre line and comment on their suitability.

STEP 1   Treat each design as a number of simple shapes (cylinders, spheres etc).

STEP 2   Use formulae where these are available from the formula sheet together with the density to calculate values for the moment of inertia I.

STEP 3   Find the sum of these I values ($I = \sum mr^2$). Integration or numerical methods will be required.

Information Bank Section 2   Unit 22.1 Integration by substitution *page 214*
Unit 26.1 Second moments of area *page 239*

☐Task 3.3

The length L of the tyre that is in contact with the road depends on the weight W that acts through the wheel.

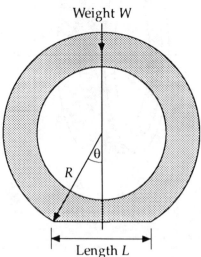

Develop a relationship between the length L in contact with the road if it is thought that:

$$\frac{dW}{dL} = 0.1W$$

(where 0.1 represents the rigidity of the tyre).

With a weight W of 2000 N, the contact length is 20 cm.

Calculate the contact length L for a weight of 1800 N.

If the wheel radius $R = 30$cm, what angle θ will be observed for this weight?

STEP 1   Separate the variables in the differential equation.

STEP 2   Integrate both sides of the equation with respect to corresponding variables.

STEP 3   Substitute values and find the particular solution.

STEP 4   Determine the length L for a weight of 1800 N.

STEP 5   Calculate the angle θ.

 Information Bank Section 2   Unit 24.1 Differential equations *page 225*
Unit 24.2 Separating variables *page 228*

☐ Extension task

For the wheel designs of Task 3.2, calculate the kinetic energy if in each case they are rotated at 500 rpm.

Suggested answer to pilot question 23

1. Mainly torsion.
2. The torque will remain the same whatever wheel radius is used.
3. Between 10000 and 20000. Heavy braking, town driving, fast acceleration.

Project K *Performance testing*

Introduction

An important stage in any design projects is the testing. Realistic road test results together with practical information are used to assess the performance of cars.

The project focuses on;

Task 1 *Straight and level*	Skills Used:	Function of a function Quotient rule Integration by substitution Partial fractions Integration by parts Differential equations Separating variables
Task 2 *Cornering*	Skills Used:	Vectors Trigonometrical waveforms Integration by substitution Integration by parts Centroids
Task 3 *Hills and inclines*	Skills Used:	Vectors Vector calculations Scalar products Maximum and minimum Trigonometrical waveforms Function of a function Second moments of area

Tasks follow on from one another and should be attempted in sequence. Each task is introduced with a brief explanation of how components work. Specific details are given about the application, these are required throughout the task.

'Pilot questions' lead students into the task by stimulating thoughts about different aspects of the problem. Appropriate mathematics can then follow. Suggested answers to these are given at the end of this project (page 88).

Task 1 *Straight and level*

The design of motor cars is an ongoing process and improvements can always be made. In order to quantify any improvements to existing models, measurements need to be taken that relate to vehicle performance. Here, we consider some of the criteria often used in the comparison of different designs.

☐ Pilot question 1

What would you consider to be the important performance factors that need to be measured?

☐ Task 1.1

During a road test, the speed of a vehicle was closely monitored. A table of these speeds is given.

Time (mins)	0	5	10	15	20	25	30	35	40	45	50
Speed (mph)	0	20	40	60	60	41.7	26.7	15	6.7	1.7	0

The journey is divided into three parts. For the first 15 minutes, the acceleration is constant. The car is then driven for 5 minutes at constant speed. Finally, the brakes are applied and the vehicle speed reduces following the equation:

$$v = \frac{2}{30}t^2 - \frac{20}{3}t + \frac{500}{3}$$

The total journey time is 50 minutes.

Find the total distance travelled and the time at which the rate of braking is equal in magnitude to the acceleration during the first part of the journey.

STEP 1   Draw an appropriate graph to represent this journey.

STEP 2   Write down an equation for each section of the graph.

STEP 3   Calculate the distance travelled by evaluating the area under the graph. Care must be taken to use consistent units (hours or minutes).

STEP 4   Develop a relationship for the acceleration in terms of time at each stage of the trip.

STEP 5   At what value of time is the braking rate (negative acceleration) equal in magnitude to half the initial acceleration.

Information Bank Section 2   Unit 21.1 Function of a function *page 207*
Unit 22.1 Integration by substitution *page 214*

☐ Task 1.2

In a controlled test, carried out on a test bed, the motion of a vehicle initially travelling at 10 mph is given by the equation:

$$\frac{dv}{dt} = 3 - kv$$

where kv represents the resistance to motion.

Resistances to the motion were created so that road conditions could be simulated. If the value of k is taken to be 0.03, calculate the time when the velocity is 25 mph.

STEP 1   Separate the variables in the differential equation.

STEP 2   Integrate both sides of the equation with respect to appropriate variables and obtain the general solution.

STEP 3   Substitute known values and evaluate the constant of integration. Hence write down the particular solution to the differential equation.

STEP 4   Find the time when the velocity is 25 mph.

 Information Bank Section 2   Unit 22.1 Integration by substitution *page 214*
Unit 24.1 Differential equations *page 225*
Unit 24.2 Separating variables *page 228*

☐ Task 1.3

The acceleration of a vehicle is often regarded as a mark of its performance. Investigate the motion of a vehicle if the acceleration is known.

If a car accelerates from rest at the constant rate of $a = 4$ m/s², determine the distance travelled in 10 seconds.

For a variable acceleration, $a = \dfrac{2t}{t^2 + 5t + 6}$. Again, find the distance travelled in this time.

STEP 1   Integrating the acceleration with respect to time will give velocity, since $\dfrac{dv}{dt} = a$.

STEP 2   Integrating a second time gives the distance travelled, since $\dfrac{ds}{dt} = v$

STEP 3   The initial conditions for distance and speed allow the constants of integration to be found.

STEP 4   Check the results by differentiation.

 Information Bank Section 2   Unit 21.3 Quotient rule *page 212*
Unit 22.2 Partial fractions *page 219*
Unit 22.3 Integration by parts *page 220*

☐ Extension task

Monitor the speed over a short car journey along with the mileage. Speed should be recorded at regular time intervals. Draw a velocity time graph to represent this journey.

Estimate the acceleration at selected points (including the highest rates of acceleration and deceleration). Develop equations for the acceleration if possible. Discuss the acceleration changes during the journey. Calculate the distance travelled from the graph and compare this with the mileage from the milometer.

Task 2 *Cornering*

When a vehicle turns a corner, a force is required to stop the wheels from skidding outwards. This is therefore an inward force towards the centre of the arc, known as centripetal force. On a level road it is provided by friction between the tyres and the road surface. Banked roads may be used to increase centripetal force and allow corners to be taken at higher speeds.

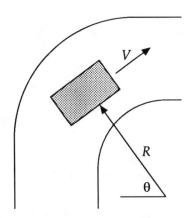

The road holding of a vehicle, together with the position of the centre of mass, will affect its cornering capabilities. Consequently, investigations are required.

☐Pilot question 2

If a vehicle turns to the left, why do you think the passengers feel a tendency to be flung to the right?

☐Task 2.1

What is the maximum speed at which a vehicle can travel round a bend of radius 20 metres if the coefficient of friction is 0.3.

STEP 1   Using appropriate formulae from the formula sheet, let the centripetal force be provided by friction, and develop an equation.

STEP 2   Substitute the radius and coefficient of friction and calculate the maximum linear speed.

STEP 3   Why is this independent of the mass of the vehicle?

STEP 4   What could be done to allow vehicles to travel faster round this bend?

   Information Bank Section 2   Unit 18.1 Vectors *page 187*

□ Task 2.2

If a road is banked at an angle θ, it allows a vehicle to corner at higher speeds without skidding.

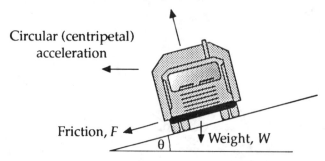

Held up by road, R

Circular (centripetal) acceleration

Friction, F ◄ ▼ Weight, W θ

With 10° of banking, what is now the maximum speed at which a vehicle can travel round a bend of radius 20 metres, where the coefficient of friction is 0.3. Consider other angles of banking.

STEP 1   Sketch the forces on a diagram and resolve them into horizontal and vertical components.

STEP 2   Consider the forces that combine to produce the centripetal acceleration (force) and write down an equation.

STEP 3   Solve this equation to obtain the maximum velocity.

STEP 4   Develop a relationship between the maximum speed and the angle of banking.

STEP 5   Sketch a curve of this relationship and comment on the practical limitations.

Information Bank Section 2   Unit 18.1 Vectors *page 187*
Unit 20.1 Trigonometrical waveforms *page 199*

□ Task 2.3

On a level bend, or even worse, a bend with reverse camber, there is a tendency for a cornering vehicle to topple over. This can be minimised by designing the shape and arrangement of components so that the centre of mass is as close to the ground as possible. The new shape of a trailer, viewed from the front, is a trapezium as shown.

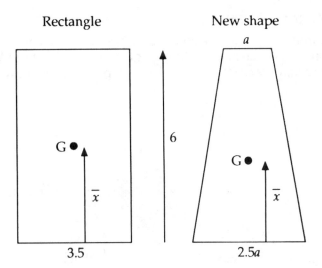

Rectangle   New shape

Calculate the height of the centre of area with this new shape. The area must remain the same.

Calculate the height of the centroid for a car if the total width $w = 2.2$ metres and the roof height is given by the equation:

$$h = 2.4 - e^{-0.2w}$$

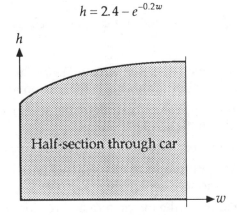

Half-section through car

STEP 1   Calculate the value of a and hence the width at the base of the trapezium.

STEP 2   Find the sum of moments of area and therefore the height of the centroid.

STEP 3   Use integration to find the area of the shape and the sum of all the moments of thin strip areas about the w axis.

STEP 4   Determine the height of the centroid.

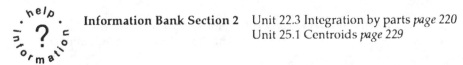

Information Bank Section 2   Unit 22.3 Integration by parts *page 220*
                                Unit 25.1 Centroids *page 229*

☐ **Extension task**

Use numerical methods to find the height of centroids for some vehicle shapes. Accurate drawings or pictures will allow measurements to be made.

Task 3 *Hills and inclines*

When a vehicle climbs a hill, an additional force has to be overcome. This is a component of the weight acting down the slope. Any height that is gained can be considered to be stored energy (potential energy) that may be used up on the way down.

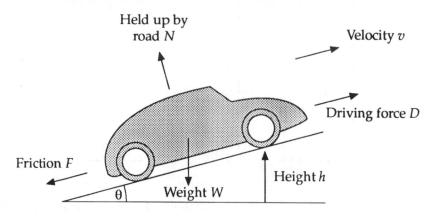

When faced with hills and slopes, the weight of a car becomes a force acting against the motion. It is therefore necessary for the power to weight ratio to be carefully designed.

☐ Pilot question 3

Why can't all the energy that is used to climb a hill be recouped on the way down?

☐ Task 3.1

If a car weighing 700 kg is driven up a hill, with angle θ = 30°, by a force of 5000 N so that all the forces are balanced (equilibrium), what is the friction force F?

With the same driving force applied on a straight and level road and assuming a friction coefficient as before, what will the acceleration be?

What is the steepest slope that can be climbed with a driving force of 6000 N?

STEP 1 Resolve the weight into force components parallel and perpendicular to the slope. Assume the acceleration due to gravity is $g = 10$ m/s².

STEP 2 Form an equation for the forces in each direction (parallel and perpendicular) and solve them to obtain the friction force, F.

STEP 3 Find the friction coefficient, μ.

STEP 4 Using this coefficient of friction and a driving force $D = 5000$ N, calculate the acceleration on a level road.

STEP 5 Again, with forces in balance, write down equations and calculate the maximum angle of a hill that can be climbed with a driving force of $D = 6000$ N.

Information Bank Section 2   Unit 18.1 Vectors *page 187*
Unit 18.2 Vector calculations *page 189*

☐ Task 3.2

Calculate the work done against gravity if the vehicle from Task 3.1 continues up the 30° incline for $\frac{1}{4}$ mile. What is the work done against friction? How much energy is stored and therefore still available? If this energy is used to simply overcome friction on the way down with the same coefficient as before, what is the minimum slope angle required?

What speed will the vehicle achieve if it rolls down the 30° incline or $\frac{1}{4}$ mile?

STEP 1   Use the scalar product to determine the work done against gravity and friction.

STEP 2   Where has the energy gone from doing the work in each case?

STEP 3   By observation of the work done against friction only down a slope (friction opposes motion), develop an equation for the angle θ and solve it.

STEP 4   Determine the acceleration down a 30° slope by consideration of the forces.

STEP 5   Calculate the velocity after $\frac{1}{4}$ mile.

Information Bank Section 2   Unit 18.3 Scalar product *page 192*
                                            Unit 20.1 Trigonometrical waveforms *page 199*

☐ Task 3.3

A hill of height H is in the shape of a sine curve. The gradient changes as a car moves a horizontal distance s from the bottom of the hill. The corresponding height is related to distance s by the given equation, where k is a constant.

$$h = \frac{H}{2}\sin\left(ks - \frac{\pi}{2}\right) + \frac{H}{2}$$

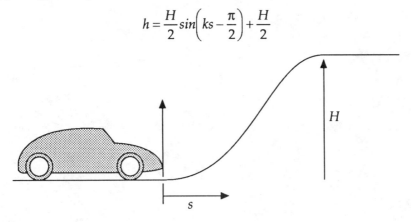

For a hill with height $H = 250$ metres, the height h is measured to be 50m at a distance $s = 300$m. Find the gradient of the slope at a distance $s = 400$ m. At this point calculate the component of weight acting against the direction of motion if the weight of the car is 980 kg. At what distance s does the road become level?

STEP 1   Substitute the height $H = 250$ into the equation for the car height h.

STEP 2   Differentiate the expression with respect to distance s (remember k is a constant value).

STEP 3   Use the particular value for the height at 300m to calculate k.

STEP 4   Give a general equation for the gradient and use this to find the gradient at 400 metres.

STEP 5   From this gradient determine the component of the weight acting down the slope.

STEP 6   Determine the distance s where the maximum height is reached $\left(\dfrac{dh}{ds} = 0\right)$.

STEP 7   Confirm that this is a maximum point.

Information Bank Section 2   Unit 18.1 Vectors *page 187*
Unit 19.0 Maximum and minimum *page 196*
Unit 21.1 Function of a function *page 207*

☐ Extension task

Find out the weight of some vehicles and complete a table with columns as shown. This should give an indication of their hill-climbing capability.

Weight (kg)	Component of weight acting against motion at angle:			
	10°	20°	30°	40°

Investigate also how the friction forces are affected by weights and angles of incline.

Section 2 – The Information Bank

Introduction

Section 2 covers all the mathematical techniques required at this level. These are divided into 'Skills Areas' (in turn, sub-divided into specific skills – see Contents below). By directing the student to refer to Section 2 as and when a particular problem needs to be solved, cross-referencing from Section 1 and Section 3 encourage a project-driven approach to the subject.

The 'Skills Areas' separate the Information Bank into logical stand-alone blocks, which also relate to up-to-date BTEC guidelines (Lecturers' Supplement provides guidance for lecturers – see Preface).

'Primary Skills' are required for the earlier part of the course (this could be the first year) and 'Secondary Skills' are extensions to these with some additional material that relates to more advanced applications.

Examples are used throughout Section 2, to introduce techniques and show how they are used to help solve an engineering problem. 'Investigations', which follow on from an 'Example', develop theory, and the mathematical principles are clarified.

Contents

Skill unit 1 *Calculators and computers*

1.1 Accuracy

Introduction

Mathematics at this level should not be attempted without access to, at the very least, a good scientific calculator. Other technological aids (such as programmable calculators and computer software) should be investigated and fully utilised.

Failure to exploit any available technological aids is wasteful and inefficient. The skills required to carry out problem solving with technology are often quite different from the, possibly redundant, skills needed without such supportive devices. It is therefore necessary for the next generation of Technicians and Engineers to be up to date and creative in their approach to using technology.

Scientific calculators

Unfortunately the layout of scientific calculators is not yet standardised (more progress in this direction has been made with computers). However, there are many similarities between the different types that are available. A typical layout is shown;

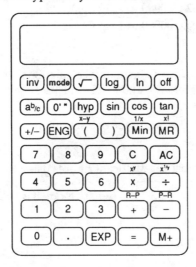

In addition there are other modes of operation including statistics that have been explained alongside the specific skills.

Some of the functions are self explanatory whereas others are not required at this level of engineering mathematics. The hyp function is not referred to here for this reason.

Example 1

The area of a rectangular steel plate is required. When a precise measuring device accurate to 0.01 mm is used the measurements are as shown in the diagram.

Find the error in calculating this area if measurements are obtained using;
a)   Callipers, accurate to 0.1 mm
b)   Ruler, accurate to the nearest mm
c)   Measuring tape, accurate to the nearest cm

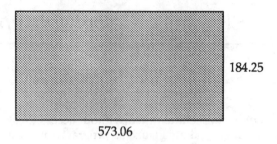

184.25

573.06

Solution 1

Using measurements accurate to five *significant figures* the area is given by;

$$184.25 \times 573.06 = 105586.31 \ (105600 \text{ to } 4 \text{ sig figs})$$

We can only guarantee that 4 significant figures are correct because the discarded (unknown) figures after the 5 and 6 would influence the 5th figure in the answer.

In the same way we must reduce the number of significant figures, in answers to other calculations, so that they are one less than measurements.

a) Callipers $184.3 \times 573.1 = 105622.33 \ (106000 \text{ to } 3 \text{ sig figs})$
b) Ruler $184 \times 573 = 105432 \ (110000 \text{ to } 2 \text{ sig figs})$
c) Tape $180 \times 570 = 102600 \ (100000 \text{ to } 1 \text{ sig fig})$

Investigations

From the example it is clear that the results of any calculations are only as accurate as measurements that are entered. It is unnecessary, and can be misleading, to quote any more figures than those that we have confidence in.

Note: In order to give an answer to an accuracy of 3 sig figs we must work with 4 sig figs.

Significant figures (sig figs)

Calculators can display a set number of significant figures using the SCI mode

| mode | 8 | 3 | (where mode 8 is SCI)

This instruction sets the calculator up to work with 3 significant figures. Additional entries will be rounded off.

Decimal places (DPs)

Calculators can operate with a set number of decimal places using the FIX mode

| mode | 7 | 3 | (where mode 7 is FIX)

This instruction sets the calculator up to work with 3 decimal places. Additional entries will be rounded off. This is particularly useful facility for calculations involving money (with 2 DPs).

Escaping

To leave this mode of operation:

| mode | 9 | (where mode 9 is NORM)

This will return to a floating point system.

1.2 Calculations

Example 2

Find the volume of paint, in litres, that is required to cover a circle of radius 250 cm with paint thickness of 8×10^{-3} mm.

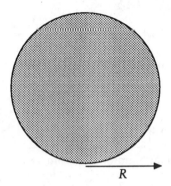

R

Solution 2

The area of the circle can be found using $A = \pi R^2$. This value is then multiplied by the thickness.

Using a calculator $A =$

| π | | $\times$ | | 250 | x^2 | | $=$ |

gives 200000 cm² (2 sig figs)

Units have to be consistent, so the thickness has to be converted to cm.

| 8 | exp | 3 | +/− | ÷ | 10 | = |

the answer here is 0.0008 cm

(EXP opens 2 smaller spaces in which the power is entered for standard form numbers)

Multiplying these gives 160 cm³ or 0.16 litres.

Investigations

Example 2 introduces the use of functions (x^2), standard form (exp) and gives the correct sequence of entering operations.

Functions

With any required function the number is entered onto the display before the function is activated.

To find sin 30°.

| 30 | sin | is CORRECT

| sin | 30 | is INCORRECT

Where index numbers other than squared values are sought the x^y button is used, here we have 3^4:

| 3 | x^y | 4 | = |

Sequence of Calculations

Calculators carry out operations in the order shown:
- ❐ Brackets
- ❐ Powers and Roots
- ❐ Multiplication and Division
- ❐ Addition and Subtraction

This order should be kept in mind when carrying out a string of calculations.

The calculation $\dfrac{6+9}{2\times 3}$ can give a number of different answers depending on how it is entered and care is required.

One method is to use brackets:

| [| 6 | + | 9 |] | | ÷ | | [| 2 | × | 3 |] |

Alternatively we can evaluate the numerator and store it in the memory;

| 6 | + | 9 | = | M+ | AC | 2 | × | 3 | = | X-M | + | MR | = |

The X-M button switches the display with the memory.

Binary, Octal and Hex

Denary (base 10) numbers can be represented in other bases where figures (columns) have different values. Columns to the left increase by multiplying by the base number.

Binary (base 2)

| 512 | 256 | 128 | 64 | 32 | 16 | 8 | 4 | 2 | Units |

The only digits required here are 1 and 0

Octal (base 8)

| 512 | | 64 | | 8 | | Units |

The only digits required here are 0–7

Hex (base 16)

| 256 | | 16 | | Units |

Here, extra digits are required, represented by the letters A to F, giving a total range:

1, 2, 3, 4, 5, 6, 7, 8, 9, A, B, C, D, E, F.

These extra symbols are necessary to avoid confusion between columns.

Eg   10 (Den) = A (Hex)

               16 (Den) = 10 (Hex)

Example

300 (Den) = 100101100 (Bin)

= 454 (Oct)

= 12C (Hex)

Converting from one number to another may be carried out very easily with a suitable calculator. A number on the display can be converted appropriately with;

| Den | Bin | Oct | Hex |

Programmable Calculators

Programmable scientific calculators allow the user to carry out a calculation repeatedly with a range of values. The calculator records a sequence of keys that have been pressed. Programs are retained in memory and executed when required. A number of programs may be held in memory simultaneously.

To enter a program (string of keys) the required sequence is entered in the LEARN mode and completed with ENTER.

For the squaring and adding 3:

$\boxed{x^2}$ $\boxed{+}$ $\boxed{3}$ $\boxed{\text{ENT}}$ enters the program

A program can be executed with

$\boxed{\text{RUN}}$ or $\boxed{\text{EXE}}$

Thus, for example:

4 $\boxed{\text{RUN}}$ will square 4 and add 3 giving answer 19

More sophisticated calculators allow formulae to be entered in a similar way.

1.3 Spreadsheets

Large and complicated tables of values can be calculated very quickly using spreadsheets.

There are a few points to note when entering formulae into spreadsheets. The notation that is used differs slightly from that which is usually written.

Conventional Expression	Spreadsheet Entry (where cell A1 contains a value)
$2x^2 + 3x - 4$	=2*A1^2+3*A1-4
$\sin \theta$	=sin(A1)
$\sqrt{x}$	=SQRT(A1)

Formulae may be copied (memorised) and pasted into other cells. When this is done the relative positions are pasted rather than exact cell numbers.

	A	B	C	D	E
1	3	=2*A1	=2*B1		
2		=2*A2			
3					
4					

In this spreadsheet, when the formula from cell B1 is copied and pasted into B2 the system is aware that it has moved down one space and the formula changes accordingly. The same applies for pasting into other columns.

2.1 Evaluating formulae

Example 1

A jug kettle holds water in the shape of a cylinder. The radius (R) and the height (H) are internal dimensions as shown.

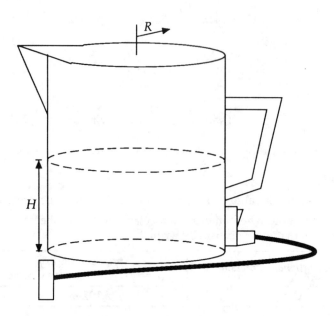

Find the volume if the radius is measured to be 7cm and the height 12cm.

Solution 1

Using the formula	$V = H\pi R^2$	where V represents the volume
Substitute values	$V = 12 \times 3.14 \times 7^2$	
Thus:	$V = 12 \times 3.14 \times 49$	
	$V = 1,850 \text{ cm}^2$	
	$V = 1.85 \text{ litres}$	

Investigations

The order of operations

When evaluating formulae, calculations are carried out in order,

FIRST	brackets
SECOND	powers and roots
THIRD	multiplication and division
FINALLY	addition and subtraction

In example 1 squaring must be carried out before multiplication.

$$V = 12 \times 3.14 \times 7^2$$

$$V = 12 \times 3.14 \times 49$$

$$V = 1,850$$

If the numbers are incorrectly multiplied first there is a large error (shown here).

$$V = (12 \times 3.14 \times 7)^2$$

$$V = 263.76^2$$

$$V = 69,600$$

This illustrates the importance of the order in which operations are carried out.

2.2 Rearranging formulae

Investigations

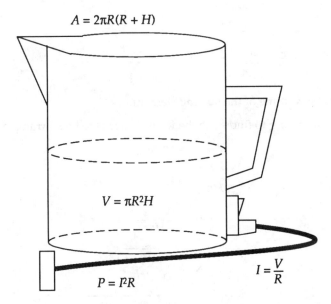

$$A = 2\pi R(R + H)$$

$$V = \pi R^2 H$$

$$I = \frac{V}{R}$$

$$P = I^2 R$$

Formulae can be used to find unknown values, but it is often necessary to rearrange them so that the unknown is the subject, given in terms of other symbols.

Rearranging $\qquad P = I^2 R$

To give us an understanding of the principles we can replace symbols with simple numbers. let $R = 2$ and $I = 3$;

$$P = I^2 R$$

$$18 = 3^2 \times 2$$

Make R the subject;

It can now be seen that $\qquad 2 = \dfrac{18}{3^2}$

and
$$R = \frac{P}{I^2}$$

In general to transfer terms that are multiplied to the other side of the equation we have to divide.

Make I the subject
$$18 = 3^2 \times 2$$

as before change and divide
$$3^2 = \frac{18}{2}$$

$$3 = \sqrt{\frac{18}{2}}$$

and
$$I = \sqrt{\frac{P}{R}}$$

In general to transfer a power we take a root.

Example 2

Find the value of R if $H = 15$ cm when the capacity is 2 litres, after allowing for the volume of a heating element estimated to be 30cm^3.

Solution 2

A formula for the volume can be used here:

$$V = H\pi R^2 - E$$

where E represents the volume of the heating element.

In this problem we are trying to find R, so the formula needs to be rearranged.

Add E:
$$V + E = H\pi R^2$$

Divide by $H\pi$:
$$\frac{(V + E)}{H\pi} = R^2$$

or
$$R^2 = \frac{(V + E)}{H\pi}$$

Square root:
$$R = \sqrt{\frac{(V + E)}{H\pi}}$$

Values can now be entered:
$$R = \sqrt{\frac{(2000 + 30)}{15 \times \pi}}$$

$$= \sqrt{\frac{2030}{47.12}}$$

Thus:
$$R = 6.56 \text{ cm}$$

Investigations

To rearrange the equation $V = H\pi R^2 - E$ we need to peel symbols away from R in a systematic, ordered procedure. Care must be taken to remove symbols in the correct sequence one step at a time.

Let us consider the order of operations if we knew the value of R;

1. square the value $\quad R^2$
2. multiply by $H \quad\quad H\pi R^2$
3. subtract $E \quad\quad\quad H\pi R^2 - E$

This would allow us to calculate V, starting with a known value of R. However, it is the reverse (or inverse) of this procedure that is required.

1. add $E \quad\quad\quad\quad V + E$
2. divide by $H\pi \quad\quad \dfrac{(V + E)}{H\pi}$ (brackets ensure that addition is carried out before division)
3. square root $\quad\quad \sqrt{\dfrac{(V + E)}{H\pi}}$

The order in which operations are removed is reversed, as well as each operation being an inverse.

Also in the evaluation of example 2 the correct order must be followed

$$R = \sqrt{\frac{(2000 + 30)}{15 \times \pi}}$$

$$R = \sqrt{\frac{2030}{15 \times \pi}} \quad\quad \text{(brackets)}$$

$$R = \frac{45.06}{3.87 \times 1.77} \quad\quad \text{(square root – each term is square-rooted)}$$

$$R = 6.56 \quad\quad \text{(multiplication and division)}$$

2.3 Extended formulae

Example 3

The heat lost when a jug kettle is boiled depends on the surface area of the cylinder of water, rearrange the formula for the surface area A to give height H in terms of A and radius R.

Solution 3

cylinder surface area= area of two circles + area of rectangle ($H \times$ circumference)

$$A = 2\pi R^2 + 2\pi RH$$

Factorise: $\quad\quad\quad\quad A = 2\pi R(R + H)$

Divide by $2\pi R \quad\quad \dfrac{A}{2\pi R} = R + H$

Subtract R: $\quad\quad\quad H = \dfrac{A}{2\pi R} - R$

Investigations

In example 3 we have taken advantage of the terms that repeat themselves and simplified by factorising, making the arrangement easier.

To rearrange the equation: $\quad\quad A = 2\pi R(R + H)$

we need to peel symbols away from H in the correct order.

Order of operations if H were known

1 Add $R \quad\quad\quad\quad H + R$
2 Multiply by $2\pi R \quad\quad 2\pi R(R + H)$

Inverse operations and reverse order

1 Divide by $2\pi R$ $\dfrac{A}{2\pi R}$

2 Subtract R $\dfrac{A}{2\pi R} - R$

Example 4

Find the radius of a cylindrical mug if it is filled to a height of 6cm from a kettle. The depth of water in the kettle goes down by 2cm and 8cm³ is spilt.

Solution 4

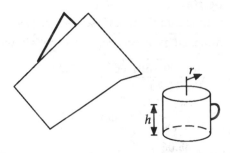

An equation can be written down because the water from the kettle is equal to the water in the mug plus spillage.

$$\text{water from kettle} = \text{water in mug} + \text{spillage}$$

$$H\pi R^2 = h\pi r^2 + s$$

The unknown value is r so we have to rearrange the equation:

$$H\pi R^2 = h\pi r^2 + s$$

subtract s: $$H\pi R^2 - s = h\pi r^2$$

divide by $h\pi$: $$\dfrac{H\pi R^2 - s}{h\pi} = r^2$$

square root: $$r = \sqrt{\dfrac{H\pi R^2 - s}{h\pi}}$$

Values can now be entered: $$r = \sqrt{\dfrac{2\pi \times 6.56^2 - 8}{6\pi}}$$

That is: $$r = 3.73 \text{ cm}$$

Investigations

When we carry out calculations the order that is followed is;

FIRST brackets

SECOND powers and roots

THIRD multiplication and division

FINALLY addition and subtraction

For rearranging, symbols must be moved across the equation away from the unknown value in the reverse of this order;

    FIRST   move added and subtracted parts

    SECOND   move multiplied and under parts of any division

    THIRD   powers and roots

    FINALLY brackets

Here is an example where we are rearranging to give B

$$A = \frac{(B+C)^2}{D} - E$$

First add E:

$$A + E = \frac{(B+C)^2}{D}$$

Second, multiply by D:

$$D(A+E) = (B+C)^2$$

Third, square root:

$$\sqrt{D(A+E)} = B + C$$

Finally, subtract C:

$$\sqrt{D(A+E)} - C = B$$

We should now be able to rearrange most equations. There are however problems with subtraction and division.

If in example 4 it had been the spillage that was required we could have written down the equation;

$$\text{water in kettle} - \text{spillage} = \text{water in mug}$$

or

$$K - s = M$$

There may be a temptation to peel the K away from the s, but clearly the spillage is not equal to $M + K$. The reason for this is that unlike addition, subtraction cannot be reversed.

$$K - s \quad \textit{is not the same as} \quad s - K$$

Instead we need to move the s itself: $K = M + s$

Now we can reverse the order: $K = s + M$

and move the M: $s = K - M$

The same approach is used if something is being divided by a symbol.

Remember that division is NOT the same when it is reversed.

Rearranging for C: $A = \dfrac{B}{C}$

Move C itself so we have a product: $AC = B$

Reverse the order: $CA = B$

Divide by A: $C = \dfrac{B}{A}$

Example

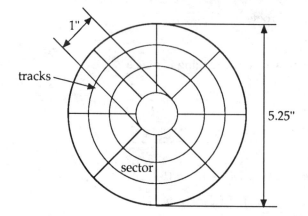

A 5.25" computer disc stores data on tracks which are divided into 8 sectors as shown. There is a hole in the centre with diameter 1". Calculate the area available for data within each sector. What is the length of the outer track in a sector.

Solution

As there are 8 sectors the angle in each will be:

$$\frac{360°}{8} = 45°$$

The radii of the disc and the hole are of course found by halving the diameter in each case.

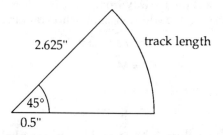

The area of the sector (including hole): $\qquad A = \dfrac{45}{360} \times \pi \times 2.625^2 = 2.71$

The area of the sector of the hole: $\qquad H = \dfrac{45}{360} \times \pi \times 0.5^2 = 0.098$

Sector area: $\qquad A - H = 2.61 \text{ in}^2$

Outer track length: $\qquad T = \dfrac{45}{360} \times 2\pi \times 2.625 = 2.06 \text{ in}$

Investigations

As an alternative to measuring angles in degrees, radians can be used. This unit of angular measurement has the advantage that in many problems the messy number π is eliminated.

In a full circle there are:

$$2\pi = 2 \times 3.1415\dots\dots$$
$$= 6.28 \text{ radians (rads) approximately}$$

So clearly radians are much bigger than degrees.

To convert from one measure to the other remember:

$$360° = 2\pi \text{ rads}$$

For convenience measurements are often quoted in terms of π. Conversions of the more common angles are worth remembering.

Half a circle:	180°	$\dfrac{180}{360} \times 2\pi$	$= \pi$ rads
Quarter of a circle:	90°	$\dfrac{180}{360} \times 2\pi$	$= \dfrac{\pi}{2}$ rads
	45°	$\dfrac{45}{360} \times 2\pi$	$= \dfrac{\pi}{4}$ rads
	60°	$\dfrac{60}{360} \times 2\pi$	$= \dfrac{\pi}{3}$ rads
	30°	$\dfrac{30}{360} \times 2\pi$	$= \dfrac{\pi}{6}$ rads

Or we could remember what fraction of 180° each angle is, and multiply by π.

Scientific calculators can be used for conversions and they will work in radians mode.

The formulae for the area of a sector and the arc length are particularly useful in radian form.

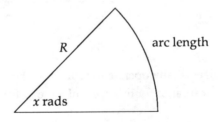

Sector area:
$$A = \frac{x}{2\pi}\pi R^2 = \frac{x}{2}R^2$$

Arc length:
$$L = \frac{x}{2\pi}2\pi R = xR$$

These simplified formulae can now be used to solve the above problem using angles in radians:

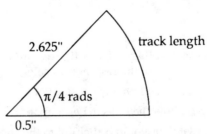

The area of the sector (including hole): $\quad A = \frac{1}{2} \times \frac{\pi}{4} \times 2.625^2 = 0.861\pi = 2.71$

The area of the sector of the hole: $\quad H = \frac{1}{2} \times \frac{\pi}{4} \times 0.5 = 0.0313\pi = 0.098$

Sector area: $\quad A - H = 0.83\pi = 2.61$ in²

Outer track length: $\quad T = \frac{\pi}{4} \times 2.625 = 0.656\pi = 2.06$ in

Technology

Calculators

 Most scientific calculators have the facility of working in radians rather than degrees, this is quite simple to achieve.

mode	5

(or the mode number that relates to the rad mode)

This changes the calculator to work in radians. Trigonometrical functions can then be used.

Radians are usually quoted as multiples of π.

The sequence to find the sin of $\pi/3$ is:

π	$\div$	3	$=$	sin

To find the angle that gives $\cos \theta = 0.5$ we use the sequence:

0	.	5	inv	cos	$\div$	π	$=$

Computers

 Spreadsheet formulae usually operate in radians without any changes being made. To find trigonometrical ratios for multiples of π the PI function should be used.

Skill unit 4 *Statistics*

4.1 Data display

Example 1

A shop stocks batteries of different voltages. Sales figures are available for two consecutive months. Use these to make comparisons of the two months sales.

a) Draw appropriate charts and comment on any observations.

b) Determine middle values, that allow the sales to be compared without misrepresentation.

c) What conclusions can be drawn that would be helpful to the shopkeeper.

Results

Voltage	Sales	
	November	December
1.5	8	11
3	9	7
6	1	3
9	16	10
12	2	3
Total	36	34

Solution 1

a) Before we leap into drawing charts, we must think about the purpose and what we are trying to show. The most appropriate type of diagram to do that job can then be drawn. Here, a shopkeeper is interested in the popularity of each battery size, so that stock can be kept without wasting shelf space. A good method of representing sales in proportion is a pie chart.

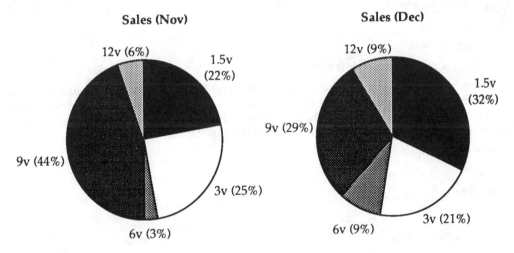

Comments

From these charts it is clear that there are 3 batteries (1.5v, 3v and 9v) that are far more popular than the other 2 types (6v and 12v).

In November 9v batteries made up a very large proportion of the months sales. Although 9v batteries were not the most popular during December they still sold well.

b) It is important to establish which battery was the most popular each month. Calculating the mean or average voltage of batteries sold is of little use here. The mode is therefore the middle value we require.

Since the data is given to us in a frequency table the mode for each month can easily be found.

November: Mode (most frequent) = 9v

December: Mode = 1.5v

c) ### Conclusions

The number of sales considered in this exercise is small, so we cannot make any conclusive statements, only tendencies can be identified.

The number of batteries kept in stock and those on shelves should reflect the proportions shown in the pie charts.

The most popular batteries (9v, 1.5v and 3v) could be used for offers or discounts and there should be good access to them in the shop.

Of course, without further information we cannot positively identify the reasons for November and December having different sales patterns, but we ought to consider;

❏ Battery sales may well be related to sales of electrical equipment.

❏ Sales may be affected by Christmas shopping.

❏ Other local shops.

Investigations

Types of Data

The results in example 1 are *discrete* data. This is data that clearly falls into one category or another. Data of this type is collected by observation or by counting. No measurement is required. Other examples of discrete data include;

❏ Number of people in a car

❏ Shoe size

❏ Nut and bolt sizes

❏ Production rates (components per hour)

We need to make the distinction between discrete and CONTINUOUS data. Continuous data is found by measuring. Values may lie anywhere within a continuous range. Whenever measurements are made (time, length or anything else) there is always some rounding, even if very precise measuring devices are used. Examples of continuous data are;

❏ Resistance (Ohms)

❏ Length

❏ Temperature

❏ Time

Charts and diagrams

Pie charts were thought to be the best way to present sales in example 1 as relative sales were sufficient, and individual types could be seen in relation to the total. A disadvantage of pie charts is that actual values are not made clear.

Bar charts and histograms

Here is the data of example 1 represented in a BAR CHART;

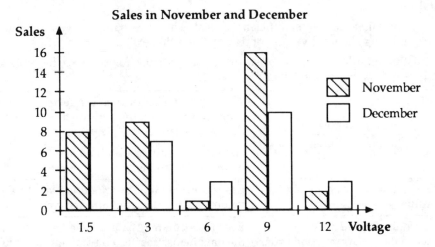

Sales in November and December

From this the sales of each battery type can be easily compared.

When continuous data is to be represented in a similar way, *histograms* are used. Here is a histogram showing the distribution of the weights of 24 dustbins full of rubbish.

Dustbin weight (kg)	Frequency
0 – 5	2
5 – 10	3
10 – 15	6
15 – 20	8
20 – 25	4
25 – 30	1

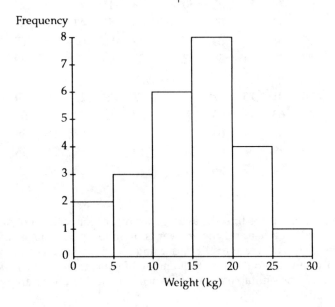

The width of the bars depends on the groups that are used in the frequency table. The area of each bar is in proportion to the total weight of the dustbins in that group.

Middle values

In example 1, modal values were sufficient to establish which batteries were the most popular each month, and the voltages given are of battery types that exist.

Before calculating middle values we must consider the reasons for doing so, the application may indicate which type is the most relevant.

Mean	$\bar{x} = \dfrac{\text{Sum of values}}{\text{Number of values}}$	The mean of a set of data is affected by every value, therefore abnormally high or low results will produce a misleading middle value. An exact result is obtained and can be used for further calculations.
Mode	Most frequently occurring value	Easy to calculate. The mode is usually a particular value from the data, not affected by abnormal results.
Median	Literally the middle value when data is arranged in order.	Easy to calculate. Again the median is usually one of the data items, unaffected by abnormal results.

4.2 Interpretation of results

Example 2

Fifty batteries from each of two manufacturers, were connected to the same load, and the time noted when they failed. Compare the life and reliability of the makes of battery from the results of this test.

Results

Life in hours (nearest hour)

Longercell

58	56	48	36	47	52	61	34	29	46
52	38	54	39	50	13	41	77	63	27
22	44	45	53	64	53	53	42	36	57
55	51	71	84	67	79	33	47	55	69
67	23	51	44	53	57	43	32	45	49

Powersure

58	21	23	17	65	77	82	23	57	89
46	63	71	93	7	70	42	29	35	56
54	51	74	63	57	33	84	62	56	38
26	49	56	69	52	10	67	59	31	46
36	84	42	96	77	27	33	62	62	37

Solution 1

A comparison can be made if we find the average (or mean) for each set of data. To calculate the mean values are added together and the answer is divided by 50. This is involves many calculations but gives us a very accurate result (assuming no errors have been made). As an alternative to this we can group the data in a frequency table and treat data as a set of ranges. With large samples this is a more suitable approach since fewer calculations are required and a good result will be obtained.

The results need to be transferred to frequency tables. Ranges of values are chosen so that all the data will fit (lowest and highest), and there are a manageable number of groups.

Frequency Tables and Charts

Longercell

Battery life	Frequency
0-10	0
10-20	1
20-30	4
30-40	7
40-50	12
50-60	16
60-70	6
70-80	3
80-90	1
90-100	0

Representing information on a histogram enables us to see how results are distributed.

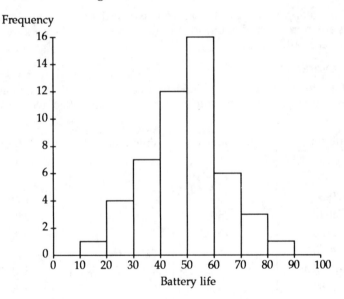

Powersure

Battery life	Frequency
0-10	1
10-20	2
20-30	6
30-40	7
40-50	5
50-60	10
60-70	8
70-80	5
80-90	4
90-100	2

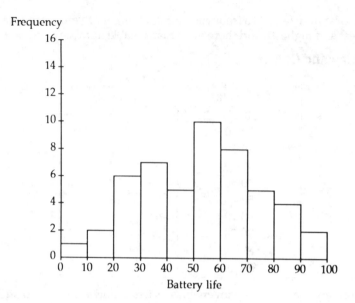

The charts allow us to appreciate the difference between the two frequency distributions. The Longercell results are more centred about the middle, whereas the Powersure chart is flatter and results are more spread out.

Calculating the averages

The frequency tables tell us how many values are in each range. If we now assume that all the values in each range are equal to the middle of that range a simplified average can be calculated;

Longercell

Battery life	Mid range (x)	Frequency (f)	fx
0-10	5	0	0
10-20	15	1	15
20-30	25	4	100
30-40	35	7	245
40-50	45	12	540
50-60	55	16	880
60-70	65	6	390
70-80	75	3	225
80-90	85	1	85
90-100	95	0	0
Total		50	2480

The mean is now found by dividing the sum of the values by 50.

$$\text{Mean, } \bar{x} \ = \frac{2480}{50} = 49.6$$

Powersure

Battery life	Mid range (x)	Frequency (f)	fx
0-10	5	1	5
10-20	15	2	30
20-30	25	6	150
30-40	35	7	245
40-50	45	5	225
50-60	55	10	550
60-70	65	8	520
70-80	75	5	375
80-90	85	4	340
90-100	95	2	190
Total		50	2630

$$\text{Mean, } \bar{x} = \frac{2630}{50} = 52.6$$

The difference between these two means is small. It only suggests that Powersure batteries on average may be slightly longer lasting.

Spread of values

Another important consideration is how consistent are each of these makes of battery. Again treating the results as grouped data we can find out how much each set of values varies from the mean. If all the batteries had the same life there would be no variation. Let us calculate the standard deviation for each manufacturer. This is a value representing consistency.

Longercell

Mid range (x)	Frequency (f)	dev	dev²	f × dev²
5	0	44.6	1989.16	0
15	1	34.6	1197.16	1197.16
25	4	24.6	605.16	2420.64
35	7	14.6	213.16	1492.12
45	12	4.6	21.16	253.92
55	16	-5.4	29.16	466.56
65	6	-15.4	237.16	1422.96
75	3	-25.4	645.16	1935.48
85	1	-35.4	1253.16	1253.16
95	0	-45.4	2061.16	0
Total	50			10442

$$\text{Standard deviation} = \sqrt{\frac{10442}{50}} = 14.5$$

Powersure

Mid range (x)	Frequency (f)	dev	dev²	f × dev²
5	1	47.6	2265.8	2265.8
15	2	37.6	1413.8	2827.5
25	6	27.6	761.8	4570.6
35	7	17.6	309.8	2168.3
45	5	7.6	57.8	288.8
55	10	−2.4	5.8	57.6
62	8	−12.4	153.8	1230.0
72	2	−22.4	501.8	2508.8
82	4	−32.4	1049.8	4199.0
92	2	−42.4	1797.8	3595.5
Total	20			23711.9

$$\text{Standard deviation} = \sqrt{\frac{23711.9}{50}} = 21.8$$

These values which give us some idea of how spread out the results are, show that there is a significant difference between the two makes of battery as far as reliability is concerned.

We can conclude that Powersure batteries are slightly longer lasting but Longercell batteries have a clear tendency to be more closely grouped around the mean.

Investigations

Spread of results

In example 2 the histograms illustrate how the results are distributed for each manufacturer. Standard deviation is a value that is calculated to establish how much results are spread out. A low value suggests consistency and a high value indicates that data varies over a large range.

To some extent, charts can give us an idea of the way data is spread out.

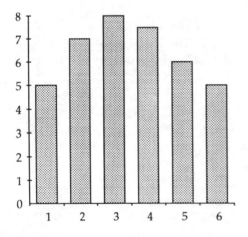
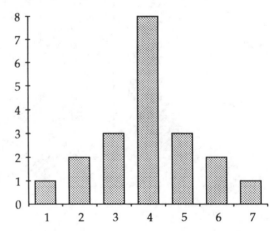

As an alternative measure of spread, semi-interquartile range can be used. To find this value a cumulative frequency curve has to be drawn.

From the data of example 2, we can calculate cumulative frequencies and draw curves.

Longercell

Battery life	Frequency	Cum Freq
0-10	0	0
10-20	1	1
20-30	4	5
30-40	7	12
40-50	12	24
50-60	16	40
60-70	6	46
70-80	3	49
80-90	1	50
90-100	0	50

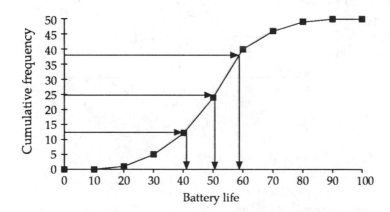

Half way through the distribution (cum freq = 25) gives us an estimate for the median: 51

The interquartile range is the range of values from a quarter to three quarters of the distribution.

    Lower quartile = 41 (quarter of 50 = 12.5)

    Upper quartile = 58 (three quarters of 50 = 37.5)

The interquartile range is therefore: 58 – 41 = 17

The semi-interquartile range is half of this value $= \dfrac{17}{2} = 8.5$

Powersure

Battery life	Frequency	Cum Freq
0-10	1	1
10-20	· 2	3
20-30	6	9
30-40	7	16
40-50	5	21
50-60	10	31
60-70	8	39
70-80	5	44
80-90	4	48
90-100	2	50

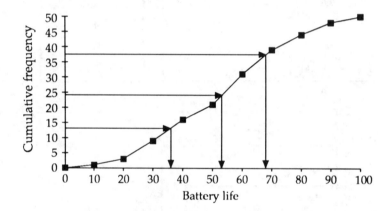

Median = 53
Lower quartile = 36
Upper quartile = 68
Interquartile range = 68 – 36 = 32
Semi-interquartile range = 16

Comment

A comparison of interquartile ranges gives a clear indication that the performance of Longercell batteries is more predictable.

Technology

Calculators

The statistics mode (SD or STAT) on calculators is particularly good value and well worth spending some time on. The large number of tedious calculations that are usually involved in statistics can be carried out quickly and accurately.

To enter the data   3, 2, 7, 2, 6, 8, 4

Enter the statistics mode;

| mode | | (or the appropriate mode symbol)

Clear any existing data;

Enter data;

The data entry button may be indicated with other symbols (×, M+, etc)

Once a set of data is entered calculations of the mean $\bar{x}$, standard deviation (σ) and other useful statistical values are calculated internally when appropriate buttons are pressed.

If it is required to enter data where there are more than one of some data items, a time saving procedure exists.

Entering data from a frequency table:

The values are followed by multiplication and the frequency.

Computers

 Computers make an excellent medium in which to deal with statistics. Graphics can be used to present data in diagrams and spreadsheets allow tables of calculations to be carried out efficiently. Integrated software packages combine both of these facilities and give us a very powerful tool.

Spreadsheets

It is worth developing a good spreadsheet that calculates all necessary statistical values using formulae, since this can be used repeatedly with different data.

An example of a possible layout;

	A	B	C	D	E	F
1	Values (x)	Frequency (f)	Value × Frequency	Deviations	(Dev)²	Frequency × (Dev)²
2			=A2*B2	=B6-A2	=D2^2	=B2*E2
3						
4						
5	Totals	=SUM(B2,B3..)	=SUM(C2,C3..)			=SUM(F2,F3..)
6	Mean	=C5/B5			SD	=SQRT(F5/B5)

Graphics

Using sets of data from spreadsheets or elsewhere, a variety of charts and diagrams can be drawn using graphics programs.

Relevant data has to be highlighted or entered. With menu driven software it is just a question of picking out the type of chart required and executing it. Labels and titles should always be added.

All computing work must be saved on a regular basis and printouts obtained.

5.1 Trigonometrical curves

Example 1

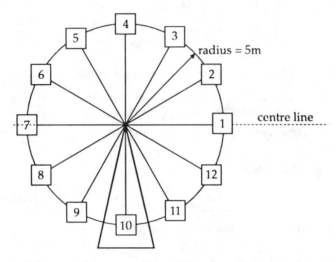

The 'Big Wheel' at a fairground has a radius of 5 metres. It is rotating at 1 revolution every 3 minutes. Find the height of chair number 1 above the centre line after,

a) 15 seconds

b) 1 minute

c) 2 minutes

Solution

1 revolution	(or 360°)	in	3 mins
$\frac{1}{2}$ revolution	180°	in	90 seconds
	90°	in	45 seconds
	30°	in	15 seconds

a) So in 15 seconds the wheel has rotated 30 degrees. This enables us to draw a triangle that represents the new position of chair 1.

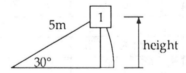

Now the height after 15 seconds can be calculated using the formula;

$$\sin x = \frac{O}{H}$$

rearranging

$$O = H \sin x$$

substituting ($H = 5$ and $x = 30$ using h for height):

$$h = 5 \sin 30$$
$$= 5 \times 0,5$$

Thus:

$$h = 2.5 \text{ metres}$$

b) After 1 minute the wheel has rotated $\frac{1}{3}$ of a revolution, or $\frac{1}{3}$ of 360°, which is 120°. To find this height a graph of heights between 0 – 360° needs to be drawn.

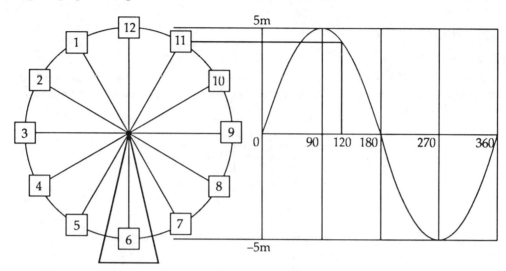

From this graph it is clear that the chair reaches a maximum height after 45 seconds and then drops down to the same level as 60 degrees. Using the formula as before:

$$\sin x = \frac{O}{H}$$

rearranging $\qquad\qquad O = H \sin x$

substituting ($H = 5$ and $x = 60$ using h for height):

$$h = 5 \sin 60$$

Thus: $\qquad\qquad h = 4.33$ metres

c) After 2 minutes the wheel has rotated $\frac{2}{3}$ of 360° which is 240°. The graph shows that the chair falls below the centre line and therefore has a negative height.

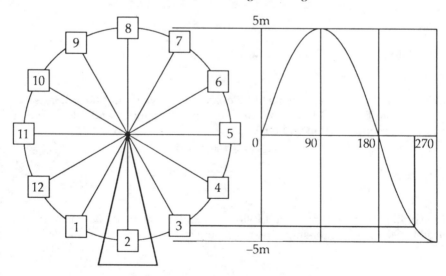

117

Although the curve is upside down beyond 180°, it is the same shape as before. 240° is 60° more than 180° so using the previously calculated value the chair is 4.33m below the centre line (or −4.33m)

Investigations

Sine curve

In example 1 the height at any point is found using $h = 5 \sin x$. If we now consider a wheel where the radius is only one metre the relationship becomes $h = \sin x$ the corresponding graph is known as a sine curve.

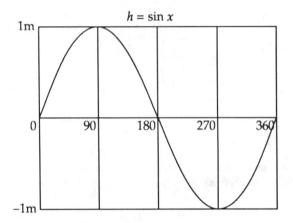

$$h = \sin x$$

We are already familiar with angles up to 90°, this curve can be used to find values for the sine ratio up to 360°.

To find: sin 160°   160° is 20° less than 180°, by symmetry sin 160 = sin 20

          sin 245°   245° is 65° more than 180°, sin 245 has the same value as sin 65 but negative

          sin 310°   310° is 50 less than 360°. sin 310 has the same value as sin 50 but negative.

Calculators can of course be used to find the sin of any angle. It is when the angle is unknown that the curve is most useful, as shown here;

What angles give: $\sin x = 0.6$

Using a calculator, $x =$ | inv | | sin | 0.6

                                     $x = 36.9°$

This is only one of the solutions, we need to look at the curve to find the other. A horizontal line drawn across from 0.6 would cut the curve again between 90° and 180°. Since the curve is symmetrical the second solution will be:

$$x = 180 - 36.9$$
$$= 143.1°$$

Cosine curve

The change of height of chair number 4 follows a similar pattern to that of chair number 1 but it is advanced by 90°. The relationship illustrated here is; $H = \cos x$

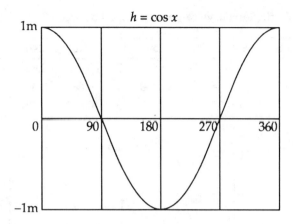

$$h = \cos x$$

Again we can use the curve to find values for angles up to 360°.

To find: cos 160°   160° is 20° less than 180°, cos 160 has the same value as cos 20 but negative

cos 245°   245° is 65° more than 180°, cos 245 has the same value as cos 65 but negative

cos 310°   310° is 50° less than 360°, by symmetry cos 310 = cos 50

Again calculators can be used to find cos of any angle, but again a calculator will only give one unknown angle.

What angles give: $\cos x = -0.3$

Using a calculator, $x = \boxed{\text{inv}} \ \boxed{\cos} \ -0.3$

$x = 107.5°$

This is only one of the solutions, we need to look at the curve to find the other. A horizontal line drawn across from –0.3 would cut the curve again between 180° and 270°.

Since the curve is symmetrical the second solution will be:

$$x = 360 - 107.5$$
$$= 252.5°$$

Tangent curve

The tan ratio is related to sin and cos in the following way.

First: $\sin x = \dfrac{O}{H}$

becomes $O = H \sin x$

Second: $\cos x = \dfrac{A}{H}$

becomes $A = H \cos x$

Thus: $\tan x = \dfrac{O}{H}$

$$= \dfrac{H \sin x}{H \cos x}$$

That is: $\tan x = \dfrac{\sin x}{\cos x}$

Using this relationship the tan curve can be developed between 0 and 360°;

angle	0	30	60	90	120	150	180	210	240	270	300	330	360
sin	0	0.5	0.866	1	0.866	0.5	0	–0.5	–0.866	–1	–0.866	–0.5	0
cos	1	0.866	0.5	0	–0.5	–0.866	–1	–0.866	–0.5	0	0.5	0.866	1
tan	0	0.577	1.732	∞	–1.732	–0.577	0	0.577	1.732	∞	–1.732	–0.577	0

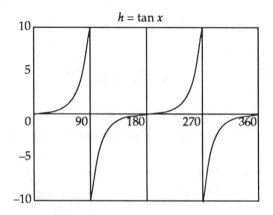

$h = \tan x$

This curve has the convenient facility that it repeats itself after 180°.

$$\tan 30 = \tan (30 + 180)$$
$$= \tan 210$$

So to determine other angles (having found one with a calculator) we can simply add 180°. In some cases calculators will give negative angles as solutions, here 180° can be added twice.

What angles give: $\qquad\qquad \tan x = -0.4$

Using a calculator, $\qquad\qquad x = \boxed{\text{inv}} \quad \boxed{\text{tan}} \quad -0.4$

$$x = -21.8°$$

This value is outside of our range so adding 180° gives:

$$x = 158.2°$$

Adding 180° again gives the second solution:

$$x = 338.2°$$

5.2 Sin, cos and tan formulae

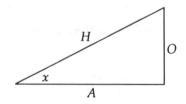

Pythagoras Theorem $\qquad\qquad H^2 = A^2 + O^2$

Rearranging $\qquad\qquad 1 = \dfrac{A^2 + O^2}{H^2}$

120

$$1 = \frac{A^2}{H^2} + \frac{O^2}{H^2}$$

We already know that $\qquad \dfrac{A^2}{H^2} = \cos^2 x$

and $\qquad \dfrac{O^2}{H^2} = \sin^2 x$

so $\qquad 1 = \cos^2 x + \sin^2 x$

This is a useful formula that we will use later. Alternatively it can be written in terms of tan;

We know that: $\qquad 1 = \cos^2 x + \sin^2 x$

Dividing by $\cos^2 x$ gives: $\qquad \dfrac{1}{\cos^2 x} = \dfrac{\cos^2 x}{\cos^2 x} + \dfrac{\sin^2 x}{\cos^2 x}$

But: $\qquad \tan^2 x = \dfrac{\sin^2 x}{\cos^2 x}$

Thus: $\qquad \dfrac{1}{\cos^2 x} = 1 + \tan^2 x$

5.3 Sin and cosine rule

Example 2

A robot arm moves a component from position A to position B as shown:

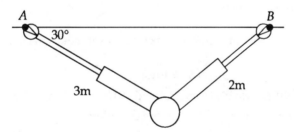

The extension of the arm is 3m to pick it up and 2m to place it down. If the arm makes an angle of 30° with the direction of movement when it is picked up find;
a) the angle that the arm makes with the direction of movement when it is positioned.
b) the distance it is moved

Solution 2

a) The triangle produced here is not right angled, however two right angled triangles can be formed by adding an imaginary line as shown;

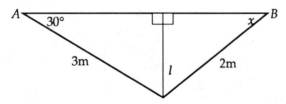

This additional line is part of both right angled triangles and links them together. If we give the link a value l and call the unknown angle x we can find a relationship between the triangles.

From triangle containing A: $\sin 30 = \dfrac{l}{3}$

Thus: $3 \sin 30 = l$

From triangle containing B: $\sin x = \dfrac{l}{2}$

Thus: $2 \sin x = l$

Combining equations: $3 \sin 30 = 2 \sin x$

Rearranging for x: $\sin x = \dfrac{3 \sin 30}{2}$

From this x can be calculated: $\sin x = 0.75$

Therefore: $x = 48.6°$

b) A similar link can be developed if an alternative imaginary line is drawn again creating two right angled triangles;

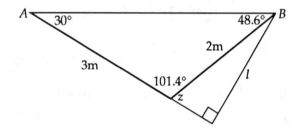

The angle between the two robot arm positions is found as it makes the sum in the triangle up to 180°.

$$180 - 30 - 48.6 = 101.4$$

Angle z will now be the difference between 180° and 101.4° which is 78.6°.

To find the length AB the right angled triangles are considered.

First: $\sin 30 = \dfrac{l}{AB}$

giving: $AB \sin 30 = l$

Second: $\sin z = \dfrac{l}{2}$

giving: $2 \sin z = l$

Combining equations: $AB \sin 30 = 2 \sin z$

Rearranging for AB: $AB = \dfrac{2 \sin z}{\sin 30}$

From this AB can be calculated: $AB = \dfrac{2 \sin 78.6}{\sin 30}$

$AB = 3.92$ metres

Investigations

Sine Rule

If we look more closely at example 2 a general formula or rule can be developed. In the example some values were known:

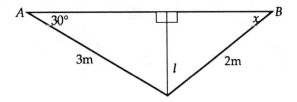

and a formula was found: $\qquad$ $3 \sin 30 = 2 \sin x$

Using symbols to represent general values:

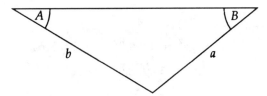

a similar formula can be produced:

$$b \sin A = a \sin B$$

This formula or rule is known as the sine rule.

It is usually rearranged and stated as:

$$\frac{\sin A}{a} = \frac{\sin B}{b}$$

Where A is any angle in a triangle (this rule works with any triangle) opposite to side a, and B is another angle opposite to side b.

Special case

Care must be taken when using the 'Sine Rule' to find angles, because as we know there are two angles between 0 and 180 degrees for any positive value. A calculator will not always give us the appropriate angle. An examination of the practical situation may be necessary.

Cosine rule

The sine rule is very useful and should be used to solve triangles where ever possible. However there are two situations where we are unable to use it successfully.

These are   1.   When only two sides and the angle between them are known
              2.   When only three sides are known

An alternative formula to the 'Sine Rule' is the 'Cosine Rule' which can be thought of as an extension to 'Pythagoras Theorem'. If a triangle is again labelled as before with side a opposite to angle A, side b opposite to angle B and also side c opposite to angle C then the 'Cosine Rule' is as follows.

Quoted as for situation 1 where we are finding a side:

$$a^2 = b^2 + c^2 - 2bc\cos A$$

Rearranged for situation 2 where we are finding an angle:

$$\cos A = \frac{b^2 + c^2 - a^2}{2bc}$$

Situation 1

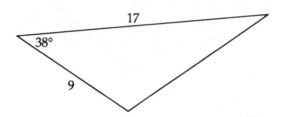

Let $A = 38°$, $b = 17$ and $c = 9$

The unknown side a can be found:

$$a^2 = 17^2 + 9^2 - 2 \times 17 \times 9 \cos 38$$

Therefore:

$$a = \sqrt{128.9}$$

Finally:

$$a = 11.4$$

Situation 2

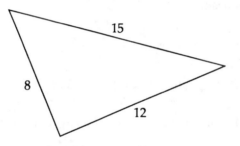

Put $a = 8$ $b = 12$ and $c = 15$.

Using the cosine rule with these values:

$$\cos A = \frac{12^2 + 15^2 - 8^2}{2 \times 12 \times 15}$$

$$= 0.847$$

giving:

$$A = 32.1°$$

If further values are required after the cosine rule has been used once (to find either an angle or a length), sufficient information is available to allow the sine rule or other methods to be used.

Example

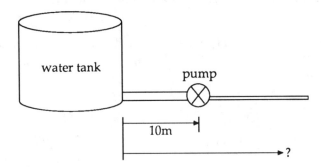

A pump is 10 metres from a supply tank as shown. How far from the tank does the water reach after 15 seconds, and how long will it take to reach a tap 50 metres away?

Solution

Initially when time = 0 the water is 10 metres from the tank.

Every second the water is pumped a further two metres away.

When $t = 1$:   distance, s $= 10 + 2$

When $t = 2$: s $= 10 + 4$

So whatever the value of t, it is multiplied by 2 and added to 10.

In a formula: s $= 10 + 2t$

This formula can now be used to solve the problem:

When $t = 15$:   distance s $= 10 + 2 \times 15$

s $= 40$

Using corresponding values of s and t a graph showing distance against time can be drawn to illustrate this problem, and determine t when $s = 50$.

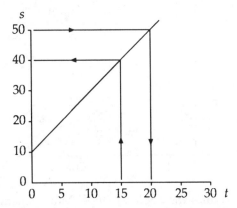

It can be seen that water will reach the tap after 20 seconds.

Investigations

The above straight line graph is represented by the equation;

$$s = 10 + 2t$$

Now let us consider how different situations affect this equation:

Situation 1

If the pump is moved so that it is only 5 metres from the tank the equation becomes;

$$s = 5 + 2t$$

The graph is as shown;

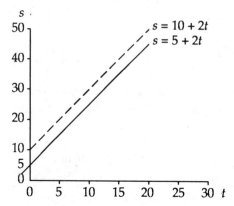

It is clear that the constant number in a straight line graph equation, corresponds to the point on the vertical axis where the line intercepts.

Situation 2

Alternatively let us increase the pump output so that the water speed is 3 metres per second. This produces the equation;

$$s = 10 + 3t$$

The graph is as shown;

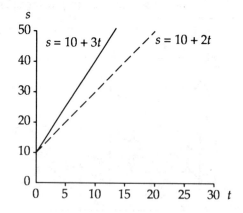

The speed therefore determines the angle of slope. More generally the value in front of the variable represents the gradient of any straight line graph.

Situation 3

If the pump was turned off the gradient would be zero and the equation would be;

$$s = 10$$

With a graph;

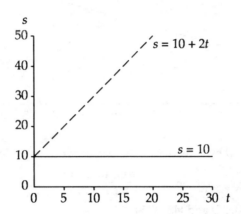

Situation 4

Reversing the pump so that water is pumped back towards the tank at 2 metres per second, is treated as a negative gradient. The equation is;

$$s = 10 - 2t$$

The graph is now;

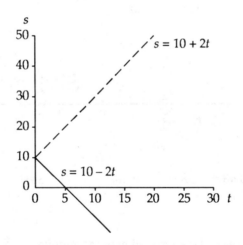

In practice it may be more appropriate to test a pump and use the results to estimate the speed of the water. These experimental results can be used to do that.

t	0	5	10	15	20	25	30	35	40	45	50
s	15	17.5	20	22.5	25	27.5	30	32.5	35	37.5	40

First points are plotted on a graph where it can be seen that they approximate to a straight line. This line is shown.

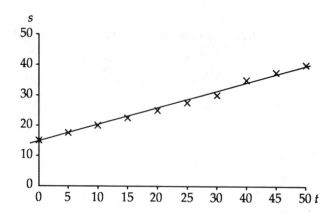

The gradient of the line is found by considering the rise between any two values of time.

$$\text{Gradient} = \frac{\text{Increase in distance}}{\text{Time interval}}$$

Consider the points shown (20, 25) and (45, 37.5)

$$\text{The increase in distance} = 37.5 - 25 = 12.5$$

$$\text{The time interval} = 45 - 20 = 25$$

$$\text{Gradient} = \frac{12.5}{25} = 0.5$$

$$\text{Speed} = 0.5$$

So the equation representing this graph: $s = 15 + 0.5t$

Skill unit 7 *Logarithms*

7.1 Logarithms

Example

An antique is valued at £500 and appreciates at 10% per annum. How many years will it take before the value exceeds £800.

Solution

A table can be constructed to show the appreciation of the antique.

Time (years)	Value	Interest
0	500.00	50.00
1	550.00	55.00
2	605.00	60.50
3	665.50	66.55
4	732.05	73.21
5	805.26	

From this it is clear that the value exceeds £800 during the fifth year. To find out more precisely when the value is £800 a graph can be used to illustrate the growth.

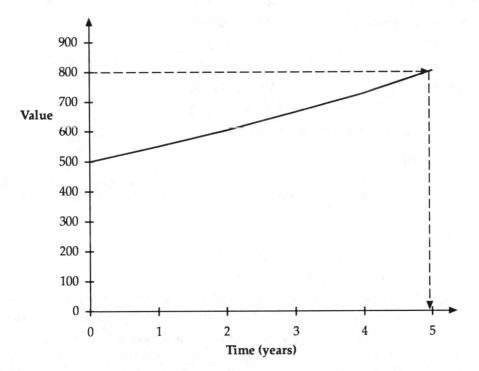

Here the actual time can be estimated to 4.9 years.

An equation can be found that gives a relationship between time and value. To do this the method of calculation is analysed more closely:

initially time, $t = 0$:   value, $b = 500$

after 1 years $= 1$: $b = 500 + 10\%$ of 500

$$= 500 + 0.1 \times 500$$
$$= 500(1 + 0.1)$$

That is: $b = 500 \times 1.1$

After 2 years $t = 2$: $b = 500 \times 1.1 \times 1.1$

That is: $b = 500 \times 1.1^2$

after 3 years $t = 3$: $b = 500 \times 1.1 \times 1.1 \times 1.1$

That is: $b = 500 \times 1.1^3$

after 4 years $t = 4$: $b = 500 \times 1.1^4$

There is clearly a pattern developing. The initial value of £500 is multiplied by 1.1 for each year of the growth. For 8 years of appreciation the value is given by;

$t = 8$: $b = 500 \times 1.1^8$

For any value of t : $b = 500 \times 1.1^t$

This equation can now be used to find the time when the value reaches £800.

$$500 \times 1.1^t = 800$$

$$1.1^t = \frac{800}{500}$$

Thus: $1.1^t = 1.6$

Guesses can be made for time t to solve this equation.

Let $t = 4$	$1.1^4 = 1.4641$
Let $t = 5$	$1.1^5 = 1.61051$
Let $t = 4.9$	$1.1^{4.9} = 1.5952331$
Let $t = 4.95$	$1.1^{4.95} = 1.6028534$

This indicates that the time t required to give a value of £800 is about **4.95 years**.

Investigations

In an equation such as $1.1^t = 1.6$ the index (t) is known as the **logarithm** of 1.6 to the base 1.1. Logarithm is often shortened to log and this equation could alternatively be written as;

$$\log_{1.1} 1.6 = t$$

or in words

'what is the power to which 1.1 must be raised to give 1.6'

This is what is meant by finding the log of a number. Here are some more obvious examples;

$\log_3 9 \Rightarrow$ 'what is the power to which 3 must be raised to give 9' $\Rightarrow$ the answer is 2

$\log_{10} 1000 \Rightarrow$ 'what is the power to which 10 must be raised to give 1000' $\Rightarrow$ the answer is 3

Finding powers is a difficult and time consuming task if carried out manually. However most scientific calculators have log facilities. They usually give log values in base 10 (if no base is specified it means base 10) and log values in base 2.7182818 (calculators usually write **ln**, this is a special number often called **e**).

7.2 Laws of Logarithms

Logs are themselves index numbers or powers so the laws of indices can be applied. Let us write them in log form;

Multiplication

$$1000 \times 100$$

In index form: $\qquad 10^3 \times 10^2$

Add the powers: $\qquad 10^{3+2} = 10^5$

The powers 3 and 2 can also be called the logs of 1000 and 100 respectively. This allows us to use the log relationship;

$$\log (1000 \times 100) = \log 1000 + \log 100$$

More generally $\qquad \log (a \times b) = \log a + \log b$

In a similar way we can develop a log relationship for division.

Division

$$\frac{1000}{100}$$

In index form: $\qquad \dfrac{10^3}{10^2}$

Subtract the powers: $\qquad 10^{3-2} = 10^1$

In log form: $\qquad \log\left(\dfrac{1000}{100}\right) = \log 1000 - \log 100$

More generally: $\qquad \log\left(\dfrac{a}{b}\right) = \log a - \log b$

Powers of Powers

$$1000^2$$

In index form: $$\left(10^3\right)^2$$

Multiply the powers: $$10^{3\times2} = 10^6$$

In log form: $$\log(1000^2) = 2 \times \log 1000$$

More generally: $$\mathbf{\log\left(a^b\right)} = \mathbf{b \times \log a}$$

These laws enable us to solve equations that involve powers where the power is the unknown value.

$$1.1^t = 1.6$$

In log form: $$t \log 1.1 = \log 1.6$$

Re-arranging: $$t = \frac{\log 1.6}{\log 1.1}$$

giving $$t = \frac{0.2041}{0.0414}$$

Therefore: $$t = 4.93$$

We are reassured that this value is correct by substituting into the equation $1.1^t = 1.6$:

$t = 4.93$ $1.1^{4.93} = 1.5998$

This calculator answer is a good check on our result.

Technology

Calculators

There are logarithms to base 10 (log) and logarithms to base 2.718... (ln, base e) available on scientific calculators. Inverse logs can also be activated (10^x and e^x)

Remembering for products we add the indices, the sequence for using logs to multiply 8 by 5 is:

| 8 | log | + | 5 | log | = | inv | log |

Computers

As with calculators, logs to base 10 are written LOG(x) and logs to base e, LN(x). Other bases can also be specified in a spreadsheet formula.

A formula using logs to multiply 8 by 5 is:

$$= 10\wedge(LOG(8) + LOG(5))$$

or, with logs to base e:

$$= EXP(LN(8) + LN(5))$$

Skill unit 8 *Solving equations graphically*

8.1 Linear equations (single straight line graphs)

Example 1

Water flows from a tap at 7 litres/minute. If a bath initially contains 8 litres, how long will it take before there is a total of 27 litres?

Solution 1

An equation needs to be written down that represents the relationship between volume and time. This is:

$$V = 8 + 7t$$

where V is the volume in litres and t is the time in minutes.

A straight line graph can now be drawn by calculating some points.

t	0	2	4
V	8	22	36

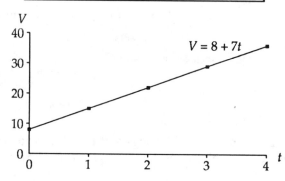

The value of t that corresponds to a volume of 27 litres is found by drawing a horizontal line, $V = 27$, and reading from the time axis where the lines cross.

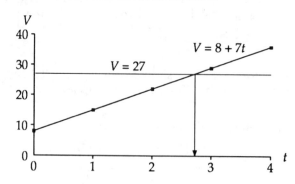

This gives a solution of about 2.7 minutes.

8.2 Simultaneous linear equations (two straight lines)

Example 2

A bath is filled by running a hot tap for 1 minute and a cold tap for 5 minutes and it then contains 42.5 litres. On another occasion the hot tap runs for 7 minutes and the cold for 2 minutes filling the bath with 33.5 litres. What are the flow rates of both the hot and cold taps?

Solution 2

Two equations can be written down to represent these situations.

1 $$h + 5c = 42.5$$
2 $$7h + 2c = 33.5$$

where h and c are the flow rates of the taps in litres/minute.

These can be rearranged to give h in terms of c.

1 $$h + 5c = 42.5$$
$$h = 42.5 - 5c$$
2 $$7h + 2c = 33.5$$
$$7h = 33.5 - 2c$$
$$h = \frac{33.5 - 2c}{7}$$

Now we can draw two straight lines on a graph that represent these. It may be helpful to calculate some points in tables.

Values of c	0	5	10
$h = 42.5 - 5c$	42.5	17.5	−7.5
$h = \dfrac{33.5 - 2c}{7}$	4.786	3.357	1.929

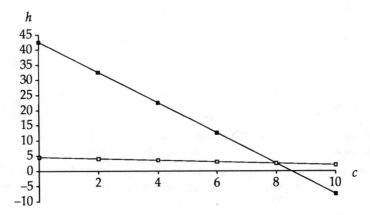

The solutions of the equations are given by the coordinates of the point (c, h) where the two lines cross and here:

$$c = 8$$
and
$$h = 2.5$$

It gives us confidence if we check our solutions by substituting them into one of the original equations.

$$h + 5c = 42.5$$

$$2.5 + 5(8) = 42.5 \text{ CHECK}$$

The units used in the equations were litres and minutes. Therefore flow rates of the hot and cold taps are 2.5 and 8 litres per minute respectively.

Investigations

Solving equations graphically may seem time consuming and inaccurate, but if graphical calculators or computers are used this becomes a very quick and precise method.

If other methods are to be employed to solve simultaneous linear equations as in example 2 they should be used in addition to the graphical approach. It is important to think of all equations as relationships that can be represented in graphical form.

8.3 Quadratic graphs

Example 3

The surface area of the water in a bath is 600,000 mm². If the length of the straight section (l) is 800 mm, determine the radius (r) that gives this area.

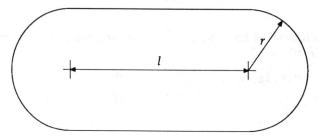

Solution 3

A formula for the surface area of the bath is found by considering that we have a circle plus a rectangle:

$$A = \pi r^2 + 2rl$$

$$A = \pi r^2 + 2 \times 800 \times r$$

$$A = \pi r^2 + 1600r$$

With this equation values of A are related to r and also r squared. Whenever we have a squared relationship it is known as a quadratic equation and if a graph is plotted a curve will result.

The graph of this equation can be drawn by calculating corresponding values in a table, or by programming a calculator/computer. As the graph will produce a curve a number of points are required.

r	0	100	200	300	400	500	600
A	0	191420	445680	762780	1142720	1585500	2091120

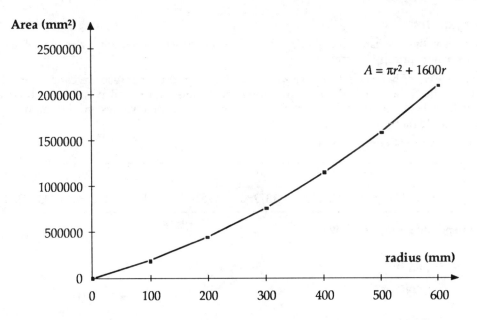

Using the graph we can find the radius that gives an area of 600,000 mm²:

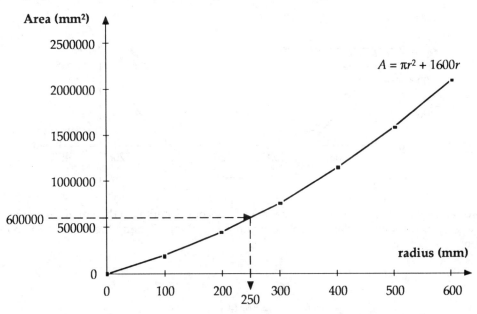

Here the radius can be seen to be about 250 mm. We can test this value in the equation to give us confidence and check our accuracy.

$$A = \pi r^2 + 1600r$$

$$A = \pi (250)^2 + 1600(250)$$

$$A = 596,000$$

Radius $r = 250$ mm is therefore a good estimate for a solution to the quadratic equation.

Investigations

It is now clear that we can solve quadratic equations in much the same way as we solve linear equations using appropriate graphs.

In example 3 we only considered positive values for the radius, because we cannot visualise a negative radius in a practical situation. However, to ensure that all possible mathematical solutions have been found let us investigate the effects of negative values and extend our graph to accommodate them.

The table of values of r and A becomes:

r	-800	-600	-400	-200	0	200	400
A	730880	171120	-137280	-194320	0	445680	1142720

The corresponding graph is shown:

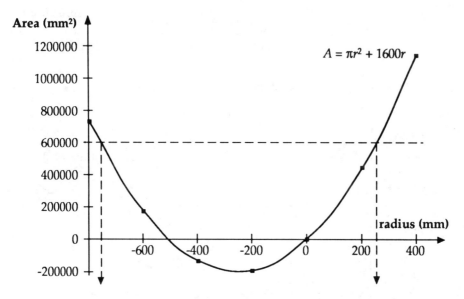

Here we can see that the curve is a 'U' shape and a second solution to the equation can be read from the graph. The solutions are $r = 250$ mm and $r = -750$ mm. Testing the other solution in the equation:

$$A = \pi r^2 + 1600r$$

$$A = \pi(-750)^2 + 1600(-750)$$

$$A = 567146$$

Again this is a good estimate for the required radius.

Note:

All quadratic graphs (squared relationships) are either 'U' shaped, or 'n' shaped. Because of this there should be two solutions.

Example 4

A bath similar to that in example 3, again with a straight length of 800mm, has the same width as a rectangular bath of length 1500 mm. If the width in each case is $2r$ determine values of r so that the surface areas are equal.

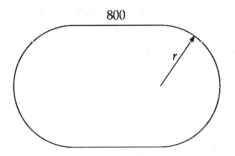

| 800 | 1500 |

For the bath with semi-circular ends, as before:

$$A = \pi r^2 + 1600r$$

For the rectangular bath:

$$A = 1500 \times 2r$$
$$A = 3000r$$

Drawing corresponding graphs on the same axes enables us to see that there are two solutions where the areas are equal:

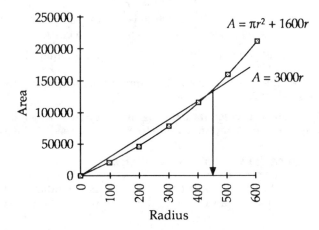

Clearly one solution is when $r = 0$ the areas will obviously be equal. The other solution can be estimated from the point where the lines cross: $r = 445$.

Checking our solution:

First:

$$A = \pi r^2 + 1600r$$
$$A = \pi(445)^2 + 1600(445)$$
$$A = 1,334,114$$

and second:

$$A = 3000\,r$$
$$A = 3000\,(445)$$
$$A = 1,335,000$$

These values are very close suggesting that $r = 445$ mm is an accurate solution.

Technology

Calculators

 Graph drawing calculators are becoming cheaper and more 'user friendly', making them an attractive proposition for graph sketching. They can also be used to zoom in on points giving very accurate graphical solutions to equations.

A cursor on the display is controlled with 4 arrows as shown (much the same as a computer mouse):

Cursor control

The first step in entering a graph into a calculator is to select the mode settings these include;

    deg/rads   (degrees or radians)

    rect/polar (x-y graph or radius and angular graph)

In addition the graph display needs to be selected. Is a background grid required? Should lines be plotted together or in sequence? Are dots to be joined with a curve?

After making all these decisions the function or functions can be entered.

| Y = | This allows the relationships to be entered. A conventional format is accepted. |

| Range | This gives an edit screen for entering the range over which the function is to be plotted. The max and min value for each axis needs to be entered. |

| Graph | This will then draw the curves (or points). |

As the cursor is moved on the display its precise coordinates are indicated with $x=$ and $y=$ at the base of the graph. Using this we can evaluate points of intersection of two graphs or values where lines cross the axes.

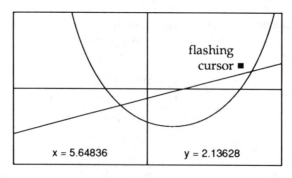

Display

| Zoom | Gives the option of zooming in to find accurate solutions to equations or zooming out to see the general shape of the graph over a larger range. The position of the cursor selects the region to be magnified. |

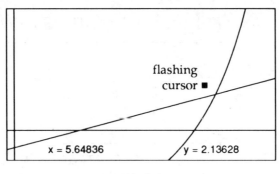

Display

Trace | The execution of this facility allows the cursor to follow a curve giving all the values as it is traced.
Again this is an invaluable feature for solving equations.

Computers

 Software for accurate x-y curve drawing is not very widespread, however, there are many systems that will join a series of points together. It is therefore necessary to plot sufficient points in order that the required accuracy is achieved.

To draw a line graph for $y = 2x^2 + 3x - 5$;

Calculating Tables of Values

By using formulae in spreadsheets tables of values can be calculated. Copying and pasting down the column saves time and reduces the chance of errors.

	A	B
1	Values (x)	y
2	-2	=2*A2^2+3*A2-5
3	-1	=2*A3^2+3*A3-5
4	0	=2*A4^2+3*A4-5
5	1	Paste
6	2	Paste

Plotting Points

Appropriate columns from the table have to be highlighted. With menu driven software it is just a question of picking out the type of graph required and executing it. Here a line graph should be selected. Labels and titles should always be added.

With integrated packages data can be updated or ranges extended and changes will automatically be made to the linked graph.

9.1 Volumes

Example 1

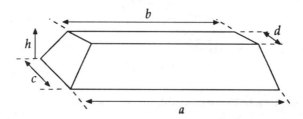

A symmetrical bar of gold is in the shape as shown with dimensions as follows

$a = 250$ mm; $b = 200$ mm; $c = 80$ mm; $d = 50$ mm; height, $h = 40$ mm.

It is to be melted down into gold coins with radius $r = 20$ mm and thickness $t = 4$ mm. Calculate how many coins can be made.

Solution 1

To begin with we need to find out the volume of the bar of gold. This is made easier by thinking of the shape as other simple shapes added together.

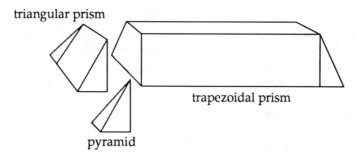

It can be considered as:

    $1 \times$ trapezoidal prism in the middle

    $2 \times$ triangular prisms one at each end

    $4 \times$ rectangular based pyramids one at each corner

Trapezoidal prism

To find the volume of a prism we use the formula:

$$\text{Volume} = \text{area of cross section} \times \text{length}$$

or, symbolically:

$$V = Al$$

In this case the cross section is a trapezium;

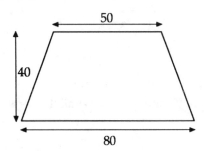

$$\text{Area} = \text{average width} \times \text{height}$$

$$A = \frac{80 + 50}{2} \times 40$$

That is:
$$A = 2{,}600 \text{ mm}^2$$

The length of the central prism is 200 mm

So the volume is given by:
$$V = 2600 \times 200$$

i.e.
$$V = 520000 \text{ mm}^3$$

Triangular Prism

Again the volume of a prism is found using the formula:

$$\text{Volume} = \text{area of cross section} \times \text{length}$$

or, symbolically:
$$V = Al$$

Here the area of cross section is a triangle;

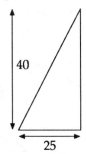

Note: The base value of 25 is found by halving the difference between lengths a and b.

$$\text{Area} = \tfrac{1}{2} \times \text{base} \times \text{height}$$

That is:
$$A = \tfrac{1}{2} \times 25 \times 40$$

$$A = 500 \text{ mm}^2$$

The length of the triangular prisms is 50 mm.

So the volume is:
$$V = 500 \times 50$$

ie
$$V = 25{,}000 \text{ mm}^3$$

Rectangular Based Pyramid

The formula for the volume of any pyramid is:

$$\text{Volume} = \tfrac{1}{3} \times \text{base area} \times \text{height}$$

or, symbolically:
$$V = \tfrac{1}{3}Al$$

The area of the base of these pyramids is:

$$A = 25 \times 15$$
$$A = 375 \text{ mm}^2$$

The volume can now be calculated:

$$V = \tfrac{1}{3} \times 375 \times 40$$
$$V = 5,000 \text{ mm}^3$$

The total volume can now be found by adding together all the parts that make up the gold bar.

Total volume is given by;

1 × trapezoidal prism	1 × 520000	520000
2 × triangular prism	2 × 25000	50000
4 × rectangular based pyramid	4 × 5000	20000
	Total	590000 mm³

Cylinder

The volume required for each coin is found by using the formula for a prism, as a cylinder may be thought of as a circular prism.

$$\text{Volume} = \text{area of cross section} \times \text{length}$$

or, symbolically:

$$V = \pi r^2 l$$

$r=20$ and $t=4$:

$$V = \pi \times 20^2 \times 4$$
$$V = 5026.5 \text{ mm}^3$$

Now we can calculate how many of these coins can be made:

$$\frac{590,000}{5,026.5} = 117.4$$

We can therefore make 117 coins, as they must be whole.

Investigations

Shapes with continuous cross sectional areas

If a shape has the same cross sectional area throughout its length then the volume is found by multiplying the area of the cross section by its length. This is the case whatever shape is involved. Here are some examples.

Cuboid

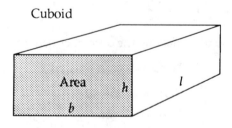

$$\text{Volume} = \text{area} \times \text{length}$$
$$V = b \times h \times l$$

Cylinder

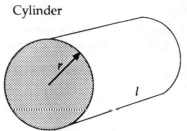

$$\text{Volume} = \text{area} \times \text{length}$$
$$V = \pi r^2 \times l$$

Irregular continuous shape

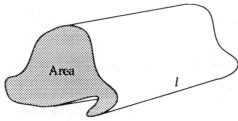

Area

$$\text{Volume} = \text{area} \times \text{length}$$
$$V = \text{area} \times l$$

Shapes where an area converges to a point

To find the volume of cones, or pyramids with different bases, again we can use a general formula. The volume is given by multiplying one third by the base area and then by the length (measured at right angles to this area).

Cone

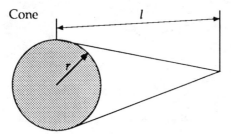

$$\text{Volume} = \tfrac{1}{3} \times \text{area} \times \text{length}$$
$$V = \tfrac{1}{3}\pi r^2 \times l$$

Triangular based pyramid

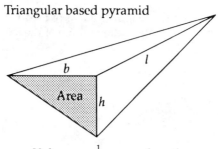

Area

$$\text{Volume} = \tfrac{1}{3} \times \text{area} \times \text{length}$$
$$V = \tfrac{1}{3} \times \tfrac{1}{2} bh \times l$$

143

Chopped off Shapes (Frustra)

In order to find the volume of shapes similar to the above (pyramids etc), except with the top removed, we calculate the volume of the total shape and subtract the volume of the missing part.

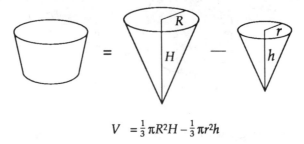

$$V = \frac{1}{3}\pi R^2 H - \frac{1}{3}\pi r^2 h$$

9.2 Estimating Volumes

Investigations

An estimate for the volume of an irregular shape can be obtained if areas are calculated at regular intervals along its length. A formula known as 'Simpsons Rule' can be adapted to determine an approximation for the volume. Areas are numbered from 0 for convenience and provided that an even number of intervals are used the method is valid.

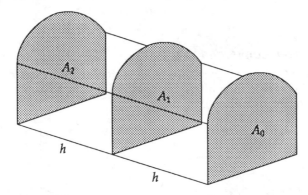

Simpson's Rule

Volume $= \frac{1}{3}h$ (first area + last area + 4(sum of odd areas) + 2(sum of other even areas))

The accuracy of the approximation can be improved by increasing the number of areas that are used. If the distance h between areas is small a good estimate may be achieved.

Example 2

Areas of slices are calculated along the length of a loaf of bread, at intervals of 4 cm. These values are given in the table. Obtain an estimate of the volume of the loaf using 'Simpsons Rule'.

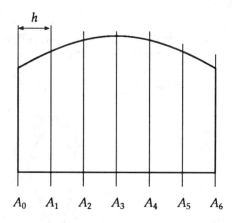

	A_0	A_1	A_2	A_3	A_4	A_5	A_6
Area cm^2	410	450	510	578	536	467	425

Solution 2

Simpson's Rule

$$\text{Volume} = \tfrac{1}{3}h \text{ (first area + last area + 4(sum of odd areas) + 2(sum of other even areas))}$$

$$V = \tfrac{1}{3} \times 4 \ (410 + 425 + 4(450 + 578 + 476) + 2(510 + 536))$$

$$V = \tfrac{1}{3} \times 4 \ (410 + 425 + 6016 + 2092)$$

$$V = 11{,}924 \text{ cm}^3$$

9.3 Surface area

Example 3

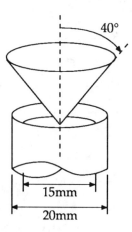

A cone is used to control the flow of liquid through a valve. The internal and external diameters of the pipe are 15 mm and 20 mm respectively, and the side of the cone makes an angle of 40° with the centre line.

Find the area of the cone that is in contact with the pipe when the valve is closed.

Solution 3

If we imagine that the curved surface area of the cone is unwrapped, there is a strip on it, that is equivalent to the area in contact with the pipe (see diagram).

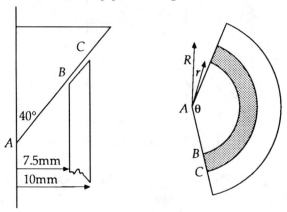

This area can be found by subtracting the inner sector area from the outer sector area.

The formula for sector area is:

$$A = \tfrac{1}{2}\theta r^2$$

where θ is the angle in radians.

It is therefore necessary to calculate each of the radii and the angle of the opened out cone (this is not 40°).

Radii

From the diagram it is clear that radius r is equal to the length AB, and using trigonometry we can calculate its value.

$$\sin 40° = \frac{7.5}{r}$$

and thus

$$R = \frac{7.5}{\sin 40°}$$

giving:

$$R = 11.67$$

In a similar way we can find R which is equal to AC.

$$\sin 40° = \frac{10}{R}$$

and thus

$$r = \frac{10}{\sin 40°}$$

giving:

$$r = 15.56$$

Angle θ

The arc lengths must be equal to the internal and external circumferences of the pipe, since they are in contact, so we can calculate these values.

$$\text{Arc length } B = \text{Internal circumference}$$
$$= 15\pi$$

$$\text{Arc length } C = \text{External circumference}$$
$$= 20\pi$$

Now using the radius (r) together with the arc length B the angle θ can be found:

$$\text{Arc length} = r\theta$$

thus: $\qquad\qquad B = r\theta$

and: $\qquad\qquad \theta = \dfrac{B}{r}$

$$\theta = \dfrac{15\pi}{11.67}$$

$$\theta = 1.29\pi$$

The area of the cone in contact with the pipe is therefore:

again working in radians: $\qquad \text{Area} = \text{Outer sector area} - \text{Inner sector area}$

$$A = \tfrac{1}{2}\theta R^2 - \tfrac{1}{2}\theta r^2$$

$$A = \tfrac{1}{2}\theta\,(R^2 - r^2)$$

$$A = \tfrac{1}{2} \times 1.29\pi(15.56^2 - 11.67^2)$$

$$A = 215 \text{ mm}^2$$

Investigations

Surface Area

In example 3 we calculated a 3 dimensional surface area by unwrapping the surface and thinking of it as a flat shape. This is a useful approach but relies on our ability to accurately represent a shape as a net (an unwrapped surface). Here are a few examples illustrated in this form. Making a shape out of paper can help us to visualise 3 dimensional shapes.

A cylinder with the top cut off at an angle produces the net shown;

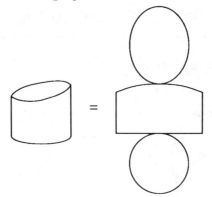

A square based pyramid has this net;

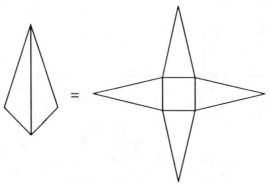

In this way the surface area of many components can be found. However, some three dimensional shapes are more difficult and we can rely on formulae to calculate surface area.

Sphere

$$\text{Volume} = \tfrac{4}{3}\pi r^3$$

$$\text{Surface area} = 4\pi r^3$$

Dome

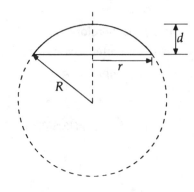

$$\text{Volume} = \frac{\pi d^2}{3}(3R - d)$$

$$\text{Surface area} = 2\pi Rd + \pi r^2$$

Skill unit 10 *Exponential relationships*

10.1 Exponential relationships

Example 1

An electrical circuit includes a capacitor and a resistance as shown.

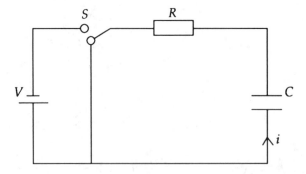

When the switch is closed the capacitor charges and the instantaneous current i varies with time t and is given by the equation:

$$i = 2e^{-\frac{t}{5}}$$

How long does it take before the current is 1.5 amperes.

Solution 1

The equation can of course be solved graphically. Values for time t allow us to calculate corresponding values for the current i.

t	0	1	2	3	4	5	6	7	8	9	10
i	2.00	1.64	1.34	1.10	0.90	0.74	0.60	0.49	0.40	0.33	0.27

Using these coordinates a graph can be drawn;

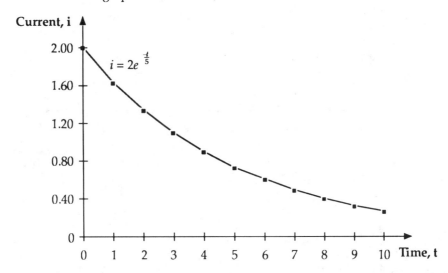

This curve enables us to estimate the time at which the instantaneous current is 1.5 amps.

Reading the graph the corresponding time is about $t = 1.44$ seconds.

Investigations

In order to help us understand the complicated exponential relationship from example 1, let us examine the curve more closely:

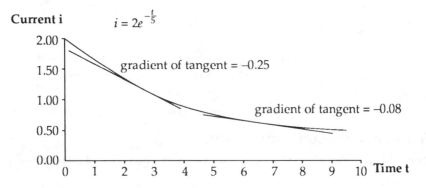

The value of i is continually reducing. However, the rate of reduction is decreasing (the gradient of the curve, although negative, is becoming shallower). This relationship is known as an exponential decay.

In practice the reason why we have an exponential decay here is; The charging current is dependent on the potential difference (PD) between the battery and the capacitor. As the capacitor is charged the PD becomes smaller, therefore reducing the charging current.

Other exponential curves

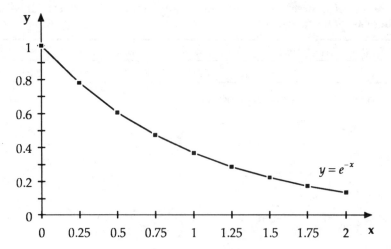

Here the curve is the same shape as before, but the initial value is $y = 1$, and the rate that y is decreasing is 5 times greater than before.

Let us now consider positive values of x;

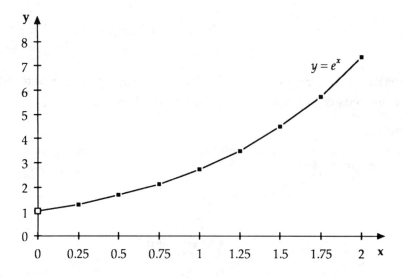

This curve shows, not only an increase in y, but also an increase in the gradient (rate of increase).

10.2 Gradients of exponential curves

To estimate the gradient at any point we can calculate the change between two points that are very close together.

The gradient at $x = 0$:

When $x = 0$:	$y = e^0 = 1$
When $x = 0.001$:	$y = e^{0.001} = 1.001$
The change in y:	$\delta y = 0.001$
The change in x:	$\delta y = 0.001$

The gradient is given by: $\dfrac{\delta y}{\delta x} = \dfrac{0.001}{0.001} = 1$

The gradient at $x = 1.5$

When $x = 1.5$: $y = e^{1.5} = 4.4817$

When $x = 1.501$: $y = e^{1.501} = 4.4862$

The change in y: $\delta y = 0.0045$

The change in x: $\delta y = 0.001$

The gradient is given by: $\dfrac{\delta y}{\delta x} = \dfrac{0.0045}{0.001} = 4.5$

The gradient at any point on this curve can be seen to be equal to the exponential value itself.

When $x = 0$ $e^x = 1$ gradient $= 1$

When $x = 1.5$ $e^x = 4.48$ gradient $= 4.5$

This is an important observation that we will refer to later.

Skill unit 11 *Simultaneous equations and matrices*

11.1 Simultaneous equations

Example 1

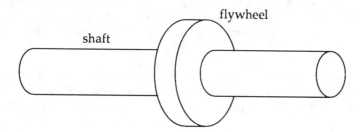

shaft

flywheel

A brass flywheel is mounted on a mild steel shaft as shown and the combined weight is 16.2kg. An alternative arrangement (the same shape) can be used with an aluminium shaft and a flywheel made from lead, here the total weight is 10.6kg. Calculate the volume of material used for the flywheels and shafts.

Solution 1

Using the table for densities of materials we can write down simultaneous equations that represent the weight of each flywheel arrangement.

Arrangement 1: $8.45f + 7.85s = 16200$ (where f = volume of flywheel; s = volume of shaft)
Densities: Brass = 8.45g/cm³ and mild steel = 7.85g/cm³

Arrangement 2: $11.3f + 2.7s = 10600$
Densities; Lead = 11.3g/cm³ and aluminium = 2.7g/cm³

Equation 1 can now be rearranged to give f in terms of s.

Subtract 7.85s: $\qquad\qquad\qquad\qquad 8.45f = 16200 - 7.85s$

Divide by 8.45: $\qquad\qquad\qquad\qquad f = \dfrac{16,200 - 7.85s}{8.45}$

This expression replaces f in equation 2 (substitute for f);

$$11.3f + 2.7s = 10600$$

$$11.3\left(\frac{16200 - 7.85s}{8.45}\right) + 2.7s = 10600$$

The resulting equation is in terms of s only, so it can be solved.

$$21700 - 10.5s + 2.7s = 10600$$

Combining terms: $\qquad\qquad 21700 - 10600 = 7.8s$

$$s = \frac{11100}{7.8}$$

Therefore: $\qquad\qquad\qquad\qquad s = 1420 \text{ cm}^3$

We can now go back to our expression for f, and replace s with this value (substitute for s):

$$f = \frac{16200 - 7.85(1420)}{8.45}$$

$$f = \frac{5050}{8.45}$$

That is: $\qquad\qquad\qquad\qquad f = 598 \text{cm}^3$

Investigations

There are a number of techniques for solving simultaneous equations, here we shall consider some of them. It is wise to learn more than just one method, because the suitability of each depends on the presentation, and numerical values involved, in particular equations.

Graphs

Graphs can of course be used to solve equations of any type and there is no exception here. This method of solution is discussed in detail in 'Graphical Solution of Equations'. There are however occasions when this is not an appropriate method (facilities may not be available).

Substitution (as in example 1)

Rearranging one of the equations for an unknown value, allows substitution into the second equation and produces a single equation that can be solved. A satisfactory solution is achieved here, but as in example 1 there may be a number of messy calculations involved. Calculators or computers can be programmed to help with this method of solution.

11.2 Matrices

Two or more equations can be combined to form one matrix equation. This is where blocks of numbers are dealt with together using a new set of rules. Let us now look at some of these rules;

Multiplying matrices

If two simple matrices are multiplied together the following result is obtained:

$$\begin{pmatrix} 1 & 2 \\ 3 & 4 \end{pmatrix}\begin{pmatrix} 5 & 6 \\ 7 & 8 \end{pmatrix} = \begin{pmatrix} (1\times5)+(2\times7) & (1\times6)+(2\times8) \\ (3\times5)+(4\times7) & (3\times6)+(4\times8) \end{pmatrix}$$

$$= \begin{pmatrix} 19 & 22 \\ 43 & 50 \end{pmatrix}$$

If this procedure is studied carefully a rule can be established. Consider how each element has been calculated;

First element (19)	Sum of the first row (1 2) multiplied by the first column (5 7)
Second element (22)	Sum of the first row (1 2) multiplied by the second column (6 8)
Third element (43)	Sum of the second row (3 4) multiplied by the first column (5 7)
Fourth element (50)	Sum of the second row (3 4) multiplied by the second column (6 8)

It should be noted that the number of columns in the first matrix, has to be the same as the number of rows in the second matrix, in order for multiplication to be possible.

The equations from example 1 can now be written as one matrix equation:

$$8.45f + 7.85s = 16200$$
$$11.3f + 2.7s = 10600$$

or, in matrix form:

$$\begin{pmatrix} 8.45 & 7.85 \\ 11.3 & 2.7 \end{pmatrix} \begin{pmatrix} f \\ s \end{pmatrix} = \begin{pmatrix} 16200 \\ 10600 \end{pmatrix}$$

Inverse matrices

When a number is multiplied by its inverse the result is always 1. In a similar way, when a matrix is multiplied by its inverse a special matrix is always obtained. This matrix is known as the identity matrix.

$$\left(\text{Matrix} \right) \left(\text{Inverse} \right) = \begin{pmatrix} 1 & 0 \\ 0 & 1 \end{pmatrix}$$

A special property of the identity matrix is that if it is multiplied by any other matrix, there is no change (as with multiplying by 1).

For convenience, matrices are given names (usually capital letters). The symbol used for the identity matrix is I. To denote an inverse the symbol is raised to the power of -1 (as with ordinary numbers). So for a matrix A we can say;

$$A.A^{-1} = I$$

or:

$$A^{-1}.A = I$$

This concept allows us to find the inverse of a simple matrix:

$$\begin{pmatrix} 1 & 2 \\ 3 & 4 \end{pmatrix} \begin{pmatrix} a & b \\ c & d \end{pmatrix} = \begin{pmatrix} 1 & 0 \\ 0 & 1 \end{pmatrix}$$

Where a, b, c and d are elements of the inverse

Multiplying we get two sets of simultaneous equations:

$a + 2c = 1$	$b + 2d = 0$
$3a + 4c = 0$	$3b + 4d = 1$

Rearrange 1st equations	$a = 1 - 2c$	$b = -2d$
Substitute into second	$3(1 - 2c) + 4c = 0$	$3(-2d) + 4d = 1$
Solve	$3 = 2c$	$-2d = 1$
	$c = 3/2$	$d = -1/2$
Substitute for c and d	$a = -2$	$b = 1$

The inverse matrix is:

$$\begin{pmatrix} -2 & 1 \\ \frac{3}{2} & -\frac{1}{2} \end{pmatrix} = -\frac{1}{2} \cdot \begin{pmatrix} 4 & -2 \\ -3 & 1 \end{pmatrix}$$

To check that this is correct, the product with the original matrix should give us the identity matrix.

Again a rule can be observed so that this lengthy procedure is not required each time an inverse is needed.

For any matrix with elements a, b, c and d :

$$\begin{pmatrix} a & b \\ c & d \end{pmatrix} \rightarrow \text{INVERSE} \rightarrow \frac{1}{ad - bc} \cdot \begin{pmatrix} d & -b \\ -c & a \end{pmatrix}$$

The value $ad - bc$ is known as the *determinant* of the original matrix. It has special properties that are discussed later.

Matrix solution of simultaneous equations

If symbols are used to represent matrices (matrix algebra), equations can be rearranged so that the unknown matrix if isolated. Labelling the matrices produced from the equations of example 1 gives us a simplified equation:

$$\begin{pmatrix} 8.45 & 7.85 \\ 11.3 & 2.7 \end{pmatrix} \cdot \begin{pmatrix} f \\ s \end{pmatrix} = \begin{pmatrix} 16200 \\ 10600 \end{pmatrix}$$

or:

$$A \cdot X = B$$

We must remember that A, B and X are matrices and the set of rules for matrices must be used. Conventional methods of rearranging equations do not apply.

The unknown matrix is X so this must be isolated.

$$AX = B$$

Multiply by the inverse of A: $\qquad A^{-1}AX = A^{-1}B$

and, since $A^{-1}A = I$: $\qquad IX = A^{-1}B$

Multiplying by I has no effect: $\qquad X = A^{-1}B$

So in order to determine X we need to find the inverse of A and multiply it by B.

Finding the inverse of A:

$$\begin{pmatrix} 8.45 & 7.85 \\ 11.3 & 2.7 \end{pmatrix} \rightarrow \text{INVERSE} \rightarrow \frac{1}{(8.45 \times 2.7) - (7.85 \times 11.3)} \cdot \begin{pmatrix} 2.7 & -7.85 \\ -11.3 & 8.45 \end{pmatrix}$$

$$A^{-1} = \frac{1}{-65.89} \cdot \begin{pmatrix} 2.7 & -7.85 \\ -11.3 & 8.45 \end{pmatrix}$$

This is now multiplied by B:

$$A^{-1}B = \frac{1}{-65.89} \cdot \begin{pmatrix} 2.7 & -7.85 \\ -11.3 & 8.45 \end{pmatrix} \begin{pmatrix} 16200 \\ 10600 \end{pmatrix}$$

$$= \frac{1}{-65.89} \cdot \begin{pmatrix} -39470 \\ -93490 \end{pmatrix}$$

$$X = \begin{pmatrix} 599 \\ 1419 \end{pmatrix}$$

These values represent the volume of the flywheel f and the volume of the shaft. They do of course agree with values found previously.

Technology

Calculators

 To work with matrices on a calculator a high powered model is required.

The first hurdle is to enter a matrix into the calculator. This is done one element at a time:

(1,1) refers to 1st row and 1st column

(1,2) refers to 1st row and 2nd column

.... and so on.

Of course more than one matrix may need to be entered, such as matrix A and matrix B. Selecting from a menu we can chose to multiply matrices or some other operation. Finding an inverse matrix is a useful function.

Computers

 Computer spreadsheets give us a much more visual approach to matrix calculations, and data as well as formulae can be stored on disks.

An example of how a spreadsheet can be laid out to calculate the inverse of a matrix is shown.

Other calculations (multiplication) may be controlled in a similar way.

	A	B	C	D	E	F
1	1	2			=B2	=-B1
2	3	4			=-A2	=A1
3						
4			determinant	=A1*B2-B1*A2		
5						
6			1/det	=1/D4		

Once spreadsheets are produced they can be kept on disk and used to deal with any numbers in cells A1, A2, B1 and B2.

12.1 Quadratic curves

Example 1

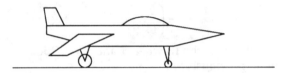

An aircraft engine produces a constant acceleration of 15 m/s². If the aircraft starts from rest, find the speed (or velocity, as these mean the same thing in this situation) after 10 seconds, and the distance it has travelled in that time.

Solution 1

The speed is increasing at a constant rate of 15 m/s every second so a straight line graph can be used to illustrate the change in velocity related to time.

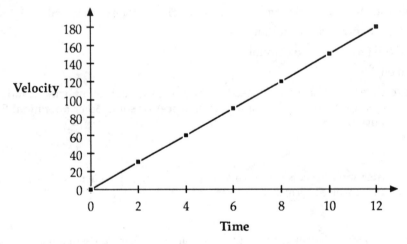

The equation represented by this graph is $v = 15t$ and we need to find the velocity after 10 seconds.

So: $$v = 15t$$

and when $t=10$: $$v = 15 \times 10$$

That is: $$v = 150 \text{ m/s}$$

To find the distance travelled, a more complicated equation needs to be used that links distance with speed and time.

We are familiar with the equation: distance = velocity × time

More generally this should be stated as: distance = average velocity × time

From our graph the product (average velocity × time) can be seen to be equivalent to the area under the graph.

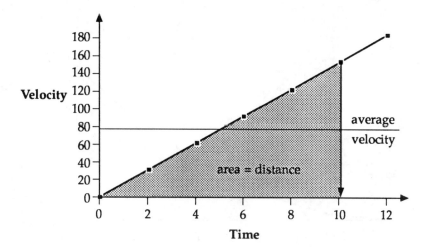

$$\text{Area} \;\; = \tfrac{1}{2} \times \text{base} \times \text{height}$$

$$= \tfrac{1}{2}\,tv \;\; \text{(where } v \text{ is the velocity after time } t)$$

So the equation is: $\qquad\qquad$ distance, $s \;\; = \tfrac{1}{2}\,tv$

When $t=10$ and $v=150$: $\qquad\qquad s \;\; = \tfrac{1}{2} \times 150 \times 10$

Therefore: $\qquad\qquad$ distance, $s \;\; = 750$ metres

Investigations

From example 1 we have two relationships:

$$v \;\; = 15t$$

and

$$\text{distance, } s \;\; = \tfrac{1}{2}\,tv$$

suggesting that both the velocity and the distance can be found for any value of time. Another relationship can be written down for distance by replacing v with $15t$ as these are equal.

So it becomes: $\qquad\qquad s \;\; = \tfrac{1}{2}\,(15t)t$

ie $\qquad\qquad s \;\; = 7.5t^2$

With this equation values of s are related to t squared. Whenever we have a squared relationship it is known as a quadratic equation and if a graph is plotted a curve will result.

Graphical solution

The graph of this equation can be drawn by calculating corresponding values in a table or by programming a calculator/computer.

As the graph will produce a curve a number of points are required:

t	0	2	4	6	8	10
s	0	30	120	270	480	750

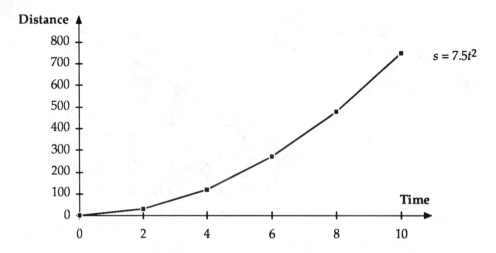

Quadratic graphs can be used in much the same way as straight line graphs to solve equations, but more care is required in plotting points and drawing curves.

Using the curve we can find the distance travelled in 10 seconds.

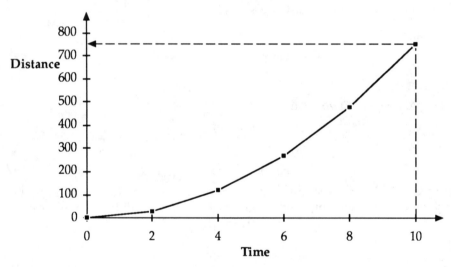

Here the distance can be seen to be 750 metres. This agrees with our previously calculated value.

Related curves

Let us consider how the relationship between distance and time is affected if the acceleration of the aircraft in example 1 is changed:

Acceleration = 30 m/s² $v = 30t$

$s = \frac{1}{2} \times 30t^2$

That is: $s = 15t^2$

Comparing this curve with $s = 7.5t^2$:

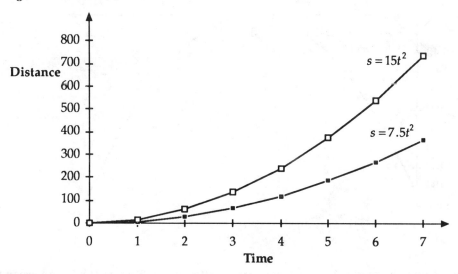

We can see that multiplying t^2 by a larger number has the effect of bending the curve upwards. This is an important observation that applies to any quadratic curve.

Negative values of time (seconds before the aircraft started) can also be used to calculate corresponding distances. This allows us to see complete quadratic curves.

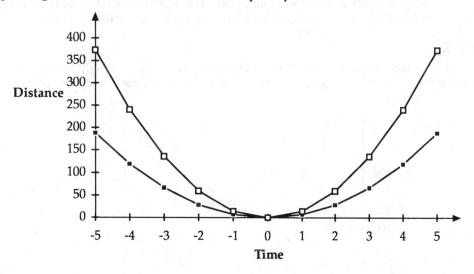

If multiplying t^2 by larger numbers bends the curve upwards then it makes sense that multiplying by smaller numbers flattens it out. This is true, and if t^2 is multiplied by 0 then a horizontal line results. Extending this idea further, multiplying by negative numbers bends the curve downwards. Here is the graph of $s = -7.5t^2$.

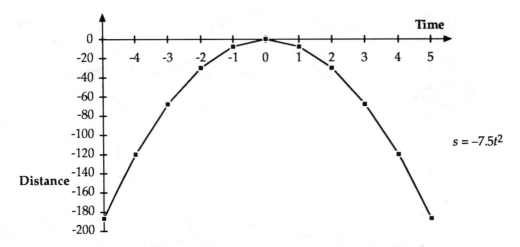

$$s = -7.5t^2$$

So we can see how the shape of the distance curve is affected by different values of acceleration.

12.2 Quadratic formulae

Example 2

An aircraft engine produces a constant acceleration of 18 m/s². If the aircraft is initially travelling at 40m/s, find the time it takes to reach the end of the runway if the distance is 650 metres.

Solution 2

The speed is increasing at a constant rate of 18 m/s every second so a straight line graph can be used to illustrate the change in velocity related to time. The graph starts with the initial velocity of 40 m/s.

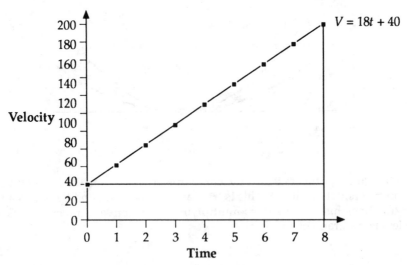

$$V = 18t + 40$$

As before, the area under the graph represents the distance travelled. An equation for this can now be written down:

$$s = \tfrac{1}{2}18t^2 + 40t$$

Using this relationship we should be able to calculate the value of t when the distance $s = 650$ metres.

Substitute $s = 650$: $$650 = 9t^2 + 40t$$

Divide by 9: $$\frac{650}{9} = t^2 + \frac{40}{9}t \qquad [1]$$

Here we have a quadratic equation involving t^2 and t. Because of this it is not possible to simply rearrange the equation in terms of t. First the equation has to be written in a different form, so that we have a bracketed term involving t that is squared.

'Complete the square' using the following identity:

$$\left(t + \frac{20}{9}\right)^2 = t^2 + \frac{40}{9}t + \frac{400}{81}$$

which is rearranged as: $$t^2 + \frac{40}{9}t = \left(t + \frac{20}{9}\right)^2 - \frac{400}{81} \qquad [2]$$

Now, substituting [2] into [1] : $$\frac{650}{9} = \left(t + \frac{20}{9}\right)^2 - \frac{400}{81}$$

Now the equation can be rearranged to give t.

$$\frac{650}{9} + \frac{400}{81} = \left(t + \frac{20}{9}\right)^2$$

$$\sqrt{\frac{6250}{81}} = \left(t + \frac{20}{9}\right)$$

giving: $$t = \sqrt{\frac{6250}{81}} - \frac{20}{9}$$

That is: $$t = 6.56 \text{ seconds}$$

It must be noted that when a square root is taken there is a positive and negative result. In this case the positive answer is the one that is required.

Investigations

Solving quadratic equations using a formula

The method of solving the quadratic equation in example 2 is a method that can always be used whatever the values of acceleration or starting velocity.

Let us solve a quadratic equation where the values are replaced with symbols and follow the same procedure as before.

If $$0 = at^2 + bt + c \text{ (where } a, b \text{ and } c \text{ could be any values)}$$

then $$-c = at^2 + bt$$

Dividing by a gives: $$\frac{-c}{a} = t^2 + \frac{b}{a}t$$

Again we have a quadratic equation involving t^2 and t. The equation has to be written in a different form, so that we have squared brackets.

Complete the square using: $$\left(t + \frac{b}{2a}\right)^2 = t^2 + \frac{b}{a}t + \frac{b^2}{4a^2}$$

which gives (after substitution): $$\frac{-c}{a} = \left(t + \frac{b}{2a}\right)^2 - \frac{b^2}{4a^2}$$

Now the equation can be rearranged to give *t*.

$$\frac{b^2}{4a^2} - \frac{c}{a} = \left(t + \frac{b}{2a}\right)^2$$

$$\sqrt{\frac{b^2 - 4ac}{4a^2}} - \frac{b}{2a} = t$$

Therefore:
$$t = \frac{-b \pm \sqrt{b^2 - 4ac}}{2a}$$

This formula can be used to solve any quadratic equation. All that is required, is that we carefully substitute values in place of the letters, and carry out the calculations. There will normally be two possible solutions (hence the ± in the formula) due to the fact that a square root may be positive or negative.

Example 3

The distance travelled by a 'Jumbo Jet' is related to time by the equation:

$$s = 8t^2 + 25t$$

If it moves along the runway towards a hedgehog, initially 200 metres away, which is travelling in the opposite direction at a constant speed of 0.5 m/s.

Calculate the time it takes before the 'Jumbo Jet' flies over the hedgehog.

Solution 3

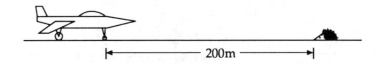

Initially the travellers are 200 metres apart. Because they are moving towards each other they should meet after the aircraft has travelled less than this distance.

Distance moved by the aircraft: $\quad s_a = 8t^2 + 25t$

Distance moved by the hedgehog: $\quad s_h = 0.5t$

The two journeys take place during the same time interval, and thus the sum of the distances must be 200m.

Algebraically: $\quad s_a + s_h = 200$

or: $\quad \left(8t^2 + 25t\right) + (0.5t) = 200$

Here we have a quadratic equation that can be solved using the formula.

$$8t^2 + 25.5t - 200 = 0$$

and thus: $\quad a = 8$

$$b = 25.5$$

and $\quad c = -200$

Substituting these values into: $\quad t = \frac{-b \pm \sqrt{b^2 - 4ac}}{2a}$

we have:

$$t = \frac{-25.5 \pm \sqrt{25.5^2 - 4 \times 8 \times 200}}{2 \times 8}$$

$$= \frac{-25.5 \pm \sqrt{650.25 - (-6400)}}{16}$$

$$= \frac{-25.5 \pm 84.0}{16}$$

giving:

$$t = 3.65 \quad \text{or} \quad t = -6.84$$

In words, the jumbo jet will fly over the hedgehog after 3.65 seconds.

Note that the negative value can be ignored here.

Technology

Calculators

Calculator care is required when the quadratic formula is used to solve equations. If we are not confident about entering the whole calculation in one go, then it should be carried out in sections and partial answers written down.

The quadratic formula:

$$x = \frac{-b \pm \sqrt{b^2 - 4ac}}{2a}$$

has to be used twice since there are generally two solutions.

To solve the equation:

$$2x^2 + 6x + 3 = 0$$

the sequence of entries is as follows.

| 6 | x^2 | − | 4 | × | 2 | × | 3 | = | √ | + | 6 | ± |

| X–Y | = | ÷ | [| 2 | × | 2 |] | = |

The other solution is obtained in a similar way.

Computers

A spreadsheet can be set up to use the formula for solving quadratic equations. This can be saved on disk and used when required.

	A	B	C
1	2	6	3
2			
3			
4	=(-B1+SQRT(B1^2–4*A1*C1))/(2*A1)		
5	=(-B1–SQRT(B1^2–4*A1*C1))/(2*A1)		

Skill unit 13 *Differentiation 1*

13.1 Differentiation

Example 1

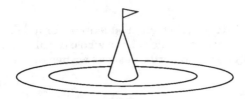

A marker buoy is dropped into the sea from a helicopter hovering overhead. The distance (*s*) of the fall from the helicopter is related to time (*t*) by the equation:

$$s = \tfrac{1}{2}gt^2$$

where *g* is the acceleration due to gravity

Calculate the velocity of the buoy on impact if it takes 3.5 seconds to complete the fall. Acceleration due to gravity (*g*) can be taken as $10\text{m}/s^2$.

Solution 1

Using the equation for distance where $g = 10$ we have:

$$s = \tfrac{1}{2}(10)t^2$$

$$= 5t^2$$

This equation allows us to calculate the displacement after 3.5 seconds.

$$s = 5 \times (3.5)^2$$

$$= 61.25 \text{ metres}$$

Velocity is distance divided by time or the rate of change of distance. The average velocity for the fall of the buoy can be calculated by using this overall distance divided by 3.5 seconds. This is quite different from the velocity at the moment of impact. For any time period during the fall we can use the distance equation to calculate the average velocity between two times. The graph shows the change of distance with time.

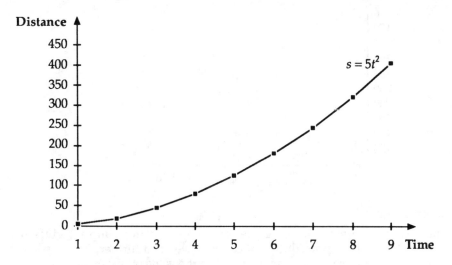

It can be seen that the rate of change of distance is increasing (a greater distance is being covered each second). The velocity is therefore continually increasing.

To determine the velocity of the buoy on impact we must consider the changes over a time interval. An estimate for the velocity can be made by calculating the distance when $t = 3.5$ and the theoretical distance just after this time (such as $t = 3.6$).

When $t = 3.5$ $s = 61.25$

When $t = 3.6$ $s = 5 \times (3.6)^2$

                                       $= 64.8$

The change in distance in 0.1 seconds is

$$64.8 - 61.25 = 3.55 \text{ metres}$$

$$\text{Velocity} = \frac{3.55}{0.1}$$

$$= 35.5 \text{ m/s}$$

This is the average velocity for the fraction of a second after impact. A better estimate is obtained by considering a smaller time interval (such as t = 3.5 to t = 3.55);

When $t = 3.5$ $s = 61.25$

When $t = 3.55$ $s = 5 \times (3.55)^2$

                                         $= 63.01$

The change in distance in 0.05 seconds is

$$63.01 - 61.25 = 1.76 \text{ metres}$$

$$\text{Velocity} = \frac{1.76}{0.05}$$

$$= 35.2 \text{ m/s}$$

Investigations

Gradient of a tangent

The rate of change of distance at a particular point on a distance/time graph is represented by a tangent drawn through that point. The gradient of the straight line is the same as the gradient at that point. In practice results of this kind are difficult to obtain with any accuracy.

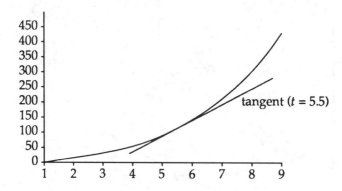

Two points on a curve

Using two points, that are very close together on a curve, as in example 1 gives reasonable results and presents us with a procedure that can be developed further. If a very small time is added to the time $t = 3.5$ there will be a small change in the value of distance.

Let the small change in time $= \delta t$ and the corresponding change in distance $= \delta s$

The distance equation $\qquad s = 5t^2$

becomes; $\qquad s + \delta s = 5(t + \delta t)^2$

$$s + \delta s = 5(t^2 + 2t\delta t + \delta t^2)$$

$$s + \delta s = 5t^2 + 10t\delta t + 5\delta t^2$$

But $s = 5t^2$ giving $\qquad \delta s = 10t\delta t + 5\delta t^2$

Dividing by δt gives $\qquad \dfrac{\delta s}{\delta t} = \dfrac{10t\delta t}{\delta t} + \dfrac{5\delta t^2}{\delta t}$

Thus the velocity is given by: $\qquad \dfrac{\delta s}{\delta t} = 10t + 5\delta t$

If we now use this equation to calculate the velocity when $t = 3.5$ as was required in example 1, and a very small change in time is used, we have:

$$\dfrac{\delta s}{\delta t} = 35 + 5(0.0000001)$$

and $\qquad v = \dfrac{\delta s}{\delta t} = 35.0000005$

But since δt is very small $5\delta t$ may be ignored $\left(\text{when this assumption is made, } \dfrac{ds}{dt} \text{ replaces } \dfrac{\delta s}{\delta t} \right).$

Therefore $\qquad v = \dfrac{ds}{dt} = 35 \text{ m/s}$

Results

Let us examine the results of this investigation

Distance is related to time by the relationship:

$$s = 5t^2$$

The rate of change of distance is: $\qquad \dfrac{ds}{dt} = 10t$

This process where we are finding a rate of change (gradient) of a variable is *differentiation*.

If other relationships are dealt with in a similar way (differentiated), the following results are obtained;

Relationship	Differentiated (gradient)
$s = 4t^3$	$\dfrac{ds}{dt} = 12t^2$
$P = 15R^2$	$\dfrac{dP}{dR} = 30R$
$V = 22r^4$	$\dfrac{dV}{dr} = 88r^3$

From these we can observe a method that saves us a lot of time. To differentiate a relationship of this type:

Multiply by the power and reduce the power by one

The general rule is as follows:

Relationship	Differentiated (gradient)
$y = ax^n$	$\dfrac{dy}{dx} = nax^{n-1}$

Where a and n are constant values.

Notes

1. Where terms similar to these are added or subtracted, each term can be differentiated separately;

$$y = 6x^3 + 4x^2 \quad \text{becomes} \quad \frac{dy}{dx} = 18x^2 + 8x$$

2. Linear expressions (such as 5x) have a power equal to 1. Differentiating reduces the power to 0 giving a constant value as the gradient;

$$y = 5x \quad \text{becomes} \quad \frac{dy}{dx} = 5$$

3. Expressions that involve fractional powers are treated in exactly the same way as whole powers;

$$y = \sqrt{x} \quad \text{can be written as} \quad y = x^{\frac{1}{2}} \quad \text{becomes} \quad \frac{dy}{dx} = \frac{1}{2}x^{-\frac{1}{2}}$$

13.2 Differentiating functions

To differentiate any relationship we can use the same procedure as before. Adding a small amount to the variable will produce a small change to the function.

If $\qquad\qquad\qquad y = \sin x$

then $\qquad\qquad\qquad y + \delta y = \sin(x + \delta x)$

If $\qquad\qquad\qquad y = e^x$

then $\qquad\qquad\qquad y + \delta y = e^{x + \delta x}$

These equations can be rearranged to give $\frac{\delta y}{\delta x}$ and then, assuming that δx is very small, allows us to eliminate negligible terms and find $\frac{dy}{dx}$.

This is a complicated time consuming procedure and inefficient to follow for each problem. It is far more convenient to use a table giving us a set of standard functions already differentiated. A table is provided giving these.

Skill unit 14 *Integration 1*

14.1 Reversing Differentiation

Investigations

Differentiation is a process that allows us to obtain the gradient of a curve. It therefore follows, that by using differentiation in reverse (carrying out the opposite processes) we can obtain the equation of a curve from the gradient. This inverse process is *integration*.

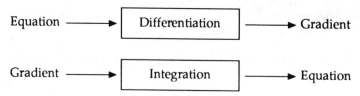

Equation $\longrightarrow$ | Differentiation | $\longrightarrow$ Gradient

Gradient $\longrightarrow$ | Integration | $\longrightarrow$ Equation

Let us try this out on an equation to see how it works.

Equation of a curve: $\qquad$ $y = 5x^2$

Differentiating: $\qquad$ $\frac{dy}{dx} = 10x$

Multiply by the power and reduce the power by one.

Now starting with the gradient and working in reverse

Gradient: $\qquad$ $\frac{dy}{dx} = 10x$

Integrating: $\qquad$ $y = 5x^2$

It can be stated that, to integrate a relationship of this type

Increase the power by one and divide by the new power

Relationship (gradient) $\qquad$ $\frac{dy}{dx} = ax^n$

where a and n are constant values.

Integrating gives: $\qquad$ $y = \frac{ax^{n+1}}{n+1}$

This is written as: $\qquad$ $\int ax^n dx = \frac{ax^{n+1}}{n+1}$

The symbol $\int$ is a summation sign and dx means 'with respect to x (the variable)'.

Note: When a constant value is differentiated the result is zero, so reversing the process (integrating) must give an unknown constant C. This is always added to an indefinite (without limits) integral.

14.2 Area under a curve

Example 1

The speed of a vehicle on a motorway is monitored by a police patrol car over a period of 1 minute. Speeds are observed every 10 seconds and the following table is constructed.

time t	0	10	20	30	40	50	60
speed v	40	47	54	61	68	75	82

When does the vehicle first exceed the limit of 70 mph, and how far has the vehicle travelled before this time.

Solution 1

From the table it can be seen that 70 mph is reached somewhere between 40 and 50 seconds.

Plotting these points on a graph indicates that there is a straight line relationship between speed and time. We can therefore write down an equation to represent this.

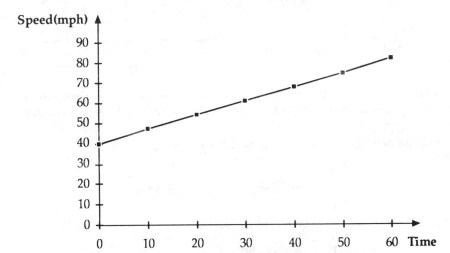

Equation of a straight line: $\qquad v = \text{intercept} + \text{gradient} \times t$

$$v = 40 + 2520t$$

(The gradient is calculated by converting 10 seconds into hours.)

The time can now be found when the speed reaches 70 mph.

Substitute this value: $\qquad 70 = 40 + 2520t$

Solve the equation: $\qquad t = 0.0119$ hours (42.84 seconds)

In order to determine the distance travelled we need to appreciate that speed is the rate of change of distance. Speed represents the gradient of a distance time graph. This means that if the relationship for speed is integrated we should have a relationship for distance.

Relationship for speed: $\qquad v = 40 + 2520t \quad$ (40 is treated as $40t^0$)

$$s = \int 40 + 2520t\, dt$$

Relationship for distance (integrating): $\quad s = 40t + \dfrac{2520t^2}{2} + C\left(\dfrac{40t^1}{1} = 40t\right)$

when $t=0$, $s=0$ and $C=0$

Substitute this value: $\qquad\qquad\qquad s = 40(0.0119) + 1260(0.0119)^2$

Solve the equation: $\qquad\qquad\qquad s = 0.654$ miles

Investigations

Another approach to solving example 1, is to consider that the distance is given by the area under the speed/time graph (as distance = speed × time).

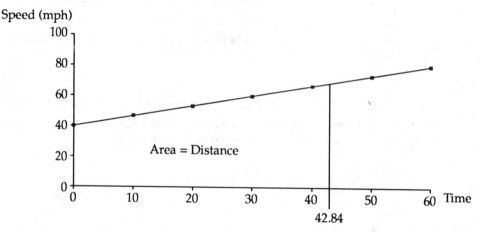

Speed (mph)

Area = Distance

42.84

This observation leads us to the conclusion that integration provides us with a method for calculating the area under a curve. This is an important property of integration that should be made full use of.

Again the summation sign is used but limits of t can be added:

$$\int_0^{0.119} (40 + 2520t)\,dt = \left(40t + 1260t^2 + C\right)_0^{0.0119}$$

The area found by replacing t with 0 is subtracted from the area with $t = 0.0119$.

That is: $\qquad \left[40(0.0119) + 1260(0.0119)^2 + C\right] - \left[40(0) + 1260(0)^2 + C\right]$

It should be noticed that the value of C is eliminated with definite integration.

Example 2

Let us consider the right angled triangle shown.

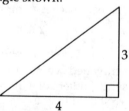

3

4

Calculate the area of a this triangle using integration.

Solution 2

The triangle can be divided up into very thin strips, it can be thought of as a composite shape (made up of an infinite number of approximate rectangles).

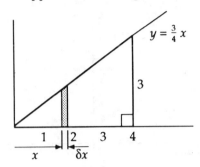

Treating the triangle as a straight line graph we can say that each rectangle has width δx and is a distance x from the origin.

The line has a gradient of $\frac{3}{4}$ and:
$$y = \frac{3}{4}x$$

The area of one strip is $\frac{3}{4}x\delta x$

This is an expression giving the area of a strip that is a distance x from the y axis. It is assumed that there are a large number of thin strips. Integration now allows us calculate the sum of strip areas between 0 and 4.

Sum of strips:
$$\int_{0}^{4}\frac{3}{4}x\,dx = \frac{3}{4}\left(\frac{x^2}{2}\right)_{0}^{4}$$
$$= \frac{3}{8}\left(4^2 - 0^2\right)$$
$$= 6 \quad \text{(as expected)}$$

Skill unit 15 *Complex numbers*

15.1 Imaginary numbers

Investigations

In electrical circuits resistance is measured in Ohms. This measurement can be considered to be a real number. That is resistances can be added together in a real or conventional way;

$$3\,\text{Ohms} + 4\,\text{Ohms} = 7\,\text{Ohms}$$

or graphically

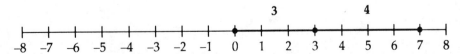

It is useful in electrical calculations to introduce another axis to this graph known as the j axis or the imaginary axis. Positive values of j are inductive reactance X_L (produced by a coil in a circuit) and negative values of j are capacitive reactance X_C (produced by a capacitor).

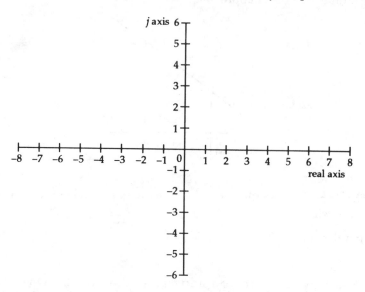

Multiplying by j, or the j operator, has the effect of rotating values by 90° in an anticlockwise direction. The magnitude is unchanged.

$j5$ represents 5 Ohms in the imaginary direction (inductive reactance)

Applying the j operator twice, j^2, has the effect of rotating values by 180° in an anticlockwise direction.

From this: $j^2 = -1$

and also: $j = \sqrt{-1}$

We cannot evaluate $\sqrt{-1}$. It is regarded as imaginary.

A number that has a real part and an imaginary part is called a complex number.

In the complex number: $Z = 3 + j5$

3 is the real part and $j5$ is the imaginary part.

Argand diagrams

If a circuit has a combination of resistance, inductance and capacitance, then the overall impedance Z of the circuit can be represented on an Argand diagram (a graph with a real and an imaginary axis).

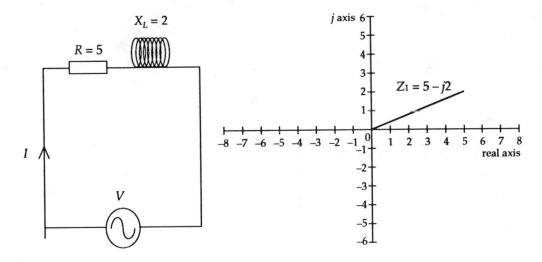

Circuit 1 has an impedance $Z_1 = 5 + j2$ represented here on an Argand diagram.

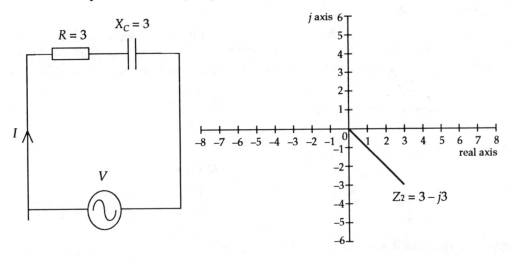

Circuit 2 has an impedance $Z_2 = 3 + j3$ represented here on an Argand diagram.

Addition and subtraction

Combining the components from the above two circuits gives an overall impedance equal to the sum of the complex numbers. To add complex numbers we simply add the components separately, the real parts together and the imaginary parts together. Subtraction is carried out in a similar way.

To demonstrate addition:

$$
\begin{aligned}
Z_1 + Z_2 &= (5 + j2) + (3 - j3) \\
&= (5 + 3) + (j2 - j3) \\
&= 8 - j1
\end{aligned}
$$

To demonstrate subtraction:

$$
\begin{aligned}
Z_1 - Z_2 &= (5 + j2) - (3 - j3) \\
&= (5 - 3) + (j2 - (-j3)) \\
&= 2 + j5
\end{aligned}
$$

Again, the impedance can be represented graphically.

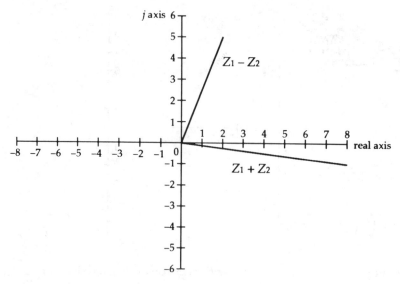

Multiplication and division

For calculations of voltage drop across a circuit and power it is necessary to be able to multiply and divide impedances. We shall therefore consider these operations with complex numbers.

If circuit 1 above carries a current of $(3 + j1)$ amps, the voltage can be found as shown.

$$V = IR$$

or, in an inductive or capacitive circuit:

$$V = IZ$$

Thus:

$$V = (3 + j1)(5 + j2)$$
$$= 3 \times 5 + 3 \times j2 + j1 \times 5 + j1 \times j2$$
$$= 15 + j6 + j5 + j^2 2$$
$$= 15 + j11 + 2(-1) \qquad \text{remember } j^2 = -1$$
$$= 13 + j11$$

In order to divide complex numbers we first need to convert the value that we are dividing by (the denominator) into a real number. A complex number will become a real number if it is multiplied by itself, after a sign change to the imaginary part.

Suppose: $\qquad Z_1 = (5 + j2)$

Then, after the change of sign, we have $(5 - j2)$ which is known as the conjugate of Z_1.

Multiplying: $\qquad (5 + j2)(5 - j2) = 25 + j10 - j10 - j^2 4$
$$= 25 + 4$$
$$= 29 \text{ (which is real)}$$

This facility can now be used to find the amount of current flowing with a supply voltage, $V = 13 + j11$.

So:

$$I = \frac{V}{Z}$$
$$= \frac{13 + j11}{5 + j2}$$
$$= \frac{13 + j11}{5 + j2} \times \frac{5 - j2}{5 - j2}$$

$$= \frac{65 - j26 + j55 - j^2 22}{29}$$

That is:
$$I = \frac{87 + j29}{29}$$

This can be written as a complex number, with real and imaginary parts.

$$I = \frac{87}{29} + j\frac{29}{29}$$
$$= 3 + j1$$

This agrees with the earlier current as expected.

15.2 Complex number calculations

Example 1

A circuit contains a resistance of 10 Ohms and an inductive reactance of 8 Ohms, connected in parallel with a resistance of 12 Ohms and a capacitive reactance of 15 Ohms. Find the current drawn if a voltage of $115 + j20$ V is applied.

Solution 1

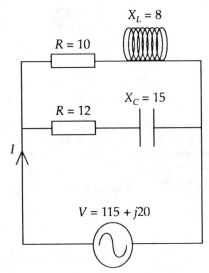

The overall impedance is found using:

$$\frac{1}{Z} = \frac{1}{Z_1} + \frac{1}{Z_2}$$

where Z_1 and Z_2 are the impedances in each branch of the circuit.

Therefore:
$$\frac{1}{Z} = \frac{1}{10 + j8} + \frac{1}{12 - j15}$$

$$= \frac{(12 - j15) + (10 + j8)}{(10 + j8)(12 - j15)}$$

Add on top and multiply under:
$$\frac{1}{Z} = \frac{22 - j7}{120 - j150 + j96 + 120}$$

$$= \frac{22 - j7}{240 - j54}$$

Taking the inverse gives:

$$Z = \frac{240 - j54}{22 - j7}$$

Divide using conjugate:

$$= \frac{240 - j54}{22 - j7} \times \frac{22 + j7}{22 + j7}$$

$$= \frac{5658 + j492}{484 + 49}$$

$$= \frac{5658 + j492}{533}$$

As a complex number:

$$Z = 10.6 + j0.92$$

Now we can use

$$I = \frac{V}{Z}$$

to give:

$$I = \frac{115 + j20}{10.6 + j0.92}$$

$$= \frac{115 + j20}{10.6 + j0.92} \times \frac{10.6 - j0.92}{10.6 - j0.92}$$

$$= \frac{1237 + j106}{112 + 0.85}$$

Therefore:

$$I = 11 + j0.9$$

15.3 Polar coordinates

Investigations

As an alternative to describing complex numbers by (x, y) coordinates (rectangular form), they can also be described by giving the radius (r called the modulus) from the origin and angle θ (called the argument) made with the x axis. This method, known as polar form, greatly simplifies calculations and is often used in preference.

Let us consider converting $Z_1 = 5 + j2$ into polar form.

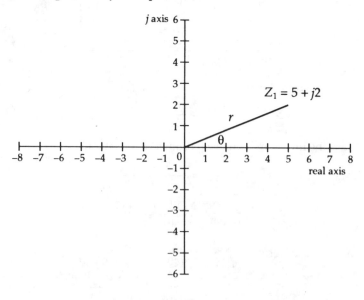

The radius r is found using pythagoras theorem:

$$r = \sqrt{5^2 + 2^2}$$
$$= 5.39$$

To find θ we use the tan ratio: $\qquad \tan \theta = \dfrac{2}{5}$

and $\qquad\qquad\qquad\qquad\qquad \theta = 22°$

Complex numbers in polar form are written modulus/argument, so here we have: 5.39/22°.

Calculators allow us to convert from rectangular to polar form or from polar to rectangular form very easily. This is discussed in detail in the calculators section.

To investigate polar form further let us consider what happens when polar complex numbers are converted into rectangular form, calculations are carried out and the answer is converted back to polar.

Multiplication in polar form

Example: Let $Z_1 = 5.385/21.8°$ and $Z_2 = 3.162/18.4°$

Converting to rectangular: $\qquad\qquad\qquad Z_1 = 5 + j2$

and $\qquad\qquad\qquad\qquad\qquad\qquad Z_2 = 3 + j1$

Multiply: $\qquad\qquad\qquad\qquad Z_1 Z_2 = (5 + j2)(3 + j1)$

$$= 13 + j11$$

Convert to polar: $\qquad\qquad\qquad Z_1 Z_2 = 17.03/40.2°$

From this it can be seen that a short cut could have been taken as follows.

The modulus of the product is:

the modulus of Z_1 multiplied by the modulus of Z_2.

or, symbolically: $\qquad\qquad$ mod $(Z_1 Z_2) = $ mod $Z_1 \times$ mod Z_2

The argument of the product is:

the sum of the two arguments.

or, symbolically: $\qquad\qquad$ arg $(Z_1 Z_2) = $ arg $Z_1 + $ arg Z_2

Division in polar form

Example: Let $Z_1 = 5.385/21.8°$ and $Z_2 = 3.162/18.4°$

Converting to rectangular: $\qquad\qquad\qquad Z_1 = 5 + j2$

and $\qquad\qquad\qquad\qquad\qquad\qquad Z_2 = 3 + j1$

Divide: $\qquad\qquad\qquad\qquad \dfrac{Z_1}{Z_2} = \dfrac{5 + j2}{3 + j1}$

$$= 1.7 + j0.1$$

Convert to polar: $\qquad\qquad\qquad \dfrac{Z_1}{Z_2} = 1.703/3.4°$

Again there is a short cut: $\qquad$ mod $\dfrac{Z_1}{Z_2} = \dfrac{\text{mod } Z_1}{\text{mod } Z_2}$

and: $\qquad\qquad\qquad\qquad$ arg $\dfrac{Z_1}{Z_2} = $ arg $Z_1 - $ arg Z_2

Square roots of complex numbers

We can use multiplication in polar form to develop rules for square roots.

Multiplying a complex number by itself (squaring) in polar coordinates can now be found.

$$Z_1^2 = 5.385^2/21.8° + 21.8°$$
$$= 29/43.6°$$

Square rooting is the opposite of this process, therefore:

$$\sqrt{29/43.6°} = 5.385/21.8°$$

or more generally, to square root a complex number, square root the modulus, and halve the argument.

Symbolically:

$$\sqrt{r/\theta} = \sqrt{r}/\frac{\theta}{2}$$

Example 2

An electrical circuit consisting of a resistor (resistance R = 5 Ohms), a coil (inductive reactance X_L = 10 Ohms) and a capacitor (capcitive reactance X_C = 6 Ohms) is connected to a 240 V ac supply. Calculate the current in the circuit.

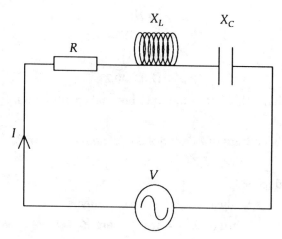

Solution 2

Complex impedance:

$$Z = R + jX_L - jX_C$$
$$Z = 5 + j10 - j6$$
$$Z = 5 + j4$$

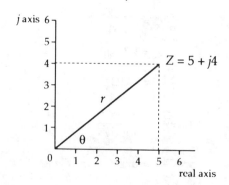

Convert to polar form:

Z = 5 + j4:

$$r = \sqrt{5^2 + 4^2}$$
$$= \sqrt{41}$$
$$= 6.4$$

and:

$$\tan \theta = \frac{4}{5}$$

giving:

$$\theta = 39°$$

We can write Z = 6.4/39°

The current can now be found.

$$I = \frac{V}{Z}$$
$$= \frac{240 \ / \ 0°}{6.4 \ / \ 39°}$$
$$= 37.5/{-}39°$$

There is a current of 37.5 Amps lagging behind the Voltage by 39°

Technology

Calculators

A particularly useful calculator facility is to convert rectangular to polar coordinates (R-P) or alternatively polar to rectangular (P-R).

To convert (3,4) into polar coordinates:

$$\boxed{3} \quad \boxed{\text{R–P}} \quad \boxed{4} \quad \boxed{=} \quad \boxed{\text{X–Y}}$$

The '=' button reveals the modulus and 'x-y' gives the angle. Angles are given in whichever mode is operational 'DEG' or 'RAD'.

Converting 8/30° to rectangular form:

$$\boxed{8} \quad \boxed{\text{P–R}} \quad \boxed{30} \quad \boxed{=} \quad \boxed{\text{X–Y}}$$

As before, the '=' button reveals the *x* coordinate and 'x-y' gives the *y* coordinate.

Computers

Formulae can be entered into a spreadsheet that carry out the conversion from rectangular to polar and vice-versa.

Pythagoras theorem looks like this in a spreadsheet formula with cells A1 and A2 containing the *x* and *y* coordinates;

$$= \text{SQRT(A1}^2\text{+A2}^2\text{)}$$

Example 1

A computer controlled machine produces bolts at the rate of 25 per hour. These are then placed into a bucket which already contains 130 bolts. How long will it take before there are a total of 680 in the bucket.

Solution 1

This problem could of course be solved the long way by continuing the pattern until 680 is reached.

Initially	130
After 1 hour	155
2 hours	180
3 hours	205
4 hours	230
5 hours	255
6 hours	280
7 hours	305
:	:

This approach is not very efficient and limited in its application. A more detailed understanding is therefore required.

From an examination of the pattern of numbers (series) an equation can be generated.

1st term	2nd term	3rd term	4th term ...
130	130 + 25	130 + 2(25)	130 + 3(25) ...

130 + (number of hours × 25) = 680

Written as an equation: $\qquad 130 + 25x = 680$

Subtract 130: $\qquad\qquad\quad 25x = 550$

Divide by 25: $\qquad\qquad\quad\quad x = \dfrac{550}{25}$

$\qquad\qquad\qquad\qquad\qquad x = 22 \text{ hours}$

Investigations

Arithmetic progressions (AP)

The series in example 1 is known as an *arithmetic progression*, where a constant is progressively added to a starting value. In general, this series is written with:

$$a = \text{first term}$$
$$d = \text{common difference}$$

1st term	2nd term	3rd term	4th term	...	nth term
a	$a + d$	$a + 2d$	$a + 3d$	...	$a + (n-1)d$

Note: The number that is multiplied by d is always one less than the term number:

$$\text{General term} = a + (n-1)d$$

This enables us to find any term in an arithmetic progression.

The 13th term in the series from example 1 is given by:

$$130 + 12(25) = 430 \quad \text{(the 13th term is after 12 hours)}$$

Sum of an arithmetic progression

In order to develop a general formula for the sum of n terms, let's try adding the terms of some series:

Sum of 5 terms	Sum of 8 terms	Sum of n terms
a	a	a
$a + d$	$a + d$	$a + d$
$a + 2d$	$a + 2d$	$a + 2d$
$a + 3d$	$a + 3d$	$:$
$a + 4d$	$a + 4d$	$a + (n - 1)d$
	$a + 5d$	$:$
	$a + 6d$	
	$a + 7d$	$:$
$5a + 10d$	$8a + 28d$	$na + \dfrac{n(n-1)}{2}d$

This can be used to calculate the sum of any AP with n terms.

$$S_n = na + \frac{n(n-1)}{2}d$$

Example 2

The sum of £1200 is invested in a bank at an annual interest rate of 7%. Interest is added to the balance each year. Determine the value of the investment after 5 full years.

Solution 2

Interest can be calculated annually, based on the balance for that particular year.

	Balance	*Interest at 7%*
Initially	1200	84
After 1 year	1284	89.88
2 years	1373.88	96.17
3 years	1470.05	102.90
4 years	1572.95	110.11
5 years	1683.06	

This procedure needs to be improved by looking at the operations in more detail.

1st term	*2nd term*	*3rd term*	*4th term*
1200	$1200 + 0.07(1200)$	$1200(1.07)^2$	$1200(1.07)^3$
	$1200(1 + 0.07)$		
	$1200(1.07)$		

Again a pattern emerges and the 6th term (after 5 years) can be found using the power 5.

Thus, 6th term: $\qquad 1200 (1.07)^5 = 1683.06 \quad \text{(as before)}$

181

Investigations

Geometric progressions (GP)

The series in example 2 is a geometric progression, where successive terms are found by multiplying by a constant.

a = first term; r = common ratio

1st term	2nd term	3rd term	4th term	...	nth term
a	$a.r$	$a.r^2$	$a.r^3$	...	$a.r^{n-1}$

Note: The power is one less than the term number.

$$\text{General term } = a.r^{n-1}$$

This formula allows us to easily calculate any term in a GP. As far as investing money is concerned, we can calculate the balance of an account at any time (n in years).

Sum of a geometric progression

A general formula for the sum of a geometric progression is apparent when we study the sum of 4 terms in detail and simplify it.

Sum of 4 terms:
$$a + ar + ar^2 + ar^3 = a\left(1 + r + r^2 + r^3\right)$$

Multiply by $\dfrac{1-r}{1-r}$:
$$= \frac{a\left(1 + r + r^2 + r^3\right)(1-r)}{1-r}$$

[Note that the above multiplier of $\dfrac{1-r}{1-r}$ is equal to 1 so multiplication does not affect the value]

Multiply sets of brackets:
$$= \frac{a(1 + r + r^2 + r^3 - r - r^2 - r^3 - r^4)}{1-r}$$

Eliminating terms where possible:
$$= \frac{a(1 - r^4)}{1-r}$$

Now, for any number of terms a similar formula applies.

Thus:
$$\text{Sum of 7 terms} = \frac{a(1 - r^7)}{1-r}$$

In general, for n terms:
$$\text{Sum of } n \text{ terms} = \frac{a(1 - r^n)}{1-r}$$

Skill unit 17 *Binomial theorem*

17.1   Binomial theorem

Example 1

The cross sectional area of a circular pipeline is required so that the flow through it can be monitored. The radius of 34 cm is measured accurate to the nearest centimetre. Determine the maximum error that could have occurred in the calculation of the flow area.

Solution 1

In measuring the radius any values in the range 33.5 to 34.4999...cm would have been rounded off to 34cm. The maximum possible error in the length measurement is therefore 0.5cm.

Calculating the area A_1 with the measured radius:

$$A_1 = \pi r^2$$
$$A_1 = \pi \times 34^2$$
$$A_1 = 3631.7 \ \text{(to 5 significant figures)}$$

Before calculating the maximum possible area let us develop a new equation introducing δr as the error. If r is increased by the error A_2 becomes;

$$A_2 = \pi(r + \delta r)^2$$
$$A_2 = \pi(r + \delta r(r + \delta r)$$

(we cannot simply square each term).

Each term from the first set of brackets is multiplied by each term in the second set.

But: $\qquad (r + \delta r)(r + \delta r) = r^2 + r\delta r + \delta r \, r + \delta r^2$

Therefore: $\qquad A_2 = \pi(r^2 + r.\delta r + \delta r.r + \delta r^2)$

$$A_2 = \pi(r^2 + 2r\delta r + \delta r^2)$$

Our values can now be used in this equation to give the largest area.

$r = 34; \ \delta r = 0.5$ $\qquad A_2 = \pi(34^2 + 2 \times 34 \times 0.5 + 0.5^2$

$$A_2 = \pi \times 1190.25$$
$$A_2 = 3739.3$$

The difference between these two areas represents the maximum possible error.

$$A_2 - A_1 = 3739.3 - 3631.7$$
$$= 107.6 \ \text{cm}^2$$

We have also to consider the case where the measurement is too large, and subtract the error in a similar way. If r is reduced by the error the area A_3 becomes;

$$A_3 = \pi(r - \delta r)^2$$
$$A_3 = \pi(r - \delta r)(r - \delta r)$$
$$A_3 = \pi(r^2 - r.\delta r - \delta r.r + \delta r^2)$$
$$A_3 = \pi(r^2 - 2r\delta \, r + \delta r^2)$$

Again values can be entered, this time giving the smallest area.

$r = 34; \ \delta r = 0.5$ $\qquad A_3 = \pi(34^2 - 2 \times 34 \times 0.5 + 0.5^2)$

$$A_3 = \pi \times 1122.25$$
$$A_3 = 3525.7$$

The difference between A_3 and A_1 represents another possible large error.

$$A_3 - A_1 = 3631.7 - 3525.7$$
$$= 106 \ \text{cm}^2$$

Investigations

Expanding Binomial Expressions

A set of brackets containing the sum of two numbers (or symbols) is known as a binomial expression. Let us use $(a + b)$ to represent any expression of this type and look at binomial expressions raised to powers as in example 1.

$$(a + b)^2 = (a + b)(a + b) = a^2 + ab + ba + b^2$$
$$= a^2 + 2ab + b^2$$
$$(a + b)^3 = (a + b)(a + b)^2$$

Using the expansion of $(a + b)^2$:
$$= (a + b)(a^2 + 2ab + b^2)$$
$$= a^3 + 3a^2b + 3b^2a + b^3$$

This procedure can be used for higher powers, but it is clearly a time consuming exercise and there is a need for an alternative approach.

The *Binomial theorem* is a series that can help us to expand these expressions.

$$\left(a + b\right)^n = a^n + na^{n-1}b + \frac{n(n-1)}{2!}a^{n-2}b^2 + \cdots + b^n$$

(where $2! = 2 \times 1$ and $3! = 3 \times 2 \times 1$ and so on. This symbol (!) is known as factorial)

In this form it may look complicated but if the power n is replaced by the number 3, the pattern becomes more obvious. The index of a is reduced by 1 for each term while the index of b increases by 1.

$$\left(a + b\right)^3 = a^3 + 3a^2b^1 + \frac{3.2}{2.1}a^1b^2 + \frac{3.2.1}{3.2.1}a^0b^3$$
$$= a^3 + 3a^2b + 3ab^2 + b^3$$

This agrees with the expansion that was developed earlier.

17.2 Error

Example 2

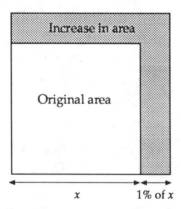

The side of a square steel plate is originally x centimetres long. After a temperature change the plate expands so that x increases in length by 1%. Find the percentage change in the area of the plate.

Solution 2

Original area	$A = x^2$
Area + increase in area:	$A + \delta A = (x + 0.01x)^2$
Factorise	$A + \delta A = (x(1 + 0.01))^2$
Square terms separately	$A + \delta A = x^2(1 + 0.01)^2$

Expand using the binomial theorem

$n = 2$. $a = 1$ and $b = 0.01$

$$A + \delta A = x^2\left(1^2 + 2(1)^1(0.01)^1 + \frac{2 \times 1}{2 \times 1}(1)^0(0.01)^2\right)$$

$$A + \delta A = x^2(1 + 0.02 + 0.0001)$$

$$A + \delta A = x^2 + 0.0201x^2$$

Since $A = x^2$ the increase in area must be equal to the additional part.

$$\delta A = 0.0201x^2$$

This suggests that there is a 2.01% increase in the area for 1% increase in the length x

Investigations

The binomial theorem can be useful in another form where $a = 1$ and b is replaced with x.

General form:

$$(a + b)^n = a^n + na^{n-1}b + \frac{n(n-1)}{2!}a^{n-2}b^2 + \ldots + b^n$$

More specific form:

$$(1 + x)^n = 1 + nx + \frac{n(n-1)}{2!}x^2 + \ldots + x^n$$

For small values of x compared to 1 (as in example 2, $(1 + 0.01)^2$, where $x = 0.01$) the significance of terms very quickly becomes negligible and have little effect on the overall sum. A good approximation can therefore be obtained by expanding only a few terms

These expansions can be used for any positive whole number values of n. Where n is a negative or fractional value, the series will continue indefinitely and there will be no final term x^n.

Example 3

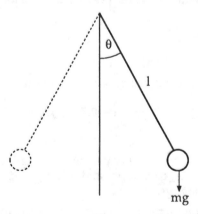

As a simple pendulum swings the time period t of each oscillation is given by the relationship:

$$t = 2\pi\sqrt{\frac{l}{g}}$$

where l is the length and g is acceleration due to gravity.

Determine the error in the calculation of t if the measurement of length l is 2% too large.

Solution 3

Here, we are replacing the correct value of l with an increased value $(l + 0.02l)$ in order to establish what error has occurred in the calculation of t.

The equation $t = 2\pi\sqrt{\dfrac{l}{g}}$ becomes: $\qquad t = 2\pi\sqrt{\dfrac{(l+0.02l)}{g}}$

Taking the square root of terme separately:

$$t = 2\pi\frac{(l+0.02l)^{\frac{1}{2}}}{g^{\frac{1}{2}}}$$

We need to expand $(l+0.02l)^{\frac{1}{2}}$

$$(l+0.02l)^{\frac{1}{2}} = \sqrt{l}(1+0.02)^{\frac{1}{2}}$$

and, using the specific form of the binomial theorem:

$$(l+0.02l)^{\frac{1}{2}} = \sqrt{l}\left(1+\tfrac{1}{2}(0.02)+\frac{\frac{1}{2}\times-\frac{1}{2}}{2\times1}(0.02)^{2}.......\right)$$

$$= \sqrt{l}(1+0.01-0.00005......)$$

The terms of the expansion are getting smaller and have little effect on the overall sum. We can therefore achieve a good estimate by considering only the first two terms

Substituting this back into the equation for t:

$$t = 2\pi\frac{\sqrt{l}(1.01)}{g^{\frac{1}{2}}}$$

$$= 2\pi\sqrt{\frac{l}{g}}(1.01)$$

This indicates that for 2% overestimates of l the calculated value for period t is approximately 1% too great.

Investigations

$$\sqrt{(1+x)} = (1+x)^{0.5}$$

Let us investigate the effects of different values of x on this series.

Put $x = 0.3$ and:

$$(1+0.3)^{0.5} = 1+(0.5)(0.3)+\frac{0.5(0.5-1)}{2!}0.3^{2}+.......$$

$$= 1+0.15-0.01125......$$

Again the significance of terms very quickly becomes negligible. The reason for this is that increasing powers of x are used in each term, and as long as x is a fraction (less than 1 and greater than –1) the series will *converge*.

Other values of x give us an infinite series and terms cannot be ignored.

Put $x = 4$ and:

$$(1+4)^{0.5} = 1+(0.5)(4)+\frac{0.5(0.5-1)}{2!}4^{2}+......$$

$$= 1+2-2.....$$

This series clearly does not produce an approximation for $\sqrt{5}$.

Where we have fractional or negative powers x must lie between –1 and +1

18.1 Vectors

Example 1

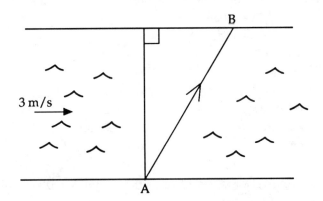

A sailor wishes to cross an estuary starting from point A. Her boat travels at 5 m/s and aims in a direction perpendicular to the bank. There is a current flowing at a constant velocity of 3 m/s which makes the boat follow the path AB. Find the resultant velocity of the boat relative to the river bed.

Solution 1

In order to determine the overall effect of the two velocities we need to add them together. We cannot simply add 3 and 5 since they are in different directions. The direction of each velocity has to be considered. A velocity diagram will help greatly:

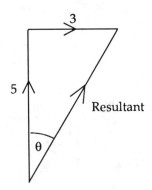

From this, trigonometry will allow us to calculate both the length of the line representing the resultant velocity, and the angle θ.

Using Pythagoras Theorem: $AB^2 = 5^2 + 3^2$

Thus $AB = \sqrt{34}$

$= 5.83$

The tan will give us the angle: $\tan \theta = \frac{3}{5}$

giving: $\theta = 31°$

Investigations

Vector quantities

Vectors (such as velocity) have to be treated differently to scalars (where addition can disregard direction) and it is therefore necessary to recognise vector quantities.

Vectors need be represented by a line which has both length and direction, whereas a value alone is sufficient for the representation of a scalar.

Some examples of these are given here:

Vectors	Scalars
displacement	energy
momentum	time
velocity	distance
acceleration	temperature
force	mass
	work

The length or magnitude of a vector is described as the modulus and vertical lines are used to represent this.

$$|a| = \text{modulus or length of vector } \mathbf{a}$$

Vector addition

Example 1 shows how two vectors can be added together. An important starting point is to produce a vector diagram where vectors are represented as straight lines. Directions need to be indicated and lines should follow end to end in the order of the calculation (the order is not so important with addition). This procedure applies however many vectors are involved. The sum is equivalent to a line joining the beginning to the end.

Let us add these lines together as if they represented vectors $\mathbf{a}$, $\mathbf{b}$ and $\mathbf{c}$:

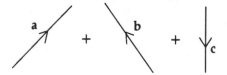

Drawing a vector diagram gives the resultant.

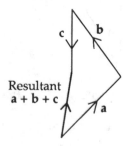

The resultant is not always bigger than its vector components. Forces, velocities or any vector quantities can have the effect of cancelling each other out if directions oppose.

The length and direction of this resultant may be found in a number of ways. Scale drawing should not be underestimated as a quick and accurate method.

Trigonometry can of course be applied, to find the resultant of any two vectors (as in example 1), since a triangle will be produced (not always right angled). Here vectors **a** and **b** form a triangle with the sum **a** + **b**.

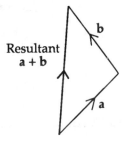

18.2 Vector Calculations

Example 2

A bottle rests on the deck of a sailing boat and is about to slip when the deck makes an angle of 35° to the horizontal.

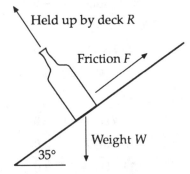

The forces which act on the bottle are: the weight $W(mg)$, the reaction of the deck holding the bottle up (R), and a friction force known to be $F = kR$ which acts in the opposite direction to which the bottle is tending to slip. Calculate the value of k (coefficient of friction).

Solution 2

Forces can be regarded as lines acting in different directions, where lengths are in proportion to the magnitude of the forces.

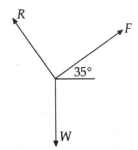

Conveniently the force W can be resolved into two components which are in the same directions as R and F. This is done by replacing W by $W\cos35$ and $W\sin35$ since W is the hypotenuse of a right angled triangle (by vector addition the sum $W\cos35 + W\sin35 = W$).

189

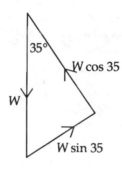

This allows us to add parallel forces and write down the resultant in terms of two components.

Treating upwards, parallel to R as positive and equating to 0 (no movement therefore no acceleration and zero resultant)

$$W\cos35 - R = 0$$

Treating upwards, parallel to F as positive and equating to 0 (no movement therefore no acceleration and zero resultant)

$$W\sin35 - F = 0$$

Using the first of these equations:

$$W\cos35 - R = 0$$

Rearranging: $$W\cos35 = R$$

Using the second of these equations:

$$W\sin35 - F = 0$$

Substitute $F = kR$: $$W\sin35 - kR = 0$$

Substitute $R = W\cos35$: $$W\sin35 - kW\cos35 = 0$$

Factorise: $$W(\sin35 - k\cos35) = 0$$

The weight of the bottle cannot be zero so the other factor $(\sin35 - k\cos35)$ must be.

That is: $$\sin35 - k\cos35 = 0$$

Rearranging: $$\sin35 = k\cos35$$

giving $$k = \frac{\sin35}{\cos35}$$

The coefficient of friction is therefore:

$$k = \tan35$$

ie $$k = 0.7$$

Investigations

Resolving vectors into components

Any vector may be replaced by another two vectors that are effectively the same (as the force W was replaced in example 2). It is often useful to replace a single vector with two components that are at right angles to each other. This simplifies calculations.

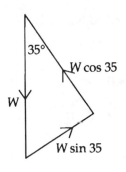

More generally, **c** can be resolved
into components **a** + **b**

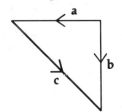

Unit vectors

Although vectors can be resolved into components in any directions, it is most convenience to use the horizontal and vertical (and also horizontally outwards for 3 dimensions). Graphically these directions are conventionally known as the x direction, y direction and z direction.

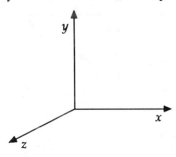

The magnitude of a vector can also be standardised, if we refer to a vector of a particular size, in this case of length 1 unit (unit vector). To allow us to simplify discussion about vectors, the unit vectors in each of the directions x, y and z are regarded as **i**, **j** and **k**.

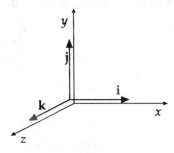

If forces are expressed in terms of these unit vectors, calculations become very easy. Illustrated here on a grid.

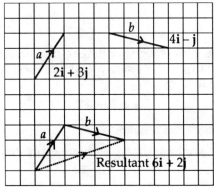

191

Since **i** and **j** are at right angles, the addition of *a* and *b* is found adding **i**'s and **j**'s separately.

$$a = 2\mathbf{i} + 3\mathbf{j}$$

and
$$b = 4\mathbf{i} - \mathbf{j}$$

Therefore:
$$a + b = (2\mathbf{i} + 3\mathbf{j}) + (4\mathbf{i} - \mathbf{j})$$
$$= 6\mathbf{i} + 2\mathbf{j}$$

18.3 Scalar product

Example 3

The estuary from example 1 is 80 metres wide and maintains a current of 3 m/s. In order to cross the estuary directly from C to D (perpendicular to the bank) the engine of a boat must apply a force *F* which has a component upstream. The force then makes an angle θ with the line CD.

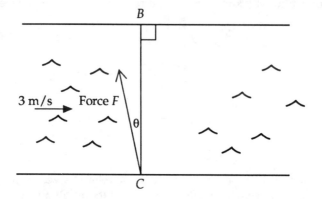

Determine the work done by the engine in the direction *CD*, if *F* = 430 Newtons and the angle θ = 26°.

Solution 3

In words: work done (*W*) = force in direction of motion × displacement

Symbolically: $W = F \cos\theta\, CD$

Substitute values: *F* = 430; *CD* = 80; θ = 26°

$$W = 430 \times 80 \cos 26$$

giving: $W = 30920$ Nm (Joules)

which is a scalar quantity and thus has no direction.

Investigations

Scalar product

Example 3 involves multiplying vectors together (force × displacement) the result of which is a scalar quantity (work). This is known as the scalar product or alternatively the dot product, since a dot is often used to indicate multiplication.

scalar product $a.b = |a|.|b| \cos\theta$

where θ is the angle between the vectors a and b.

Let us consider using the scalar product when vectors are expressed in terms of unit vectors i, j and k.

If we have two vectors: $a = 3i + j - 4k,$

and: $b = i - 2j + 5k:$

the scalar product gives: $a.b = (3i + j - 4k).(i - 2j + 5k)$

That is: $a.b = 3i.i - 6i.j + 15i.k + j.i - 2j.j + 5j.k - 4k.i + 8k.j - 20k.k$

The angle between i and i is of course 0° and i, j and k are all at 90° with each other. This allows us to simplify our product, since cos 0° = 1 and cos 90° = 0.

Thus:

$i.i = 1 \times 1 \cos 0° = 1$	$j.i = 0$	$k.i = 0$
$i.j = 1 \times 1 \cos 90° = 0$	$j.j = 1$	$k.j = 0$
$i.k = 0$	$j.k = 0$	$k.k = 1$

The product now becomes: $a.b = 3 - 2 - 20$

$= -19$

Again, the result is a scalar as we would expect.

Note: The order of multiplication does not affect the result.

That is: $a.b = b.a$

18.4 Vector product

Example 4

The propeller of a boat has a radius of 0.1 metres and rotates at a constant angular velocity W of 5 rads/sec. Water is projected outwards (in addition to rearwards).

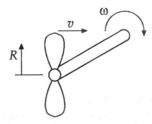

Find the horizontal component of the water velocity as it comes into contact with the outer tip of the propeller in a direction towards the port side of the boat.

Solution 4

We are to find the component of velocity which is at right angles to the drive shaft. The distance of the propeller tip from the centre is always r, but the direction changes and therefore the displacement also changes. The vertical component of this position vector ($r \sin \theta$) gives us the effective displacement to calculate the moment. A vector diagram helps us to visualise the situation (angular velocity is represented as a line through the centre of rotation).

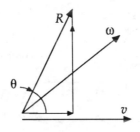

$$\text{Linear velocity} = \text{angular velocity} \times \text{radius}$$

ie: $$V_{horizontal} = \text{angular velocity} \times R_{vertical}$$

or: $$V_h = W R \sin\theta$$
$$= 5 \times 0.1 \sin\theta$$
$$= 0.5 \sin\theta$$

A graph shows us how this velocity varies with the angle of the propeller.

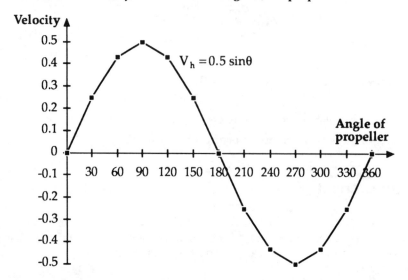

Note: **When the propeller is horizontal there is no horizontal velocity as the moment $WR_V = 0$**

Investigations

Vector product

Example 4 involves multiplying vectors together (angular velocity × displacement) the result of which this time is a vector quantity (linear velocity). This is known as the vector product or alternatively the cross product, a cross is used here for multiplication distinguishing the vector product from the scalar product.

Vector product: $$|a \times b| = |a|.|b| \sin\theta$$

where θ is the angle between the vectors a and b.

This gives the modulus of the vector product, but, because the result is a vector, the direction is also required.

In example 4 we had clockwise angular velocity this is represented on a vector diagram by a line, using the convention that clockwise is inwards (as with a screw).

Clockwise rotation

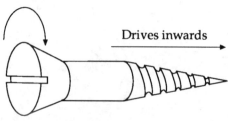

Drives inwards

This convention is also used to give the direction of the vector product.

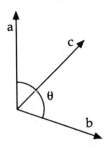

a × b = vector in the direction of c

Vector product b × a would be anticlockwise (from b up to a) and therefore reverse the direction of c.

Again let us consider using the vector product with vectors expressed in terms of unit vectors i, j and k.

If we have two vectors:
$$a = 3i + j - 4k$$
and:
$$b = i - 2j + 5k:$$

the vector product gives:
$$a \times b = (3i + j - 4k) \times (i - 2j + 5k)$$

That is: $\quad a \times b = 3\,i \times i - 6\,i \times j + 15\,i \times k + j \times i - 2\,j \times j + 5\,j \times k - 4\,k \times i + 8\,k \times j - 20\,k \times k$

The angle between i and i is of course 0° and i, j and k are all at 90° to each other. This allows us to simplify our product, since sin 0° = 0 and sin 90° = 1

$i \times i = 1 \times 1 \sin 0 = 0$	$j \times i = -k$	$k \times i = j$
$i \times j = 1 \times 1 \sin 90 = k$	$j \times j = 0$	$k \times j = -i$
$i \times k = -j$	$j \times k = i$	$k \times k = 0$

The product now becomes: $\qquad a \times b = -3i - 19j - 7k$

The result here is a vector.

Note: Reversing the order of multiplication has the effect of reversing the direction of the vector result.

That is: $\qquad a \times b = -(b \times a)$

18.5 Determinants

A systematic approach to the vector product can be taken by using determinants

If we have two vectors: $\quad a = 3i + j - 4k$

and: $\qquad b = i - 2j + 5k:$

they can be arranged in a 3 × 3 matrix as: $\begin{pmatrix} i & j & k \\ 3 & 1 & -4 \\ 1 & -2 & 5 \end{pmatrix}$

The determinant (or modulus) of this matrix represents the vector product a × b.

This is written as $\begin{vmatrix} i & j & k \\ 3 & 1 & -4 \\ 1 & -2 & 5 \end{vmatrix}$

195

We have already found determinants for 2 × 2 matrices. It was used in finding an inverse matrix. For any matrix with elements a, b, c and d:

$$\begin{pmatrix} a & b \\ c & d \end{pmatrix} \Rightarrow \text{INVERSE} \Rightarrow \frac{1}{ad-bc} \cdot \begin{pmatrix} d & -b \\ -c & a \end{pmatrix}$$

The value $ad - bc$ is known as the *determinant* of the matrix.

For a 3 × 3 matrix an extension is made to this process:

$$\begin{vmatrix} i & j & k \\ 3 & 1 & -4 \\ 1 & -2 & 5 \end{vmatrix} = i \begin{vmatrix} 1 & -4 \\ -2 & 5 \end{vmatrix} - j \begin{vmatrix} 3 & -4 \\ 1 & 5 \end{vmatrix} + k \begin{vmatrix} 3 & 1 \\ 1 & -2 \end{vmatrix}$$

Note: The elements in the first row are multiplied by the determinants of 2 × 2 matrices made from the remaining elements when corresponding columns are excluded. The second product is subtracted.

Thus:
$$\begin{vmatrix} i & j & k \\ 3 & 1 & -4 \\ 1 & -2 & 5 \end{vmatrix} = i\left[(1\times5)-(-4\times-2)\right] - j\left[(3\times5)-(-4\times1)\right] + k\left[(3\times-2)-(1\times1)\right]$$

That is:
$$a \times b = -3i -19j -7k$$

This agrees with our previous answer as we are carrying out the same processes systematically.

Skill unit 19 *Maximum and minimum*

Example

A rectangular field is to be enclosed by 200metres of fencing and an existing hedge. The hedge is to be used as one of the sides, therefore fencing is only required for three sides. Determine the maximum area for the field.

Solution

The field has to be rectangular so a sketch can be drawn. If we call the unknown width of the field x, then because there is 200m of fencing the length will be:

$$200 - 2x.$$

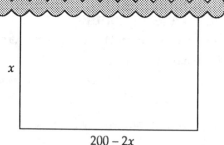

The area (A) of the field is now given by the equation;

$$A = x(200 - 2x)$$

This becomes: $A = 200x - 2x^2$

Area is dependent on the value of x. The graph allows us to appreciate that the maximum area is achieved at the top of a curve.

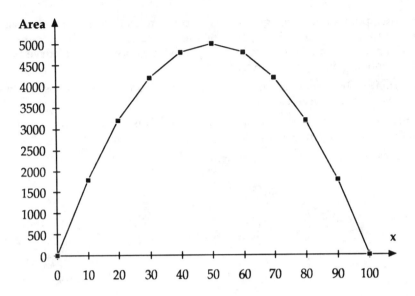

To find the value of x that gives the maximum area we must consider the gradient of the curve by at different points. It is clear that at the point that represents the maximum area the tangent is horizontal and has a gradient of zero.

$$A = 200x - 2x^2$$

The gradient of the curve is found by differentiating:

$$\frac{dA}{dx} = 200 - 4x$$

Since the gradient at the maximum point must be zero, we can find the value of x that gives this area.

At maximum: $\quad\quad\quad\quad\quad\quad\quad\quad \dfrac{dA}{dx} = 0 \quad\quad\quad$ and $200 - 4x = 0$

The vaue of x can now be found: $\quad\quad 4x = 200$

$$x = 50$$

This value gives the maximum area $\quad\quad A = 200(50) - 2(50)^2$

$$A = 5000 \text{ m}^2$$

Investigations

Maximum and minimum points

Curves may have a number of points where the gradient is zero. This will of course depend on the complexity of the relationship.

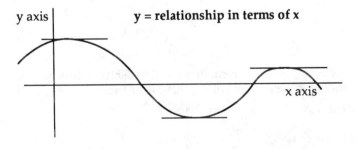

y axis | y = relationship in terms of x | x axis

Here, there are three points where the gradient is zero. A sketch allows us to visualise the relationship, giving us an idea of where these points of interest are. It can also be seen that points are either maximum or minimum. To determine the precise positions on the curve where these points occur differentiation is used as in example 2.

The nature of turning points (max or min) is established by considering values just before, and values just after, the point is reached.

In example 2 it is clear that the point is a maximum point. This can be confirmed by looking at the gradient of the curve either side of $x = 50$.

The equation of the curve is: $$A = 200x - 2x^2$$

Differentiating: $$\frac{dA}{dx} = 200 - 4x$$

Finding the gradient when $x = 49$

$$\frac{dA}{dx} = 200 - 4(49)$$

$$\frac{dA}{dx} = 4$$

Finding the gradient when $x = 51$

$$\frac{dA}{dx} = 200 - 4(51)$$

$$\frac{dA}{dx} = -4$$

Before we reach the turning point (at $x = 49$) the gradient is positive (slopes upwards) and after the turning point (at $x = 51$) the gradient is negative (slopes downwards). This is evidence that the turning point is maximum.

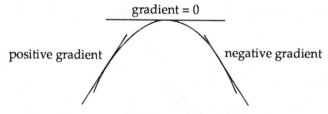

gradient = 0

positive gradient

negative gradient

Maximum point

This is distinct from a minimum point because the gradient would have changed from negative to positive.

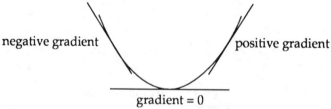

negative gradient

positive gradient

gradient = 0

Minimum point

When the equation of a curve is differentiated a relationship results for the gradient. Let us examine this relationship for the gradient of the curve from example 2.

The equation of the curve is $$A = 200x - 2x^2$$

The equation of the gradient is $$\frac{dA}{dx} = 200 - 4x$$

The gradient itself can therefore be represented as a straight line graph;

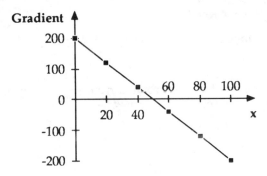

From this we can see that the gradient is positive until $x = 50$, it is then zero, and after this it becomes negative. Here we have an alternative approach to finding the nature of turning points.

If we now differentiate the equation of the gradient (giving the gradient of the gradient) we have;

$$\frac{d}{dx}\left(\frac{dA}{dx}\right) = \frac{d^2 A}{dx^2}$$

$$= -4$$

This is known as the second derivative usually written as shown.

The second derivative helps us to understand how the gradient is changing. In this case it indicates that the gradient is continually decreasing (negative second derivative). This suggests that the change is from positive gradient to negative gradient hence a maximum point. The reverse is also true, a positive second derivative suggests a minimum point.

Skill unit 20 *Trigonometry 2*

20.1 Trigonometrical waveforms

Example 1

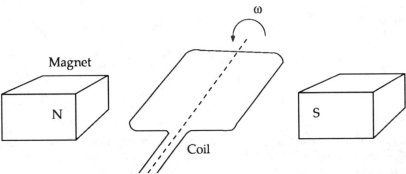

A coil is initially perpendicular to a magnetic field. As the coil is rotated, at constant angular velocity ω radians/second, between the poles of the magnet (so that the coil cuts the magnetic flux) a voltage is induced in the coil. This voltage alternates (AC) due to the changing position of the coil. The maximum voltage is measured to be $E = 18$volts.

The induced voltage is given by: $\quad e \quad = E \sin \omega t$.. ①

where t is the time after the start of rotation

Draw a graph to show the change of voltage with ωt.

Solution 1

The angle through which the coil has been rotated from its starting position is given by the angular velocity ω (rads/secs) multiplied by the time t (secs).

The angle $\theta = \omega t$

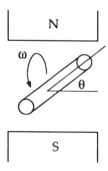

The maximum induced voltage occurs when the direction of motion of the coil is at right angles to the magnetic field (when $\theta = 90°$).

The graph showing change of voltage can now be drawn.

Putting $E = 18$ (maximum voltage) into equation ① above, we have:

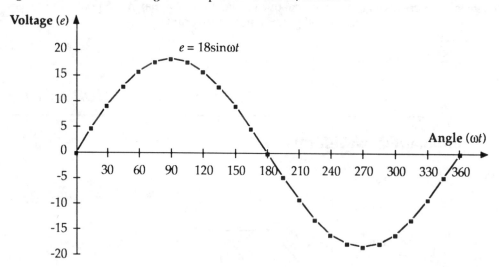

Investigations

Let us consider variations on example 1, where we look at other values of E and different angular velocities ω. These changes will allow an appreciation of trigonometric functions to be gained.

Maximum voltage

The maximmum value of $\sin \omega t$ is 1, which occurs for angle $\omega t = 90°$. It is also clear that the minimum value is -1, for $\omega t = 270°$. The maximum voltage is therefore E and the minimum is $-E$. A negative voltage suggests that current will flow in the opposite direction.

Here are graphs showing the curves $e = E \sin \omega t$, $e = \frac{1}{2} E \sin \omega t$ and $e = 2E \sin \omega t$.

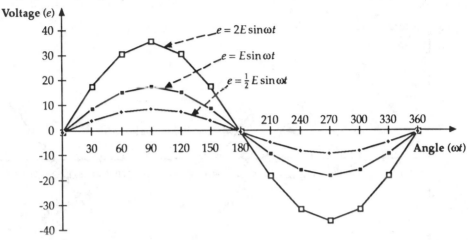

We can conclude that any increase in the maximum voltage (more generally called *amplitude*) does not affect the sinusoidal shape of the curve, but simply increases the peak value. The same applies to any decrease in the maximum voltage.

Increasing angular velocity

If the coil from example 1 is rotated at an increased angular velocity 2ω (double the original value) we can replace ω with 2ω in the equation for voltage.

The equation becomes: $e = E \sin 2\omega t$

This has the effect of increasing the *frequency* (number of cycles per second). There is no change in the amplitude.

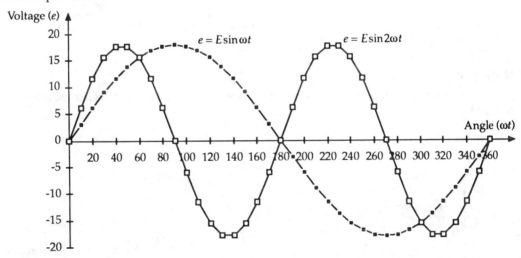

Also the effect of reducing the velocity of rotation will reduce the frequency and the time *period* for a complete cycle is made longer.

Phase angles

We have considered situations where our initial angle θ is zero, but in practice this will depend on the position of the coil when it starts to turn. If instead of zero the initial angle is α (refered to as a *phase* angle) then our equation for voltage becomes:

$$e = E \sin (\omega t + \alpha)$$

If we use a phase angle of 35°, again this change can be represented on a graph along with the original curve.

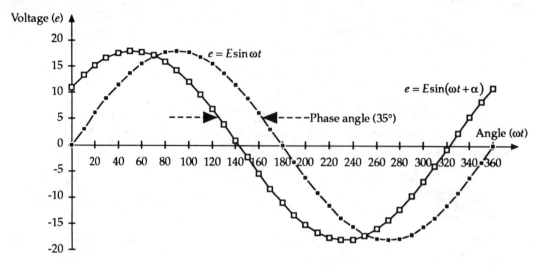

So introducing a phase angle gives us the same shaped curve that is advanced by the phase angle itself.

20.2 Addition of sine curves

Example 2

Find the resultant waveform from the addition of voltages induced in two coils. These voltages are given by:

$$e_1 = 12\sin 2\omega t$$

$$e_2 = 8\sin(\omega t + 30)$$

Solution 2

If these two curves are plotted on the same graph we can see that a complicated waveform will result from the addition.

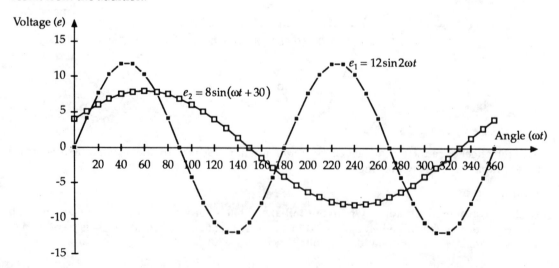

A table of values allows us to systematically calculate the sum of the two curves. This can be carried out using a calculator, but a spreadsheet package on a computer will save a lot of time.

ωt	0	30	60	90	120	150	180	210	240	270	300	330	360
e_1	0.0	10.4	10.4	0.0	-10.4	-10.4	0.0	10.4	10.4	0.0	-10.4	-10.4	0.0
e_2	4.0	6.9	8.0	6.9	4.0	0.0	-4.0	-6.9	-8.0	-6.9	-4.0	0.0	4.0
$e_1 + e_2$	4.0	17.3	18.4	6.9	-6.4	-10.4	-4.0	3.5	2.4	-6.9	-14.4	-10.4	4.0

The resultant curve can now be shown:

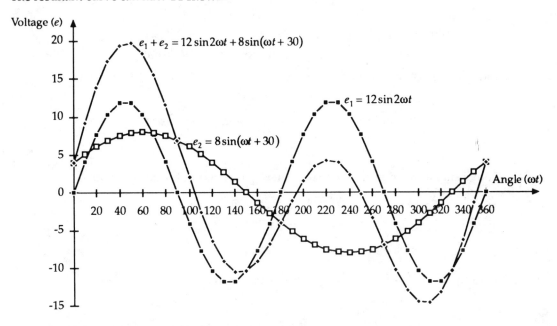

Again it is sensible to use a computer to draw curves of this complexity.

Investigations

20.3 Combining trigonometrical equations

There is of course a relationship that defines the curve from example 2. This can be written down by adding the two equations:

$$e_1 + e_2 = 12\sin 2\omega t + 8\sin(\omega t + 30)$$

In order to combine the expressions we have to write them in alternative forms.

The trigonometrical identities from the formulae sheet enable us to expand compound angles (sum or difference):

$$\sin(A + B) = \sin A \cos B + \sin B \cos A$$

$$\sin(A - B) = \sin A \cos B - \sin B \cos A$$

$$\cos(A + B) = \cos A \cos B - \sin B \sin A$$

$$\cos(A - B) = \cos A \cos B + \sin B \sin A$$

From these identities a compound angle formula can be developed for $\tan(A+B)$:

$$\tan(A+B) \ = \ \frac{\sin(A+B)}{\cos(A+B)}$$

$$= \ \frac{\sin A \cos B + \sin B \cos A}{\cos A \cos B - \sin A \sin B}$$

and dividing throughout by $\cos A \cos B$ gives:

$$\tan(A+B) \ = \ \frac{\tan A + \tan B}{1 - \tan A \tan B}$$

We can now expand $\sin(\omega t + 30)$.

$$\sin(\omega t + 30) \ = \ \sin \omega t \cos 30 + \sin 30 \cos \omega t$$

This identity can also be used to expand $\sin 2\omega t$

$$\sin 2\omega t \ = \ \sin(\omega t + \omega t)$$

$$= \ \sin \omega t \cos \omega t + \sin \omega t \cos \omega t$$

$$= \ 2 \sin \omega t \cos \omega t$$

Note

This and other similar relationships are sometimes quoted as double angle formulae:

$$\sin 2A \ = \ 2 \sin A \cos A$$

$$\cos 2A \ = \ \cos^2 A - \sin^2 A$$

$$\tan 2A \ = \ \frac{2 \tan A}{1 - \tan^2 A}$$

The relationship for our combined curve can now be restated.

$$e_1 + e_2 \ = \ 12 \sin 2\omega t + 8 \sin(\omega t + 30)$$

$$= \ 24 \sin \omega t \cos \omega t + 8(\sin \omega t \cos 30 + \sin 30 \cos \omega t)$$

This may look more cumbersome than before, but we have eliminated the double and compound angles.

Input values for $\cos 30$ and $\sin 30$ and we have:

$$e_1 + e_2 \ = \ 24 \sin \omega t \cos \omega t + 6.928 \sin \omega t + 4 \cos \omega t$$

Example 3

Find the combined trigonometrical relationship from the addition of voltages induced in two coils. These voltages are given by:

$$e_1 \ = \ \sin \omega t$$

$$e_2 \ = \ 3 \sin(\omega t - 45)$$

Draw the resultant waveform.

Solution 3

The sum of expressions: $e_1 + e_2 \ = \ \sin \omega t + 3 \sin(\omega t - 45)$

Expand with compound formula: $= \ \sin \omega t + 3(\sin \omega t \cos 45 + \sin 45 \cos \omega t)$

Simplify: $= \ \sin \omega t + 3 \sin \omega t \cos 45 + 3 \sin 45 \cos \omega t$

$$= \ 3.121 \sin \omega t + 2.121 \cos \omega t$$

If we now compare this with the compound angle formula it is seen to be very similar. Introducing a contant value R allows us to simplify the expression.

Thus: $$R(\sin A \cos B + \sin B \cos A) = R \sin(A + B)$$

can be compared to:

$$\sin \omega t(3.121) + (2.121)\cos \omega t = R\sin(\omega t + B)$$

From this observation R and angle B can be found, since (from the two equations above):

$$R\cos B = 3.121 \quad \dotsfill ②$$

$$R \sin B = 2.121 \quad \dotsfill ③$$

③ + ② gives:
$$\frac{R \sin B}{R \cos B} = \frac{2.121}{3.121}$$

That is:
$$\tan B = 0.680$$

giving:
$$B = 34.2°$$

③² + ②² gives:
$$R^2 \sin^2 B + R^2 \cos^2 B = 2.121^2 + 3.121^2$$

or:
$$R^2 (\sin^2 B + \cos^2 B) = 14.24$$

Since $\sin^2 B + \cos^2 B = 1$, we have:
$$R^2 = 14.24$$

giving:
$$R = 3.77$$

Substituting these values of B and R into:

$$\sin \omega t(3.121) + (2.121)\cos \omega t = R\sin(\omega t + B)$$

gives:
$$\sin \omega t(3.121) + (2.121)\cos \omega t = 3.77\sin(\omega t + 34.2)$$

The curve $e = 3.77\sin(\omega t + 34.2)$ can now be drawn.

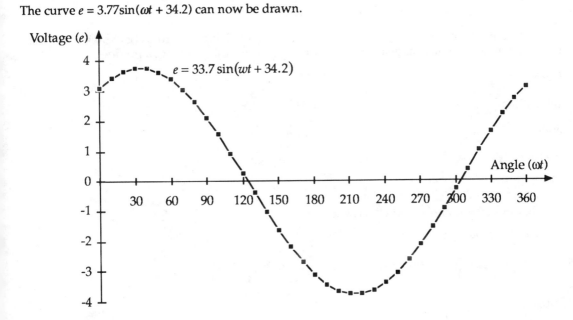

Voltage (e)

$e = 33.7 \sin(wt + 34.2)$

Angle (ωt)

Investigations

Example 3 demonstrates another use of the compound angle formulae. Let us develop these into other useful forms.

We know that:
$$\sin(A+B) = \sin A \cos B + \sin B \cos A \dotfill ④$$

and:
$$\sin(A-B) = \sin A \cos B - \sin B \cos A \dotfill ⑤$$

Adding together equation ④ and ⑤ gives:
$$\sin(A+B) + \sin(A-B) = 2\sin A \cos B$$

Subtracting ⑤ from ④ gives:
$$\sin(A+B) - \sin(A-B) = 2\sin B \cos A$$

Similar developments can be carried out with the following equations ⑥ and ⑦.

Since we know that:
$$\cos(A+B) = \cos A \cos B - \sin B \sin A \dotfill ⑥$$

and:
$$\cos(A-B) = \cos A \cos B + \sin B \sin A \dotfill ⑦$$

Adding together equation ⑥ and ⑦ gives:
$$\cos(A+B) + \cos(A-B) = 2\cos A \cos B \dotfill ⑧$$

Subtracting ⑦ from ⑥ gives:
$$\cos(A+B) - \cos(A-B) = -2\sin A \sin B$$

Use can be made of these formulae when it is helpful to change the form of expressions. The following shows how to change the sum of two trigonometrical ratios into a product.

Consider: $\cos\theta + \cos 3\theta$

By writing: $\theta = 2\theta - \theta$

and: $3\theta = 2\theta + \theta$

we have: $\cos\theta + \cos 3\theta = \cos 3\theta + \cos\theta$

$$= \cos(2\theta + \theta) + \cos(2\theta - \theta)$$

and, putting $2\theta = A$ and $\theta = B$ in ⑧ gives:
$$\cos\theta + \cos 3\theta = 2\cos 2\theta \cos\theta$$

21.1 Function of a function

Example 1

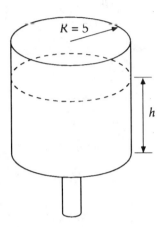

$R = 5$

h

Water drains from a cylindrical tank of radius 5 metres. As the height h falls the pressure reduces and it is observed that the relationship between h and time t is given by:

$$h = 3e^{\frac{t}{20}}$$

Determine the rate that the height is falling after 2 seconds, and also the flow rate in litres per second after 4 seconds.

Solution 1

The height of water depends on the value of t (h is a function of t). The rate of change of height with time is found by differentiating this function with respect to t (ie by evaluating $\dfrac{dh}{dt}$).

The table of standard derivatives from the formulae sheet gives us some help in differentiating exponential functions.

If: $$y = e^x$$

then: $$\frac{dy}{dx} = e^x$$

The function for h is more complicated than this, but introducing a 'dummy' variable simplifies our function and enables us to differentiate it.

Now: $$h = 3e^{-\frac{t}{20}}$$

and putting: $$u = \frac{-t}{20}$$

gives: $$h = 3e^u$$

The variable u has no real meaning it is only introduced to simplify our expression. Dummy variables must be replaced by other symbols after differentiation.

We can now differentiate (with respect to u):

$$\frac{dh}{du} = 3e^u$$

Note: multiplying by a constant does not affect the differentiation.

The result is the rate of change of height with u (the dummy), not with time t which is required.

By introducing u we can say that h depends on u, but u in turn depends on t, or h is equal to a function which is a function of something else (*function of a function*).

To eliminate the dummy so that we have $\dfrac{dh}{dt}$ the derivative $\dfrac{dh}{du}$ must be multiplied by $\dfrac{du}{dt}$.

Thus we also have to find $\dfrac{du}{dt}$.

Now:
$$u = \frac{-t}{20}$$

Therefore:
$$\frac{du}{dt} = -\frac{1}{20}$$

The rate of change of height with time, $\dfrac{dh}{dt}$ can now be found.

$$\frac{dh}{dt} = \frac{dh}{du}\frac{du}{dt}$$

$$= 3e^u . -\frac{1}{20}$$

Substituting for u gives:
$$\frac{dh}{dt} = 3e^{-\frac{t}{20}} . -\frac{1}{20}$$

So, when $t = 2$:
$$\frac{dh}{dt} = -\frac{3}{20}e^{-\frac{2}{20}}$$

The rate of fall in height after 2 seconds is 0.1357 m/s. The negative sign suggests that h is reducing.

The flow rate or rate of change of volume $(\frac{dV}{dt})$ is determined by differentiating an expression for the volume in terms of time.

Now:
$$V = \pi R^2 h$$

Substituting $R = 5$:
$$V = 25\pi h$$

Differentiating with respect to h:
$$\frac{dV}{dh} = 25\pi$$

As before, we have a function of a function.

That is:
$$\frac{dV}{dt} = \frac{dV}{dh}.\frac{dh}{dt}$$

But:
$$\frac{dh}{dt} = -\frac{3}{20}e^{-\frac{t}{20}} \quad \text{from above.}$$

Thus:
$$\frac{dV}{dt} = 25\pi . -\frac{3}{20}e^{-\frac{t}{20}}$$

and when $t = 4$:
$$\frac{dV}{dt} = -\frac{75}{20}.\pi.e^{\frac{-4}{20}}$$

$$= -9.645 \text{ m}^3/\text{s}$$

The flow rate when $t = 4$ is 9.645 m³/s. Again the negative indicates that the volume of water in the tank is going down.

Converting to litres/second: $9.645 \times 1000 = 9645$

Investigations

Function of a function

Where a function has another function within it, a dummy (possibly the letter u) needs to replace the inner function to allow differentiation. Here are some examples;

$\sin(3t + 40)$	Let $u = 3t + 40$	$\sin u$
$\sqrt{a^2 + 9}$	Let $u = a^2 + 9$	$\sqrt{u}$
$\cos^2 x$	Let $u = \cos x$	u^2
$\ln(x^2 - 5)$	Let $u = x^2 - 5$	$\ln u$

We then require both the derivatives. The product gives us the final rate of change.

If y is a function of a function of x then:

$$\frac{dy}{dx} = \frac{dy}{du} \cdot \frac{du}{dx}$$

21.2 Product rule

Example 2

Water flows into a trough which is in the shape of half a cylinder, of radius $R = 0.4$ metres, and length $l = 2$ metres.

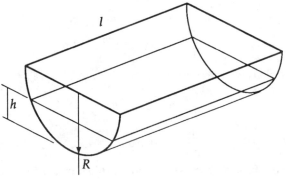

Viewed from the end:

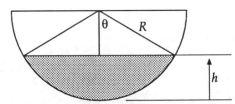

Write down a formula for the volume of water in the trough in terms of the angle θ (rads) and differentiate this to give the rate of change of volume with θ. What is the value of this rate when the depth h of water is 0.25 metres.

Solution 2

The area of the cross section of the water can be found by subtracting an isosceles triangle from a sector.

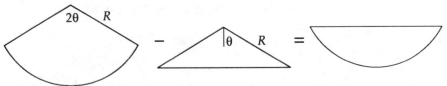

$$\text{Sector area} = \tfrac{1}{2}(2\theta)R^2$$

Putting $R = 0.4$ gives:
$$\text{Sector area} = \theta(0.4)^2$$
$$= 0.16\theta.$$

$$\text{Triangle area} = (R\sin\theta)(R\cos\theta)$$

and with $R = 0.4$:
$$\text{Triangle area} = 0.16\sin\theta\cos\theta$$

$$\text{Resulting area} = 0.16\theta - 0.16\sin\theta\cos\theta$$

But the volume of water, V, is given by multiplying this area by the length.

That is:
$$V = 2(0.16\theta - 0.16\sin\theta\cos\theta)$$
$$= 0.32\theta - 0.32\sin\theta\cos\theta$$

We can differentiate this function in two parts. The first part is quite easy, but to differentiate a product the 'product rule' from the formula sheet is required.

Differentiating $0.32\,\theta$ gives 0.32.

To differentiate $0.32\sin\theta\cos\theta$ we treat it as a product of two functions.

Call these w and z. with:
$$w = 0.32\sin\theta$$

and
$$z = \cos\theta$$

Thus we have:
$$V = 0.32\theta - wz$$

and, differentiating:
$$\frac{dV}{d\theta} = 0.32 - \frac{d(wz)}{d\theta}$$

But, using the definitions of w and z above, we have:

$$\frac{dw}{d\theta} = 0.32\cos\theta$$

and
$$\frac{dz}{d\theta} = -\sin\theta$$

We can now substitute these functions into the product rule formula from the formula sheet.

Product rule

If:
$$y = u.v$$

where u and v are both functions of x, then:

$$\frac{dy}{dx} = v\frac{du}{dx} + u\frac{dv}{dx}$$

Thus (using the product rule):
$$\frac{d(wz)}{d\theta} = z\frac{dw}{d\theta} + w\frac{dz}{d\theta}$$
$$= \cos\theta\,(0.32\cos\theta) + 0.32\sin\theta\,(-\sin\theta)$$
$$= 0.32\cos^2\theta - 0.32\sin^2\theta$$
$$= 0.32(\cos^2\theta - \sin^2\theta)$$

That is:
$$\frac{d(wz)}{d\theta} = 0.32\cos 2\theta \quad \text{[double angle formula]}$$

But:
$$\frac{dV}{d\theta} = 0.32 - \frac{d(wz)}{d\theta} \text{ [from above]}$$

Therefore:
$$\frac{dV}{d\theta} = 0.32 - 0.32\cos 2\theta$$

$$= 0.32(1 - \cos 2\theta)$$

A relationship between h and θ can be found by looking at the sector dimensions.

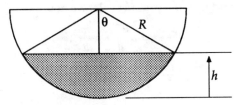

From the diagram:
$$R\cos\theta = R - h$$

Substituting $R=0.4$ and $h=0.25$ gives:
$$0.4\cos\theta = 0.15$$

giving:
$$\cos\theta = 0.375$$

Therefore:
$$\theta = 1.186 \text{ rads}$$

The rate of change of volume with θ when $h = 0.25$ metres is found by substituting this value into $\frac{dV}{d\theta}$.

This gives:
$$\frac{dV}{d\theta} = 0.32(1 - \cos 2(1.186))$$

$$= 0.32 \times 1.718$$

$$= 0.55 \text{ m}^3/\text{rad}$$

Investigations

The 'Product Rule' is required in order to differentiate products of functions of a variable. Examples of such products are given as follows.

i) Consider
$$y = x.\ln x$$

Putting $u = x$ and $v = \ln x$:
$$\frac{du}{dx} = 1$$

$$\frac{dv}{dx} = \frac{1}{x}$$

Using the product rule:
$$\frac{dy}{dx} = v\frac{du}{dx} + u\frac{dv}{dx}$$

gives:
$$\frac{dy}{dx} = \ln x(1) + x\left(\frac{1}{x}\right)$$

That is:
$$\frac{dy}{dx} = \ln x + 1$$

Another example giving w in terms of the variable t follows.

ii) Given
$$w = e^t.\cos t$$

Putting $u = e^t$ and $v = \cos t$:
$$\frac{du}{dt} = e^t$$

$$\frac{dv}{dt} = -\sin t$$

If we replace x and y by t and w in the product rule, we get:
$$\frac{dw}{dt} = v\frac{du}{dt} + u\frac{dv}{dt}$$

giving:
$$\frac{dw}{dt} = e^t\cos t - e^t\sin t$$

21.3 Quotient rule

Example 3

The volume of water contained in a conical flask as shown (in the following diagram) depends on the radius r and the depth h. These are connected by the angle θ. If the depth is required to be $h = 0,7$ metres, find a relationship between the volume and the angle θ.

Determine the rate of change of volume with $\theta\left(\dfrac{dV}{d\theta}\right)$.

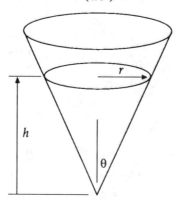

Solution 3

If a section is cut through the centre of the cone, a right angled triangle allows us to use trigonometry to develop relationships.

The relationship between r and h is:
$$\tan\theta = \frac{r}{h}$$

Rearranging:
$$r = h\tan\theta$$

This is used to replace r and give a relationship for volume.

The volume of a cone is given by the formula:
$$V = \frac{1}{3}\pi r^2 h$$

and, substituting for r:

$$V = \frac{1}{3}\pi(h\tan\theta)^2 h$$

$$= \frac{1}{3}\pi h^3 \tan^2\theta$$

Let $h = 0.7$:

$$V = 0.359\tan^2\theta$$

Here the volume is a function of a function, so to differentiate we have to make a substitution and separate the functions.

$$V = 0.359\tan^2\theta$$

Putting $u = \tan\theta$ gives:

$$V = 0.359u^2$$

and

$$\frac{dV}{du} = 0.718u \dots\dots\dots\dots\dots\dots\dots\dots\dots\dots\dots\dots\dots\dots\dots\dots\dots\dots\dots\dots①$$

Differentiating a quotient (a fraction) is carried out with reference to the 'quotient rule' from the formulae sheet.

Quotient rule

If:

$$y = \frac{u}{v}$$

where u and v are both functions of x, then:

$$\frac{dy}{dx} = \frac{1}{v^2}\left(v\frac{du}{dx} - u\frac{dv}{dx}\right)$$

Symbols need to be changed but the principle can be applied to the quotient $u = \tan\theta = \dfrac{\sin\theta}{\cos\theta}$.

Let $w = \sin\theta$ and

$$\frac{dw}{d\theta} = \cos\theta$$

Let $z = \cos\theta$ and

$$\frac{dz}{d\theta} = -\sin\theta$$

In a similar way to using the 'product rule', substitutions can be made into the formula.

That is:

$$\frac{du}{d\theta} = \frac{1}{z^2}\left(z\frac{dw}{d\theta} - w\frac{dz}{d\theta}\right)$$

$$= \frac{1}{\cos^2\theta}(\cos\theta\cos\theta - \sin\theta(-\sin\theta))$$

$$= \frac{1}{\cos^2\theta}\left(\cos^2\theta + \sin^2\theta\right)$$

Thus, with $\cos^2\theta + \sin^2\theta = 1$:

$$\frac{du}{d\theta} = \frac{1}{\cos^2\theta} \dots\dots\dots\dots\dots\dots\dots\dots\dots\dots\dots\dots\dots\dots\dots②$$

The overall derivative can now be found by using the two expressions ① and ②.

$$\frac{dV}{d\theta} = \frac{dV}{du}\frac{du}{d\theta}$$

$$= 0.718u\left(\frac{1}{\cos^2\theta}\right)$$

and finally:

$$\frac{dV}{d\theta} = 0.718\frac{\tan\theta}{\cos^2\theta}$$

Investigations

Quotient rule

Differentiating quotients (fractions), where one function of x (or some other variable) is divided by another function of the same variable, requires the use of the 'Quotient Rule'.

This is a formula involving derivatives of each function, as with the 'Product Rule'. An important difference to note here, however, is that subtraction must be carried out in the correct order.

Another example of its use is shown.

We have:
$$y = \frac{e^x}{x^2}$$

Put $u = e^x$ and:
$$\frac{du}{dx} = e^x$$

and $v = x^2$ gives:
$$\frac{dv}{dx} = 2x$$

The 'Quotient Rule' can now be used.

$$\frac{dy}{dx} = \frac{1}{v^2}\left(v\frac{du}{dx} - u\frac{dv}{dx}\right)$$

$$= \frac{1}{x^4}\left(x^2 e^x - e^x.2x\right)$$

That is:
$$\frac{dy}{dx} = \frac{e^x}{x^4}\left(x^2 - 2x\right)$$

Skill unit 22 *Integration 2*

22.1 Integration by substitution

Example 1

The alternating current I in a circuit with frequency 50 Hz is given by $I = 13 \sin 100\pi t$ where t is time in seconds. Determine the r.m.s value of this current.

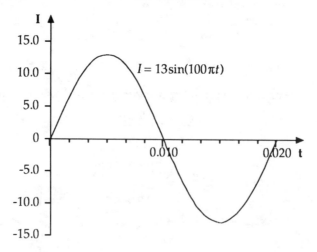

Solution 1

The root mean square (r.m.s) is a useful type of average that can be used as a representative value of an alternating current. It gives the value of an equivalent steady current that will expend the same energy.

$$\text{r.m.s.} = \sqrt{\frac{\text{Sum of } I^2}{\text{period}}}$$

The equation for current is:
$$I = 13\sin 100\pi t$$

Therefore:
$$I^2 = (13)^2(\sin 100\pi t)^2$$

This relationship can be illustrated on a graph, and the area under the curve represents the sum of I^2 between the limits of 0 and $\frac{1}{50}$. If the area is divided into very thin strips it can be thought of as the sum of a series of rectangles (accuracy depends on the number of rectangles). Here, each strip has a width δt height I^2 and is a distance t from the I^2 axis.

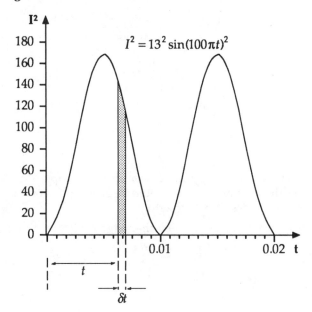

The area of each strip is:
$$I^2.\delta t = (13)^2(\sin 100\pi t)^2 \delta t$$

Integration can be used to find the sum of these thin rectangles between the limits of 0 and $\frac{1}{50}$. When integrating, dt replaces δt suggesting that infinitely small thicknesses are used (a theoretical limit).

$$\text{sum of } I^2 = 169\int_0^{\frac{1}{50}} \sin^2 100\pi t \, dt$$

As it is the expression is difficult to integrate. Trigonometrical equations allow us to change the form of the expression by replacing it with other functions.

From the formula sheet:
$$\cos 2\theta = 1 - 2\sin^2\theta$$

and rearranging gives:
$$\sin^2\theta = \tfrac{1}{2}(1 - \cos 2\theta)$$

Using appropriate symbols:
$$\sin^2 100\pi t = \tfrac{1}{2}(1 - \cos 200\pi t)$$

The integral now becomes:

$$\text{sum of } I^2 \;=169\int_0^{\frac{1}{50}} \sin^2 100\pi t\, dt$$

$$=169\int_0^{\frac{1}{50}} \tfrac{1}{2}(1-\cos 200\pi t)\, dt \quad \text{[substituting]}$$

$$=\frac{169}{2}\left[t-\frac{1}{200\pi}\sin 200\pi t\right]_0^{\frac{1}{50}} \quad \text{[integrating]}$$

$$=\frac{169}{2}\left(\frac{1}{50}-0\right)$$

Thus: $\qquad\qquad\qquad$ sum of I^2 $= 1.69$

The r.m.s. can now be calculated.

$$\text{r.m.s.} \;=\sqrt{\frac{\text{Sum of } I^2}{\text{period}}}$$

$$=\sqrt{\frac{1.69}{\frac{1}{50}}}$$

giving $\qquad\qquad\qquad$ r.m.s. $= 9.19$

Investigations

Mean

The mean or average value of the alternating current from example 1 can also be calculated by using integration to find the sum of areas. It should be clear however, that negative values will cancel out with positve and the result will be zero.

A value can be obtained for the mean between the range t = 0 and t = 0.1 since only a positive area is produced.

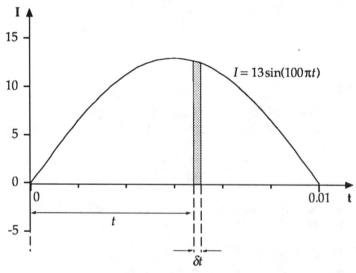

Integration allows us to find the sum of thin strip areas between these limits.

The area of each strip is: $\qquad\qquad I.\delta t \;= 13\sin 100\pi t\ \delta t$

Integrating:
$$\int_0^{0.01} 13\sin 100\pi t\, dt \;=\; -13\left[\frac{1}{100\pi}\cos 100\pi t\right]_0^{0.01}$$

The limits can now be substituted for t. The lower limit value is subtracted from the upper limit value.

Thus:
$$\text{Sum} \;=\; \frac{-13}{100\pi}\big(\cos 100\pi(0.01) - \cos 100\pi(0)\big)$$

$$=\; \frac{-13}{100\pi}(-1-1)$$

giving
$$\text{Sum} \;=\; 0.08276$$

The mean is found by dividing this sum by the period t.

Thus
$$\text{Mean} \;=\; \frac{0.0828}{0.01}$$

$$=\; 8.28$$

Substitution

A method of simplifying an expression so that it may be integrated is to use the method of substitution. Here, we replace part of the function with a 'dummy' variable. There is an opportunity to apply this in example 1.

To find
$$\int \cos 200\pi t\, dt$$

where limits are ignored.

We can let $u = 200\pi t$ simplifying the expression $\int \cos u\, dt$

A substitution is also required for dt.

$$u \;=\; 200\pi t$$

$$\frac{du}{dt} \;=\; 200\pi$$

and rearranging gives:
$$dt \;=\; \frac{du}{200\pi}$$

The integral now becomes
$$\int \cos 200\pi t\, dt \;=\; \int \cos u \frac{du}{200\pi}$$

$$=\; \frac{1}{200\pi}\sin u$$

Substitute for u:
$$=\; \frac{1}{200\pi}\sin 200\pi t$$

This is of course one of our standard integrals from the formula sheet, but it gives us an understanding of a procedure that can be used to help integrate other functions.

Substitution can help with:
$$\int \frac{x}{x^2+1}\, dx$$

Let
$$u \;=\; x^2 + 1$$

Then
$$\frac{du}{dx} \;=\; 2x$$

and
$$dx = \frac{du}{2x}$$

The integral becomes
$$\int \frac{x}{u} \frac{du}{2x} = \int \frac{1}{2u} du$$

$$= \frac{1}{2} \ln u$$

$$= \frac{1}{2} \ln(x^2 + 1) + C$$

Note: Substitution is often suitable where the top (numerator) of a quotient is the derivative of the bottom function (denominator).

Trigonometrical equations

Trigonometrical equations from the formula sheet can often help to change the form of an expression so as to enable us to integrate. This is demonstrated in example 1. Experience is needed so that we can recognise easily integrated forms. Trial and error will build up this experience. It is often easier to integrate a sum or difference than a product.

Example 2

Find the area of a circle with a radius R = 15cm, using integration. Confirm that this is correct using the standard formula.

Solution 2

If the centre of the circle is placed at the origin of an x, y graph an equation can be developed for the curve. The area is considered as a series of thin strips where the width is δx, and each strip is a distance x from the y axis.

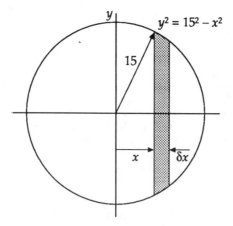

The area of a strip is given by: $\qquad 2y \, \delta x$
(assuming thin strips are rectangles).

Substitute $y = \sqrt{15^2 - x^2}$ $\qquad 2y \, \delta x = 2\sqrt{15^2 - x^2} \, \delta x$

Putting A = area of circle and integrating to find the sum of strips between $x = -15$ and $x = 15$,

we have:
$$A = \int_{-15}^{15} 2\sqrt{15^2 - x^2} \, dx$$

A substitution is now required to allow us to integrate the function.

Let $\qquad x = 15 \cos \theta$

Then: $\qquad \dfrac{dx}{d\theta} = -15 \cos \theta$

and $\qquad dx = -15 \sin \theta d\theta$

It is also necessary to change the limits.

Since $\qquad x = 15 \cos \theta$

then $\qquad \theta = \text{inv}\left(\cos \dfrac{x}{15}\right)$

Thus: when $x = -15$, $\theta = \pi$

and when $x = 15$, $\theta = 0$.

The integral becomes:

$$A = \int_{\pi}^{0} 2\sqrt{15^2 - 15^2 \cos^2 \theta} - 15(\sin\theta)d\theta$$

$$= -30 \int_{\pi}^{0} \sqrt{15^2\left(1 - \cos^2 \theta\right)} \sin \theta \, d\theta$$

Substitute $1 - \cos^2 \theta = \sin^2 \theta$:

$$A = -450 \int_{\pi}^{0} \sin^2 \theta \, d\theta$$

Substitute $\sin^2\theta = \frac{1}{2}(1 - \cos2\theta)$

$$A = \dfrac{-450}{2} \int_{\pi}^{0} (1 - \cos 2\theta)d\theta$$

$$= -225\left[\theta - \dfrac{1}{2}\sin 2\theta\right]_{\pi}^{0}$$

$$= 225\pi$$

This is of course πR^2 which is what we would expect.

Investigations

To complete our investigation into integration we must look at other functions that cannot be integrated using methods discussed so far.

22.2 Partial fractions

Consider a simple looking expression: $\qquad \dfrac{1}{x^2 - 1}$

Integration by substitution is not suitable here, because when a 'dummy' is introduced, x cannot be eliminated without producing an even worse situation.

A good start is to factorise the denominator

Thus: $\qquad \dfrac{1}{x^2 - 1} = \dfrac{1}{(x + 1)(x - 1)}$

From our experience of adding fractions it is useful to work in reverse and replace the quotient with a sum of two fractions (partial fractions).

As with $\dfrac{5}{6} = \dfrac{A}{2} + \dfrac{B}{3}$: $\qquad \dfrac{1}{(x + 1)(x - 1)} = \dfrac{A}{x + 1} + \dfrac{B}{x - 1}$

It is now required to evaluate A and B.

As with $5 = 3A + 2B$: $\qquad 1 = A(x - 1) + B(x + 1)$

This equation enables us to find constant values for A and B. In contrast x is of course a variable and can take any value. It is convenient to let $x = 1$ (giving $x - 1 = 0$) and subsequently to let $x = -1$ (giving $x + 1 = 0$).

Let $x = 1$
$$1 = A(0) + B(1 + 1)$$
$$1 = 2B$$
$$B = \tfrac{1}{2}$$

Let $x = -1$
$$1 = A(-1 - 1) + B(0)$$
$$1 = -2A$$
$$A = -\tfrac{1}{2}$$

Substituting these values into the partial fractions gives:
$$\frac{1}{(x+1)(x-1)} = \frac{1}{-2(x+1)} + \frac{1}{2(x-1)}$$

Integration can now be carried out, since each fraction lends itself to the substitution method.

Thus:
$$\int \frac{1}{x^2+1}\,dx = \int \frac{1}{(x+1)(x-1)}\,dx$$
$$= \int \left(\frac{1}{-2(x+1)} + \frac{1}{2(x-1)} \right) dx$$
$$= \int \left(\frac{1}{-2(x+1)} \right) dx + \int \left(\frac{1}{2(x-1)} \right) dx$$

We will integrating the two terms separately.

Let $u = x + 1$
$$\int \left(\frac{1}{-2(x+1)} \right) dx = \int \frac{1}{-2u}\frac{du}{1} \quad [\text{since } \frac{du}{dx} = 1]$$
$$= -\tfrac{1}{2}\ln u$$

Let $u = x - 1$
$$\int \left(\frac{1}{2(x-1)} \right) dx = \int \frac{1}{2u}\frac{du}{1} \quad [\text{since again } \frac{du}{dx} = 1]$$
$$= \tfrac{1}{2}\ln u$$

The combined result is therefore given by:
$$\int \frac{1}{x^2-1}\,dx = \tfrac{1}{2}\ln(x-1) - \tfrac{1}{2}\ln(x+1)$$

22.3 Integration by parts (products)

The integration of products is often a difficult task, but it depends largely on the form that they take (some trigonometrical products have already been considered). Unfortunately there is not a rule that will always work, and there could be more than one successful approach. The 'product rule' for differentiation can be adapted to produce a formula that sometimes helps to integrate products.

From the formula sheet for differentiation we have the product rule as follows.
If:
$$y = u.v$$
where u and v are both functions of x, then:
$$\frac{dy}{dx} = v\frac{du}{dx} + u\frac{dv}{dx}$$

Integrating both sides of this equation with respect to x gives:

$$\int \frac{dy}{dx}dx \;=\; \int v\frac{du}{dx}dx + \int u\frac{dv}{dx}dx$$

That is:

$$y \;=\; \int v\frac{du}{dx}dx + \int u\frac{dv}{dx}dx$$

Replacing y with uv:

$$uv \;=\; \int v\frac{du}{dx}dx + \int u\frac{dv}{dx}dx$$

Rearranging:

$$\int u\frac{dv}{dx}dx \;=\; uv - \int v\frac{du}{dx}dx$$

This is a formula that enables us to integrate certain types of products, it is called integrating by parts.

Integrating by Parts

Given a product $u\dfrac{dv}{dx}$:

$$\int u\frac{dv}{dx}dx \;=\; uv - \int v\frac{du}{dx}dx$$

Example 3

Find the area under the curve for the product $x^2.\ln x$ between $x = 1$ and $x = 5$.

Solution 3

To evaluate $\displaystyle\int_1^5 x^2.\ln x\,dx$

Let

$$u \;=\; \ln x$$

giving

$$\frac{du}{dx} \;=\; \frac{1}{x}$$

Also let

$$\frac{dv}{dx} \;=\; x^2$$

giving

$$v \;=\; \frac{x^3}{3} \quad \text{[ignoring the arbitrary constant]}$$

Using integration by parts:

$$\int u\frac{dv}{dx}dx \;=\; uv - \int v\frac{du}{dx}dx$$

we have:

$$\int_1^5 \ln x.x^2\,dx \;=\; \left[\ln x.\frac{x^3}{3}\right]_1^5 - \int_1^5 \frac{x^3}{3}\frac{1}{x}dx$$

$$=\; \left[\frac{x^3}{3}.\ln x - \frac{x^3}{9}\right]_1^5$$

$$=\; \left[\frac{x^3}{9}(3\ln x - 1)\right]_1^5$$

$$=\; \left[\frac{5^3}{9}(3\ln 5 - 1) - \frac{1^3}{9}(3\ln 1 - 1)\right]$$

$$=\; 53.28 \text{ (to 2 dec pl)}$$

Example 1

The alternating current I in a circuit is given by $I = 13 \sin 100\pi\, t$ with frequency 50 Hz where t is time in seconds. Determine an approximate value for the r.m.s of this current.

Solution 1

The root mean square (r.m.s) is given by;

$$\text{r.m.s.} = \sqrt{\frac{\text{Sum of } I^2}{\text{period}}}$$

The equation for current is:

$$I = 13 \sin 100\pi t$$

Therefore:

$$I^2 = (13)^2 (\sin 100\pi t)^2$$

This relationship can be illustrated on a graph, and the area under the curve represents the sum of I^2.

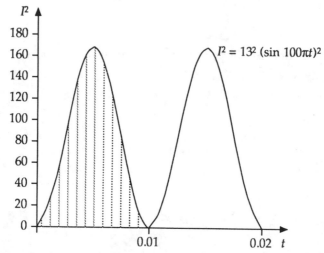

Since the cycle for I^2 repeats itself after 0.01 seconds the r.m.s can be calculated over this period. If the area is divided into strips it can be thought of as the sum of a series of rectangles (accuracy depends on the number of rectangles). Let us consider 10 strips, each of width 0.001 seconds.

The height of each rectangle is estimated to be the height of the function I^2 at the middle of the strip. These values are calculated in a spread sheet.

Time t	I^2
0.0005	26.44
0.0015	76.72
0.0025	119.50
0.0035	150.58
0.0045	166.92
0.0055	166.92
0.0065	150.58
0.0075	119.50
0.0085	76.72
0.0095	26.44

An approximation for the area under the curve can now be obtained by adding together these areas. This is easily achieved by finding the sum of rectangle heights and multiplying this by the common width.

$$\text{Sum of heights} = 1080.33 \text{ (using the same spreadsheet as before)}$$
$$\text{Area} = 1080.33 \times 0.001$$
$$= 1.080 \text{ (to 4 sig figs)}$$

The r.m.s can be estimated using this value;

$$\text{r.m.s.} = \sqrt{\frac{\text{Sum of } I^2}{\text{period}}}$$
$$= \sqrt{\frac{1.08}{0.01}}$$
$$= 10.4$$

Investigations

Mid-ordinate rule

The method of obtaining an approximation to the area under a curve, used in example 1, is known as the 'Mid-ordinate Rule'. The accuracy of the approximation can be improved by increasing the number of strips.

Mid-ordinate rule

$$\text{Area} = \text{Sum of mid-ordinates of strips} \times \text{Strip width}$$

Integration utilises a similar approach to this, taking a theoretical infinite number of strips. This gives a value of 0.845 for the area under the curve, suggesting that there is a large error using the 'Mid-ordinate rule' with only 10 strips. Let us consider alternative methods of achieving approximations for the area under curves.

Trapezium rule

Rather than treating strips as rectangles, with heights equal to the mid-ordinate, we can consider them to be trapeziums. The top is assumed to be a staight line joining the sides of a strip. This method is conveniently called the 'Trapezium Rule'.

To determine another approximation for the area of example 1 this rule can be applied.

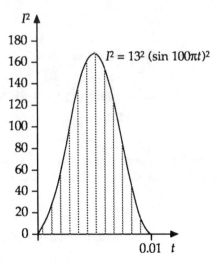

Again 10 intervals are used (11 ordinates) and the height of each ordinate is found using a spreadsheet.

Ordinate	Time t	I^2
0	0	0
1	0.001	52.22387
2	0.002	99.33571
3	0.003	136.7239
4	0.004	160.7286
5	0.005	169
6	0.006	160.7286
7	0.007	136.7239
8	0.008	99.33571
9	0.009	52.22387
10	0.01	0

An approximation to the total area is given by the sum of the trapezium areas found by considering each strip.

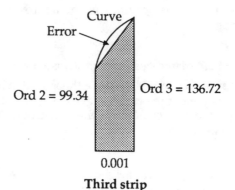

Third strip

$$\text{Area of third strip} = \text{Strip width} \times \tfrac{1}{2}(\text{Ord 2} + \text{Ord 3})$$

The 'Trapezium Rule' is now stated.

Trapezium Rule

$$\text{Area} = \text{Strip width} \times (\tfrac{1}{2}(\text{First ordinate} + \text{Last ordinate}) + \text{Sum of other ordinates})$$

For the curve:

$$\text{Approximate Area} = 0.001 \times (\tfrac{1}{2}(0 + 0) + 1067)$$
$$= 1.067$$

Simpson's rule

A third rule that allows us to calculate an approximation to the area under a curve, is 'Simpson's Rule'. This works in a similar way to the other methods in that strips are used to estimate the area.

Simpson's Rule

$$\text{Area} = \tfrac{1}{3} \times \text{Strip width} \times (\text{First} + \text{last} + 4(\text{Sum of odd ordinates}) + 2(\text{Sum of other even ordinates}))$$

Ordinates are as for the 'Trapezium Rule'

Ordinate	Time t	I^2
0	0	0
1	0.001	52.22387
2	0.002	99.33571
3	0.003	136.7239
4	0.004	160.7286
5	0.005	169
6	0.006	160.7286
7	0.007	136.7239
8	0.008	99.33571
9	0.009	52.22387
10	0.01	0

Using Simpson's Rule:

$$\text{Area} = \tfrac{1}{3} \times 0.001 \times (0 + 0 + 4(546.9) + 2(520.1))$$

$$= 1.076$$

This method often gives a better approximation to areas under curves, but this depends on the actual shape of the relationship being plotted.

Skill unit 24 *Differential equations*

24.1 Differential equations

Investigations

Differential equations are equations that contain a differential component $\left(\text{such as } \dfrac{dy}{dx}\right)$.
Ordinarily this component represents the limiting value of the gradient of a curve, and is maintained as a function itself. When working with differential equations it is convenient to regard such terms as quotients (dy divided by dx). Hence, equations can be rearranged and variables can be separated. Equations of this type are shown as follows.

1.

$$\frac{dy}{dx} = x^2 + 4$$

   becomes

$$dy = (x^2 + 4)dx \dotfill ①$$

2.

$$\frac{dy}{dx} = 2y$$

   becomes

$$\frac{dy}{y} = 2dx \dotfill ②$$

Integration allows us to obtain a general solution (an equation without differential components) of a differential equation. A general solution represents a number of curves. It does not give a specific curve because an unknown constant of integration (C or K) is included.

Integrating both sides of equation ①:

$$y = \frac{x^2}{3} + 4x + C$$

This result is the equation of an infinite number of curves crossing the y axis at C, or a family of cuves. It is called the *general solution* of the differential equation. More information, about the relationship, is needed in order to determine a value for C, and to find the *particular solution*.

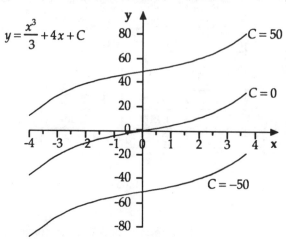

Integrating both sides of equation ②:

$$\ln y = 2x + C$$

Taking the inverse log of both sides gives:

$$y = e^{2x+C}$$
$$= e^C . e^{2x}$$

Putting constant $K = e^C$: $\qquad y = Ke^{2x}$

Again a family of curves is given by the general solution.

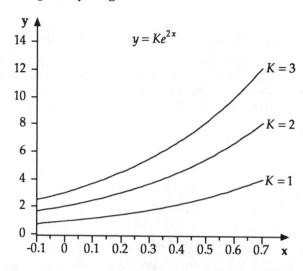

The constant C can be found if one point on the curve is known, in practice we may have a value for y when x = 0.

Example 1

A 3 μF capacitor with initial charge $Q = 50 \times 10^{-6}$ Coulombs (Amp seconds) is discharged through a 1000Ω resistor as shown.

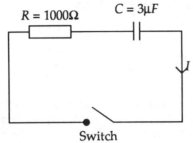

The rate of discharge $\dfrac{dQ}{dt}$ is given by the equation:

$$\frac{dQ}{dt} = -\frac{1}{CR}Q$$

Find the remaining charge after 0.004 seconds, and the time before 90% of the charge is lost.

Solution 1

We can substitute the constant values for R and C to simplify the differential equation.

So putting R = 1000 and C = 3 x 10^{-6}:

$$\frac{dQ}{dt} = -\frac{1}{3 \times 10^{-6} \times 1000}Q$$

$$= -333.3Q$$

The equation can be rearranged to collect similar terms together (separate variables).

$$\frac{1}{Q}dQ = -333.3dt$$

and integrating both sides:

$$\int \frac{1}{Q}dQ = \int -333.3dt$$

giving:

$$\ln Q = -333.3t + K \ [K = \text{constant of integration}]$$

In exponential form:

$$Q = e^{-333.3t+K}$$

or:

$$Q = e^{K}.e^{-333.3t} \ [\text{where } e^{K} \text{ is again a constant}]$$

This is an equation (general solution) giving the relationship between the charge Q and time t. The initial charge at time $t = 0$ can now be used to evaluate the constant (e^{K}).

When $t = 0$, $Q = 50 \times 10^{-6}$. Thus:

$$50 \times 10^{-6} = e^{K}.e^{-333.3 \times 0}$$

That is:

$$e^{K} = 50 \times 10^{-6} \ [\text{since } e^{-333.3 \times 0} = 1]$$

This constant may be used in the equation for Q (particular solution of the differential equation).

Thus:

$$Q = 50 \times 10^{-6}.e^{-333.3t}$$

We can now calculate the remaining charge by substituting $t = 0.004$ seconds.

That is:

$$Q = 50 \times 10^{-6}.e^{-333.3 \times 0.004}$$

$$= 13.1 \times 10^{-6} \text{Coulombs}$$

The time to reduce the charge by 90% is also found by substitution into this equation.

$$Q = 10\% \text{ of } 50 \times 10^{-6}$$

and therefore:

$$5 \times 10^{-6} = 50 \times 10^{-6}.e^{-333.3t}$$
$$0.1 = e^{-333.3t}$$
$$\ln 0.1 = -333.3t$$

Therefore:
$$t = 0.0069 \text{ seconds}$$

24.2 Separating variables

Investigations

Differential equations may be complicated expressions where it is not possible to separate the variables completely. If this is the case an alternative approach must be sought. However, with conventional techniques for rearranging equations, and splitting up the differential quotient $\left(\text{such as } \dfrac{dQ}{dt} \text{ in example 1}\right)$, many differential equations can be solved in this way.

Example 2

A vehicle, initially at rest, of mass 420 kg is propelled by a constant driving force F of 1000 Newtons. The combined resistance R (friction, air resistance etc) acts against the direction of motion.

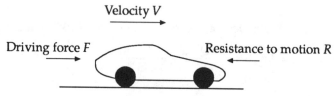

The driving force overcomes resistance and provides acceleration giving:

$$F = R + m\frac{dv}{dt}$$

As the velocity of the vehicle increases resistance to motion also increases, following the relationship:

$$R = 100 + 36v^2$$

After 9 seconds the vehicle is travelling at a velocity of $v = 2$ m/s. Find the time it takes to reach a velocity of 4 m/s.

Solution 2

The differential equation
$$F = R + m\frac{dv}{dt}$$
has to be solved.

Making substitutions $F = 1000$, $m = 420$ and $R = 100 + 36v^2$

$$1000 = 100 + 36v^2 + 420\frac{dv}{dt}$$

Simplifying:
$$900 - 36v^2 = 420\frac{dv}{dt}$$

Separating variables:
$$dt = \frac{420}{900 - 36v^2}dv$$

Integrating both sides:
$$\int dt = \int \frac{420}{900 - 36v^2}dv$$

It is easier to integrate the right hand function if it is first split into partial fractions.

$$\frac{420}{900 - 36v^2} = \frac{7}{30 + 6v} + \frac{7}{30 - 6v}$$

Thus:

$$\int dt = \int \frac{7}{30 + 6v} dv + \int \frac{7}{30 - 6v} dv$$

giving:

$$t = \frac{7}{6}\ln(30 + 6v) - \frac{7}{6}\ln(30 - 6v) + C$$

or:

$$t = \frac{7}{6}\ln\left(\frac{30 + 6v}{30 - 6v}\right) + C$$

This is the general solution of the differential equation. The constant of integration C is found, hence the particular solution, using the result $v = 2$ m/s when $t = 9$.

That is:

$$9 = \frac{7}{6}\ln\left(\frac{30 + 6(2)}{30 - 6(2)}\right) + C$$

giving:

$$C = 8$$

With this constant, the particular solution is now:

$$t = \frac{7}{6}\ln\left(\frac{30 + 6v}{30 - 6v}\right) + 8$$

The time to reach a velocity of 4 m/s can now be calculated.

Time required:

$$t = \frac{7}{6}\ln\left(\frac{30 + 6(4)}{30 - 6(4)}\right) + 8$$

$$= 10.6 \text{ seconds}$$

Skill unit 25 *Centroids*

25.1 Centroids

Investigations

The weight W of a circular flat disc acts effectively through the centre, and produces a turning moment $W\bar{x}$ about an axis YY (where $\bar{x}$ is the perpendicular distance from YY to the centre).

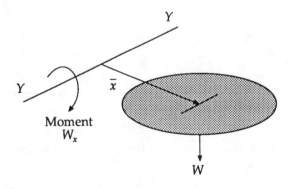

The weight of a disc with uniform thickness is directly proportional to the **area**. The moment of area is found in a silmilar way:

$$\text{Moment of Area} = A.\bar{x}$$

This is a more convenient moment to work with as the thickness and density of the material are ignored.

Example 1

The top of a boiler has to be supported at its centre of area. The shape is a rectangle with a hole cut out of it as shown.

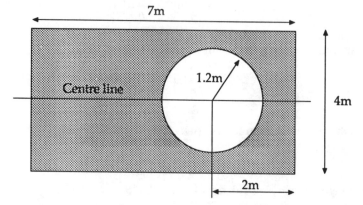

Find the position of the centre of area if it is made from steel plate of uniform thickness.

Solution 1

The shape has an axis of symmetry (the centre line) and the centroid must lie on this line. Selecting an edge (YY) as an axis about which moments can be taken, it is therefore required to find the distance $\bar{x}$ measured from this axis.

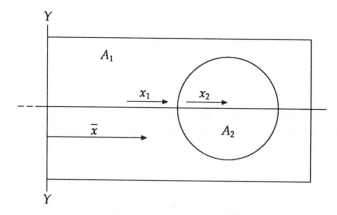

Letting the rectangle be area A_1 and the hole A_2 we can consider moments about the axis YY. To find $\bar{x}$ we make use of the following equation.

The moment of the whole area = The sum of moments of component areas

Using areas and the distances of their centroids from YY (we are subtracting the moment of the hole), we have:

$$A\bar{x} = A_1x_1 - A_2x_2 \dots\dots\dots\dots\dots\dots\dots\dots\dots\dots\dots\dots\dots①$$

Representing values in a table saves confusion.

230

Shape	Area	Distance of centroid from YY (x)
1	$A_1 = 7 \times 4 = 28$	$x_1 = 3.5$
2	$A_2 = 1.2^2 \times \pi = 4.52$	$x_2 = 5$
Total	$A = A_1 - A_2 = 23.48$	$\bar{x}$

Subtituting values into the formula ①:　　$23.48\bar{x} = 28 \times 3.5 - 4.52 \times 5$

$$\bar{x} = \frac{75.4}{23.5}$$

$$= 3.2$$

This seems a reasonable result, we would expect it to be less than 3.5.

Investigations

Where shapes are symmetrical, axes of symmetry can help us to find the centroid.

For a combination of symmetrical shapes, or shapes with defined centroids, the approach used in example 1 gives us the overall centroid.

moment of the whole area = sum of moments of component areas

Triangles

Some triangles have axes of symmetry (equilateral and isosceles), but more generally a method is required here for finding the centroid.

Let us consider the right angled triangle shown:

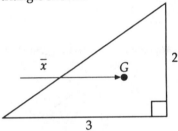

If it is divided up into very thin strips it can be thought of as a composite shape (made up of an infinite number of approximate rectangles).

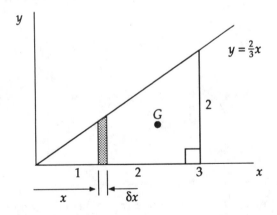

Treating the triangle as a straight line graph we can say that each rectangle has width δx and is a distance x from the origin.

The line has a gradient of $\frac{2}{3}$ and thus: $\quad y = \frac{2}{3}x$

$$\text{Area of one strip} = \frac{2}{3}x\delta x$$

Distance of centroid of strip from y-axis $= x + \dfrac{\delta x}{2}$

$$= x \text{ [since strips are thin and } \frac{\delta x}{2} \text{ is able to be ignored]}$$

Moment of area of strip about y axis $= \frac{2}{3}x\delta x.x$

$$= \frac{2}{3}x^2\delta x$$

This is an expression giving the moment, for a strip that is a distance x from the y axis. It is assumed that there are a large number of thin strips. Integration now allows us calculate the sum of moments for strips between 0 and 3.

$$\int_0^3 \frac{2}{3}x^2 dx = \frac{2}{3}\left[\frac{x^3}{3}\right]_0^3$$

$$= \frac{2}{3}\left[\frac{3^3}{3} - 0\right]$$

$$= 6$$

Again: moment of the whole area = sum of moments of component areas

$$A\bar{x} = \text{Sum of moments}$$

Area of triangle $A = 3$, giving $\qquad 3\bar{x} = 6$

Thus: $\bar{x} = 2$

From this particular solution we can generalise and suggest that for any triangle shown:

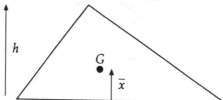

The height of the centroid G (using any of the sides as a base) is one third of the overall height.

$$\bar{x} = \frac{1}{3}h$$

Example 2

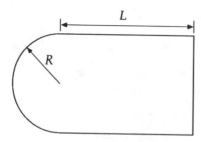

The lid of a container is made in the shape of a rectangle and a semi-circle from steel plate of uniform thickness. It is required to attach a lifting ring somewhere on the surface of the lid so that it will hang in a horizontal position. Find the centre of area where this ring should be attached if the length $L = 4$ metres and the radius $R = 1.5$ metres.

Solution 2

In order for the lid to remain horizontal, the lifting point must be at its centroid G (or centre of gravity) so that the moments are in balance.

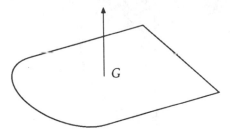

The shape has an axis of symmetry and the centroid must lie on this line.

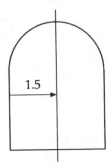

The lifting point needs to be 1.5 metres in from the edge.

It is now required to determine the distance that G must lie in the other direction.

Labelling the lid as two areas, each with its centroid measured from the edge YY.

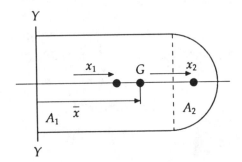

As before in example 1, we can write down an equation for the combined shape.

moment of the whole area = sum of moments of component areas

Using areas and distances of their centroids from YY:

$$A\bar{x} = A_1 x_1 + A_2 x_2$$

The difficulty here is that we are unable to find the centroid of a semi-circle without integration. The semi-circle (sector with angle π rads) is considered here to be made up of a large number of thin sectors with small angles $\delta\theta$ measured θ rads from the x-axis.

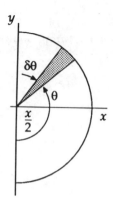

$$\text{Small sector area} \quad = \tfrac{1}{2}(1.5)^2\delta\theta \dots\dots\dots\dots\dots\dots\dots\dots\dots\dots②$$

Assuming a thin sector approximates to a triangle, then G is $\tfrac{2}{3}$ radius from the origin. Measured horizontally from the y-axis:

$$x \ =\tfrac{2}{3}R\cos\theta$$

Thus: distance of centroid from y-axis $=\tfrac{2}{3}R\cos\theta$
and, substituting for $R=1.5$ gives:

$$\text{distance of centroid from y-axis} \ = 1.\cos\theta\dots\dots\dots\dots\dots\dots\dots\dots\dots\dots③$$

But the moment about the y-axis is given by ② × ③.

Thus: moment about y-axis $=\tfrac{1}{2}(1.5)^2\delta\theta\times 1.\cos\theta$

$$= 1.125\delta\theta\cos\theta$$

Using the expression for one sector, we can integrate and find the sum of moments between $-\tfrac{\pi}{2}$ and $\tfrac{\pi}{2}$.

$$\text{Sum of moments} \ = 1.125\int_{-\frac{\pi}{2}}^{\frac{\pi}{2}}\cos\theta\, d\theta$$

$$= 1.125\big[\sin\theta\big]_{-\frac{\pi}{2}}^{\frac{\pi}{2}}$$

$$= 1.125(1-(-1))$$

$$= 2.25$$

The distance of the centroid ($\bar{x}$) from the centre is found by dividing this sum by the area of the semi-circle (A_2), as the following shows.

Since: $A_2\bar{x}$ $=$ sum of moments

we have: $\bar{x}$ $= \dfrac{\text{sum of moments}}{A_2}$

Also: A_2 $= \dfrac{1}{2}\pi(1.5)^2$

$$= 3.534$$

Therefore:
$$\bar{x} = \frac{2.25}{3.534}$$
$$= 0.637$$

The distance of this centroid from the y axis (x_2) is therefore:
$$4 + 0.637 = 4.637$$

Constructing a table of values as before:

Shape	Area	Distance of centroid from YY (x)
1	$A_1 = 3 \times 4 = 12$	$x_1 = 2$
2	$A_2 = 3.534$	$x_2 = 4.637$
Total	$A = A_1 + A_2 = 15.534$	$\bar{x}$

Subtituting values into formula ①:
$$15.534\,\bar{x} = 12 \times 2 + 3.534 \times 4.637$$
$$\bar{x} = \frac{40.4}{15.53}$$
$$= 2.6$$

This is acceptable as it lies between x_1 and x_2 which is expected.

Investigations

Sectors

In example 2 we found the centroid of a semi-circle, which can be thought of as a sector with an angle of π radians (or 2 ($\pi/2$) as symmetry is used). The same approach can be taken to find the centroid of any sector with angle 2α (where α is the angle from the line of symmetry), and with any radius R.

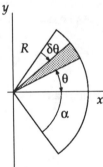

Using these more general values we can follow the same procedure as before:

The sector (with angle 2α rads) is considered to be made up of a large number of thin sectors with small angles $\delta\theta$ measured θ rads from the x axis.

$$\text{Small sector area} = \tfrac{1}{2} R^2 \delta\theta$$

Assuming a thin sector approximates to a triangle then G is $\tfrac{2}{3} R$ from the origin.

Measured horizontally from the y axis:
$$\bar{x} = \tfrac{2}{3} R \cos\theta$$

Thus:　distance of centroid from y-axis $= \tfrac{2}{3} R \cos\theta$

Therefore: moment about y-axis $= \frac{1}{2}R^2\delta\theta\frac{2}{3}R\cos\theta$

$$= \frac{1}{3}R^3\cos\theta\delta\theta$$

Using the expression for one sector, we can integrate and find the sum of moments between $-\alpha$ and α.

$$\text{Sum of moments} = \frac{1}{3}\int_{-\alpha}^{\alpha}R^3\cos\theta\,d\theta$$

$$= \frac{1}{3}R^3[\sin\theta]_{-\alpha}^{\alpha}$$

$$= \frac{1}{3}R^3[\sin\alpha - \sin(-\alpha)]$$

Substituting $\sin(-\alpha) = -\sin\alpha$. $\qquad \text{Sum} = \frac{1}{3}R^3\,2\sin\alpha$

$$= \frac{2}{3}R^3\sin\alpha$$

The distance of the centroid ($\bar{x}$) from the centre is found by dividing this sum by the area of the sector (A), as the following shows.

Since: $\qquad A\bar{x} = \text{sum of moments}$

we have: $\qquad \bar{x} = \dfrac{\text{sum of moments}}{A}$

Also: $\qquad A = \frac{1}{2}(2\alpha)R^2$

$$= \alpha R^2$$

Therefore: $\qquad \bar{x} = \dfrac{\frac{2}{3}R^3\sin\alpha}{\alpha R^2}$

Simplifying, we have: $\qquad \bar{x} = \frac{2}{3}\dfrac{R\sin\alpha}{\alpha}$

This formula may be used directly to find the position of the centroid of a sector, provided that α is given in radians. The development of this and other formulae using integration should be carefully followed as many more shapes can be dealt with in a similar way.

25.2 Volumes of revolution

Example 3

A large, bucket full of concrete has dimensions as shown, in metres.

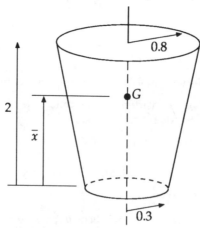

Determine the height of the centroid, and in order to establish how stable it is, calculate the maximum angle that it can lean, before it will topple over.

Solution 3

The bucket shape can be considered as a trapezium, rotated about its centre line. If this trapezium is represented on an x, y graph a straight line equation can be stated. Integration is now required to find the sum of moments of thin strips rotated about the x axis (thin discs).

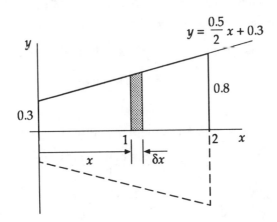

$$y = \frac{0.5}{2}x + 0.3$$

The distance of a thin strip from the y axis is x and the thickness is δx.

As a strip is rotated about the x axis a thin disc is formed with radius y and thickness δx.

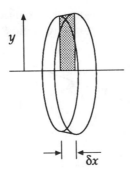

The volume of a disc is given by: $v = \pi y^2 \delta x$

The distance of the centroid of the disc from the y axis (for very thin discs) is x.

$$\text{Moment of volume} = vx$$

$$= \pi x y^2 \delta x$$

Substitute $y = 0.25x + 0.3$ $= \pi x(0.25x + 0.3)^2 \delta x$

$$= \pi(0.0625x^3 + 0.15x^2 + 0.09x)\delta x$$

Integration allows us to find the sum of moments between 0 and 2.

Thus, sum of moments of volume $= \pi \int_0^2 \left(0.0625x^3 + 0.15x^2 + 0.09x\right)dx$

$$= \pi\left[0.0156x^4 + 0.05x^3 + 0.045x^2\right]_0^2$$

ie sum of moments of volume $= 2.61$

The volume of the bucket is given by $V = \frac{1}{3}\pi h\left(R^2 + Rr + r^2\right)$

$$= \frac{2}{3}\pi\left(0.8^2 + 0.8 \times 0.3 + 0.3^2\right)$$

$$= 2.03$$

Now: $V\bar{x} = $ Sum of moments

giving: $\bar{x} = \dfrac{\text{Sum of moments}}{V}$

$$= \frac{2.61}{2.03}$$

$$= 1.29$$

Again it is worth considering how sensible this answer is: 1.29 metres is above half the height but less than 2 metres so it seems a feasible value.

The weight of the bucket acts through the centroid suggesting that it will topple over when G is vertically above the pivot point. The corresponding angle θ can therefore be calculated using the tan ratio.

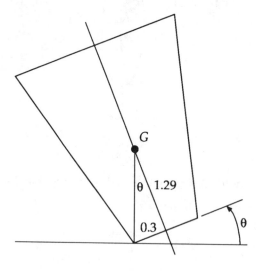

$$\tan\theta = \frac{0.3}{1.29}$$

$$\theta = 13.1°$$

26.1 Second moments of area

Investigations

The second moment of area is a property of the cross sectional area of a beam, often used in stress calculations. Its value is an indication of the bending strength of a beam.

Rectangles

Let us consider the second moment of area of a beam with a rectangular cross section as shown. As with moments of area an axis of reference is required. It is most convenient to use an axis through the centroid.

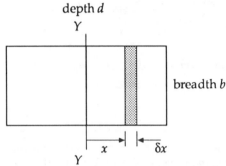

A thin strip as shown has:

$$\text{moment of area about } YY: = Ax$$

where A is the area of the strip.

The second moment of area is denoted by I and given by:

$$I_{YY} = Ax^2$$

$$= b\delta x . x^2$$

Using integration the sum of second moments of strips between $-\dfrac{d}{2}$ and $\dfrac{d}{2}$ can be found.

$$I_{YY} = \int_{-\frac{d}{2}}^{\frac{d}{2}} bx^2 \, dx$$

$$= b\left[\frac{x^3}{3}\right]_{-\frac{d}{2}}^{\frac{d}{2}}$$

$$= \frac{b}{3}\left[\left(\frac{d}{2}\right)^3 - \left(-\frac{d}{2}\right)^3\right]$$

$$= \frac{b}{3}\left(\frac{d^3}{8} + \frac{d^3}{8}\right)$$

That is:

$$I_{YY} = \frac{bd^3}{12}$$

This formula for the second moment of a rectangle is important and should be noted.

In a similar way, using integration, formulae can be developed for other regular areas.

Circle

The equation for a circle gives us a complicated expression for y, and some tricky integration is required. Second moments are taken about the y axis.

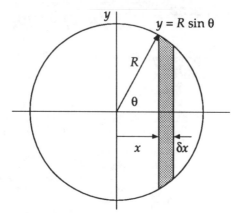

The second moment of area is given by:

$$I_{YY} = Ax^2$$

(assuming thin strips are rectangles)

ie

$$I_{YY} = 2y.\delta x.x^2$$

Substitutions can be made for x and y, and using integration the sum of second moments of strips can be found. The limits are between $-R$ and R for a full circle.

The formula here becomes:

$$I_{YY} = \frac{\pi R^4}{4}$$

This is often quoted in terms of the diameter D as:

$$I_{YY} = \frac{\pi D^4}{64}$$

For a semi-circle, again about the y axis (the diameter) the limits are modified and the sum is from 0 to R. The value is naturally half of that for a full circle.

$$I_{YY} = \frac{\pi D^4}{128}$$

Triangles

The centroid of a triangle is more difficult to relate to than symmetrical shapes, so this time we will find the second moment of area about the base B. Again thin strips are used with width δx and distance x from the y axis.

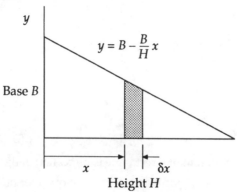

An equation of a straight line gives us a relationship between y and x, and the sum of second moments of strips can be found.

Second moment of a strip about the base is:

$$I_{\text{base}} = y.\delta x.x^2$$

$$= (B - \frac{B}{H}x).x^2.\delta x$$

Finding the sum using integration between the limits 0 and H gives:

$$I_{\text{base}} = \int_0^H (B - \frac{B}{H}x).x^2\,dx$$

$$= \int_0^H (Bx^2 - \frac{B}{H}x^3)\,dx$$

$$= \left[(B\frac{x^3}{3} - \frac{Bx^4}{4H}) \right]_0^H$$

$$= \frac{BH^3}{3} - \frac{BH^3}{4}$$

giving:
$$I_{\text{base}} = \frac{BH^3}{12}$$

This is another useful formula, but this time it represents the second moment of area about the base of a triangle, and not a line through the centroid (this will be developed later).

26.2 Composite areas

Example 1

A joist is required to support a load. Beams are available with the two different cross-sectional areas shown. Calculate which has the greatest bending strength and is therefore the most suitable.

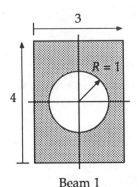

Beam 1

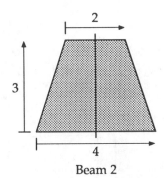

Beam 2

Solution 1

Beam 1

This beam can be used either horizontally or vertically, so we need to calculate values for the second moments of area in these two positions (I_{YY} and I_{XX}). The centre line YY passes through the centroid of both the rectangle and the circular hole. The second moment of area for the beam about this axis is therefore given by subtracting I_{YY} for the hole from I_{YY} for the rectangle.

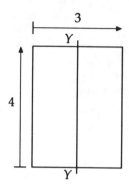 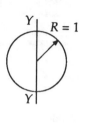

Rectangle:
$$I_{YY} = \frac{bd^3}{12}$$
$$= \frac{4 \times 3^3}{12}$$
$$= 9$$

Circle:
$$I_{YY} = \frac{\pi R^4}{4}$$
$$= \frac{\pi(1)^4}{4}$$
$$= \frac{\pi}{4}$$

The second moment of area for the beam can now be found.
$$I_{YY}(beam) = I_{YY}(\text{rectangle}) - I_{YY}(\text{circle})$$
$$= 9 - \frac{\pi}{4}$$
$$= 8.21$$

This value represents 8.21 cm³ (the units of second moment of area).

Alternatively, the second moment of area about XX could give us a larger value and needs to be calculated.

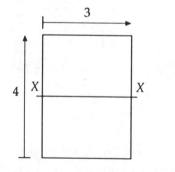 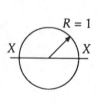

Rectangle:

$$I_{XX} = \frac{bd^3}{12}$$

$$= \frac{3 \times 4^3}{12}$$

$$= 16$$

Circle:

$$I_{XX} = \frac{\pi R^4}{4}$$

$$= \frac{\pi(1)^4}{4}$$

$$= \frac{\pi}{4}$$

The second moment of area for the beam about XX can now be found.

$$I_{XX}(\text{beam}) = I_{XX}(\text{rectangle}) - I_{XX}(\text{circle})$$

$$= 16 - \frac{\pi}{4}$$

$$= 15.21 \text{ cm}^4$$

It is now clear that the beam has greater handling strength about XX (it will support a heavier load in a vertical position).

Beam 2

The shape of this beam prohibits its use in a vertical position and we are therefore required to determine the second moment of area about a horizontal axis. The centroid of this area has to be found using the procedure for a composite shape. Let us initially consider the second moments of area about the base.

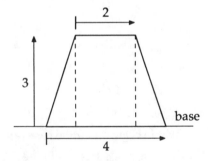

Here we have a rectangle and two similar triangles that can be dealt with separately to begin with.

To find I_{base} for the triangles (this will be the same for each) the formula can be used.

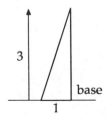

For the triangle:
$$I_{base} = \frac{BH^3}{12}$$

$$= \frac{1 \times 3^3}{12}$$

giving:
$$I_{base} = 2.25$$

We already have a formula for calculating the second moments of area for a rectangle about an axis through its centroid (I_{XX}). It is now required to change from this reference axis to a parallel axis (the base).

A particularly useful theorem can be applied here.

Parallel axis theorem

$$I_{base} = I_{XX} + Ah^2$$

(where A is the area and h the distance between the axes).

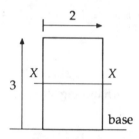

Second moments about XX:
$$I_{XX} = \frac{bd^3}{12}$$

$$= \frac{2 \times 3^3}{12}$$

$$= 4.5$$

Using the parallel axis theorem:
$$I_{base} = I_{XX} + Ah^2$$

and, substituting $I_{XX} = 4.5$, $A = 6$ and $h = 1.5$:

$$I_{base} = 4.5 + 6(1.5)^2$$

$$= 18$$

The second moments of area for the whole beam about the base can now be found.

$$I_{base}(\text{beam}) = I_{base}(\text{rectangle}) + 2 \times I_{base}(\text{triangle})$$

$$= 18 + 2 \times 2.25$$

$$= 22.5 \text{ cm}^4$$

The parallel axis theorem can now be used again to find the second moment of area about an axis through the centroid.

$$I_{base} = I_{XX} + Ah^2$$

Re-arranging:
$$I_{XX} = I_{base} - Ah^2$$

It is therefore necessary to determine the height of the centroid from the base (h).

The moment of the whole area = The sum of moments of component areas

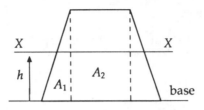

Using areas and the distances of their centroids from the base (triangles have the same moment about XX):

$$A.h = 2.A_1.x_1 + A_2.x_2$$

That is:

$$9h = 2(1.5)(1) + 6(1.5)$$

Re-arranging:

$$h = \frac{12}{9}$$

Thus:

$$h = 1.33$$

Therefore:

$$I_{XX} = I_{base} - Ah^2$$

$$= 22.5 - 9(1.33)^2$$

giving:

$$I_{XX} = 6.5 \text{ cm}^4$$

A comparison of the bending strength of the beams can now be made.

Beam 1:

horizontal: $I_{XX} = 8.21 \text{ cm}^4$

vertical: $I_{XX} = 15.21 \text{ cm}^4$

Beam 2: $I_{XX} = 6.5 \text{ cm}^4$

From this, beam 1 in a vertical position is considerably stronger than the other arrangements.

Investigations

There are some important observations that can be made from example 1.

1	The lowest numerical value for the second moment of area is found about an axis through the centroid of a shape. The 'parallel axis theorem' indicates that Ah^2 is added to second moments about other axes.
2	If a shape has a large proportion of its area away from the axis through the centroid, the bending strength will be greater.

A cross section that is often used in engineering structures is that of an 'I' section. This is a particularly good shape with a high value for the second moment of area.

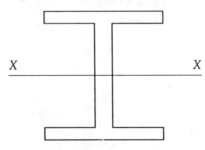

26.3 Polar second moments of area

Example 2

The strength of a shaft in torsion about the centre line depends on the polar second moment of area. Calculate this value for the shaft shown.

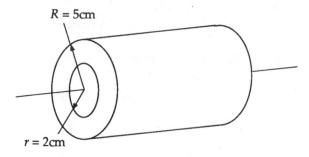

$R = 5\text{cm}$

$r = 2\text{cm}$

Solution 2

Let us consider the polar second moment of area about the centre of a thin ring with radius r and thickness δr.

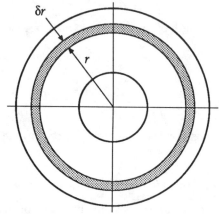

δr

r

The thin ring has polar second moment of area about the centre (axis perpendicular to the plane) given by:

$$J_{centre} = Ar^2$$

(J is used to denote polar second moment)

That is:

$$J_{centre} = 2\pi.r.\delta r.r^2$$

(the area of a thin ring is approximately equal to the circumference)

Integration can now be used to find the sum of all such thin rings, between the two radii.

So:

$$J_{centre} = 2\pi \int_2^5 r^3 \, dr$$

$$= 2\pi \left[\frac{r^4}{4} \right]_2^5$$

$$= 2\pi \left[\frac{5^4}{4} - \frac{2^4}{4} \right]$$

That is:

$$J_{centre} = 956.6$$

Investigations

A formula can be developed for the polar second moment of area about the centre of a circle, by integrating as in example 2 between the limits of 0 and R.

$$J = 2\pi \int_0^R r^3 \, dr$$

$$= 2\pi \left[\frac{r^4}{4} \right]_0^R$$

$$= 2\pi \left[\frac{R^4}{4} \right]$$

That is:

$$J = \frac{\pi R^4}{2}$$

The axis about which J acts is perpendicular to the plane of an area.

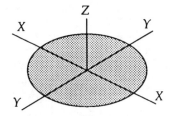

Another useful theorem that gives us a relationship between second moments of area about these perpendicular axes is given as follows.

Perpendicular Axis Theorem

$$I_{ZZ} = I_{XX} + I_{YY}$$

Note. I_{ZZ}(circle) = J

The use of this theorem can be demonstrated by appying it to the shaft from example 2:

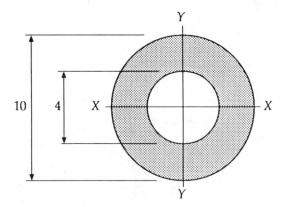

The second moment of area for circles is given by the formula:

$$I_{ZZ} = \frac{\pi(10)^4}{64} - \frac{\pi(4)^4}{64}$$

$$= 478.3$$

Using the perpendicular axis theorem:

$$I_{ZZ} = I_{XX} + I_{YY}$$
$$= 478.3 + 478.3$$

That is: $I_{ZZ} = 956.6$

This agrees with the value found for J in example 2.

Section 3 – Developing Knowledge and Skills

Introduction

In this section, projects from other fields of Engineering provide the opportunity to use skills learned in Section 1 for new applications, thereby reinforcing learning.

A 'Project/Skill Areas' table is again provided so that it is clear which skills are involved in each project. A skills list for each project also makes this clear. Some projects require only the use of primary skills. Projects are again independent units and may be attempted in any sequence. It is recommended that all relevent Section 1 projects are successfully completed before progress is made to any Section 3 projects (see page x, 'Progress to Section 3 Projects'). Tasks within a project need to be tackled in sequence.

This section can be used to set assignment work, since each project covers a combinations of skills. Answers for this section are not provided in the book. (They are available in the Lecturers Supplement – see Preface for details.)

Step by step support is also not given at this stage to encourage more independent working. Help references are broader, referring only to 'Skill Areas'. Students are expected to use their experience to select for themselves the most appropriate techniques for solutions.

Contents

Skill table

Unit No.	Skill Areas	A	B	C	D	E	F	G	H	I	J	K	L	M
	Section 2 reference							*Projects*						
1	Calcs and Comps												●	
2	Formulae	●					●	●						
3	Radians										●			
4	Statistics								●					
5	Trigonometry 1									●				●
6	Straight Line Graphs		●		●			●		●				
7	Logarithms			●				●		●				
8	Solving Equations Graphically	●					●	●						
9	Volumes and Surface Areas	●			●		●			●	●			
10	Exponential Relationships			●				●		●				
11	Sim Equations and Matrices	●	●											
12	Quadratic Curves			●	●		●							
13	Differentiation 1						●			●				
14	Integration 1										●			
15	Complex Numbers					●		●						
16	Series			●			●							
17	Binomial Theorem			●										
18	Vectors						●				●	●		●
19	Max and Min			●		●								
20	Trigonometry 2					●								
21	Differentiation 2				●			●						
22	Integration 2			●	●	●						●		
23	Numerical Methods					●	●							
24	Differential Equations			●										
25	Centroids				●							●		
26	2nd Moments of Area											●		

Power generation *Introduction*

Electrical power generation is a major field of engineering. Detailed projects consider the use of alternative energy sources. The design of a turbine and supporting shaft is carried out and the generator itself receives attention. Projects focus on;

Project A   Hydroelectric   Skill Areas Used: Formulae
                                                                Solving Equations Graphically
                                                                Volumes and Surface Area
                                                                Simultaneous Equations and Matrices

Project B   Coal and Oil   Skill Areas Used: Simultaneous Equations and Matrices
                                                                Straight Line Graphs

Project C   Nuclear Power   Skill Areas Used: Logarithms
                                                                Exponential Relationships
                                                                Quadratic Curves
                                                                Series
                                                                Binomial Theorem
                                                                Maximum and Minimum
                                                                Integration 2
                                                                Differential Equations

Project D   Gas Turbines   Skill Areas Used: Straight Line Graphs
                                                                Volumes and Surface Area
                                                                Quadratic Curves
                                                                Differentiation 2
                                                                Integration 2
                                                                Centroids

Project E   Generators   Skill Areas Used: Complex Numbers
                                                                Maximum and Minimum
                                                                Trigonometry 2
                                                                Integration 2
                                                                Numerical Methods

Each project is introduced with a brief explanation of how components work. Specific details are given about the application, these are required throughout the project.

Project A *Hydroelectric*

Task 1 *Energy*

The energy available for driving a water turbine depends on the height (or head) of water. This energy can be utilised by allowing it to drive a turbine.

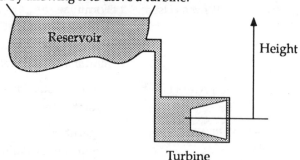

Turbine

The pressure of water at the turbine P_T and the fluid (water) velocity v can be related to the height h by using an important equation for fluid flow (Bernouli's Equation).

$$P_T + 0.5\rho v^2 = P_{surface} + \rho g h$$

where $\quad$ $P_{surface}$ = atmospheric pressure

ρ = density of the fluid

g = acceleration due to gravity (10 m/s²)

If the operating pressure for the turbine is 2 times atmospheric pressure, what will be the velocity of the fluid for the heights given in the table.

Height h (metres)	20	30	40	50	60
Velocity v (m/s)					

Construct a similar table for the same heights, but using olive oil as the fluid rather than water (assuming it would flow).

In a test the velocity at a turbine was measured for reservoir heights as before.

Height h (metres)	20	30	40	50	60
Velocity v (m/s)	15.69	21.12	25.42	29.09	32.34

Draw a graph from the data given. Estimate the height that corresponds to a velocity of 40 m/s. From the coordinates at a point and with $P_T = 250\rho$ form simultaneous equations, and solve them. What is the density of the fluid.

Write down an equation for the height h. Calculate more accurately the height when $v = 40$.

Information Bank Section 2 $\quad$ Unit 2 Formulae *page 96*
$\qquad\qquad\qquad\qquad\qquad\quad$ Unit 8 Solving Equations Graphically *page 132*
$\qquad\qquad\qquad\qquad\qquad\quad$ Unit 11 Simultaneous Equations *page 151*

Task 2 *Pipes and water flow*

Water flows through two sections of pipe, firstly through a conical shape and secondly down a slope with angle θ. Assume that friction has a negligible effect on the flow.

At the inlet diameter $D = 0.7$ m (point A) the water is flowing at velocity $v = 8$ m/s.

For the conical section;

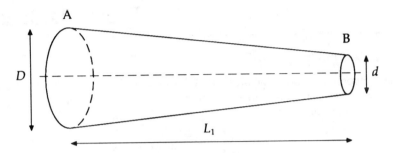

If the outlet diameter $d = 0.2$ m, what is the outlet velocity.

What diameter is required to give an outlet velocity of 25 m/s.

How long will it take for water to flow the full length of this section of pipe, if the length $L_1 = 7$ m and $d = 0.2$ m.

For the slope;

At the inlet diameter $d = 0.2$ m (point B) the water velocity $v = 25$ m/s.

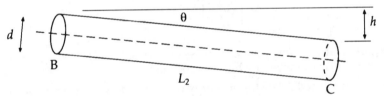

Calculate the water velocity after flowing through a pipe of length $L_2 = 9$ m at an angle of 15° to the horizontal.

Again with a pipe length $L_2 = 9$ m, what angle θ of slope is required to increase the velocity to 28 m/s.

For the conical section;

Consider the flow rate to be constant. This can be established from the inlet specifications

Calculate outlet velocity when $d = 0.2$ and the diameter that corresponds to $v = 25$ m/s.

Use the volume of the cone together with the flow rate to find the time taken for flow through the pipe.

For the slope;

Water loses potential energy (mgh) and gains kinetic energy ($0.5mv^2$) as it flows down the slope. Develop a relationship between the height h and the velocity.

Draw a graph to represent this relationship. Determine the velocity that corresponds to 9 m of pipe at 15°, and the height that gives a velocity of 28 m/s.

Information Bank Section 2 Unit 9 Volumes and surface areas *page 140*
Unit 8 Solving equations graphically *page 132*
Unit 2 Formulae *page 96*

Project B Coal and oil

Task 1 *Coal and Oil Burning*

In conventional power generation coal and oil are burned in a boiler which drives steam through a turbine. Energy is therefore released in the form of heat. The amount of energy available is determined by the quality of the fuel.

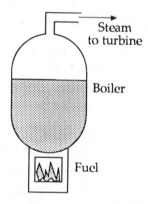

The energy requirement of a small generating system is 30000 MJ. Investigate all the different combinations for this to be achieved by burning coal and oil.

When 960 kg of fuel is burned 30000 MJ of energy is delivered by a system which is 80% efficient. The fuel is a combination of both coal and oil. Use appropriate calorific values and calculate the weight of each fuel type.

A batch of fuel is suspected to be poor quality. When 430 kg of coal and 380 kg of oil are burned only 28710 MJ are available. Using the same batch of fuel 290 kg of coal and 620 kg of oil produces 35730 MJ of energy. Determine the calorific values of the fuels from this batch.

Alternative fuels are tested in order to assess their suitability for use. The results are recorded in matrix form;

Fuel Test 1 (with fuels 1 and 2)

$$\begin{pmatrix} 230 & 410 \\ 330 & 520 \end{pmatrix} \begin{pmatrix} c_1 \\ c_2 \end{pmatrix} = \begin{pmatrix} 18870 \\ 24890 \end{pmatrix}$$

where Weights, Calorific values, and Energy are the labelled quantities.

Fuel Test 2 (with fuels 3 and 4)

Weights   Calorific
values   Energy

$$\begin{pmatrix} 570 & 280 \\ 340 & 625 \end{pmatrix} \cdot \begin{pmatrix} c_3 \\ c_4 \end{pmatrix} = \begin{pmatrix} 20030 \\ 30725 \end{pmatrix}$$

Calculate the calorific values of each of these fuels (1 – 4). Suggest which of these, together with coal and oil, are the most suitable in terms of their energy capacity.

Information Bank Section 2   Unit 6 Straight line graphs *page 125*
Unit 11 Simultaneous Equations and matrices
page 151

☐Extension task

Find out the calorific values for a host of alternative energy sources (including sugar).

Calculate the weight of each fuel required to produce 30000 MJ of energy. How much energy is supplied by a small power station per day.

Comment on the availability of each material (some research may be required).

Discuss these fuels as realistic alternatives to coal or oil.

Project C *Nuclear power*

Task 1 *Fuel Rods*

☐Task 1.1

Radioactive cylindrical fuel rods are contained in nuclear reactors to produce heat. It is required that they are arranged in shapes that have small suface areas (relative to the volume) so as to minimise heat loss.

If 300 fuel rods can be accommodated by a vessel with an area of cross section A = 4 m², determine what shape will give the smallest perimeter and hence minimise the surface area of the vessel.

Rectangular Cross Section

Find the required dimensions b and h to minimise the perimeter of a rectangular shape. What perimeter do these give?

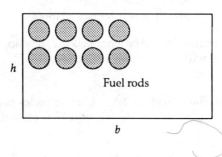

Fuel rods

Triangular Shape

Could this be improved with a triangular cross section. Again calculate the dimensions b and h that produce the smallest possible perimeter. How does this perimeter compare with the rectangular minimum?

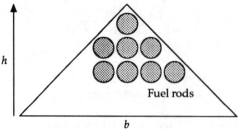

h

Fuel rods

b

Other Shapes

Investigate other shapes in a similar way. What conclusions can be drawn?

Information Bank Section 2   Unit 12 Quadratic curves *page 156*
                                  Unit 19 Maximum and minimum *page 196*

☐Task 1.2

In a particular nuclear reactor the fuel rods are arranged in a pattern as shown in the diagram.

With a total of 13 rows, how many rods will there be in the final row? What is the total number of fuel rods in this reactor?

How many rows are required to accommodate at least 300 rods using this pattern?

What alternative A.P pattern could be used to contain exactly 300 rods?

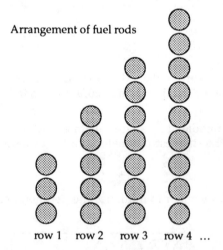

Arrangement of fuel rods

row 1   row 2   row 3   row 4 ...

Considering the analysis of a triangular shape from task 1.1, develop a series to allow exactly 300 rods to be contained in a shape with a minimum surface area.

Information Bank Section 2   Unit 16 Series *page 180*
                                  Unit 17 Binomial theorem *page 182*

Task 2 *Radioactive Decay*

Radioactivity is the process that occurs when nuclei (central parts of atoms) from material are unstable and emit 'radiations' or particles in order to reach a more stable state. Nuclei are therefore said to disintegrate or decay.

Investigate the radioactivity and decay times for materials used for nuclear power generation.

A useful law of radioactive decay gives the rate of disintegration of nuclei

$$\frac{dN}{dt} = -\lambda N$$

where N is the number of nuclei remaining and λ is the decay constant of the material

Element X

A radioactive material (unknown element X) has decay constant $\lambda = 3 \times 10^{-7}$. If the initial number of nuclei when $t = 0$ is $N_o = 4 \times 10^{27}$, Find an equation that relates the number of remaining nuclei N to time t.

How long will it take before half of the nuclei in this material have decayed? What material is being considered.

Note: The time for half the nuclei in a material to disintegrate is known as the 'half life'. A table giving the half life for other elements is available in the reference section.

Other elements

If the initial number of nuclei is $N_o = 4 \times 10^{27}$ for each material, complete the table for the elements given;

Element	Half Life (seconds)	Decay Constant λ	Radioactivity $\frac{dN}{dt}$
Uranium			
Radium			
Radon			

Suitability of Elements

How long will it take before a uranium fuel rod has expended 90% of its nuclei? What is the radioactvity after this time?

If a fuel rod is only efficient with a rate of decay greater than -1.8×10^9 nuclei/second then what will be the useful life for a fuel rod made from:

a)   Uranium?
b)   Radium?
c)   Radon?

Information Bank Section 2   Unit 7 Logarithms *page 128*
Unit 10 Exponential relationships *page 148*
Unit 22 Integration 2 *page 214*
Unit 24 Differential equations *page 225*

Task 3 *Radioactive Intensity*

Radiation is less intense at a distance. If a Geiger counter (for measuring radiation) is moved away from a source of radiation the number of particles detected per unit area is reduced. A relationship to represent this change can be developed by considering the increase in area over which particles have been spread.

A Small Spherical Source

Since radiation is dispersed in all directions particles are regarded as if they are spread over the surface area of a sphere.

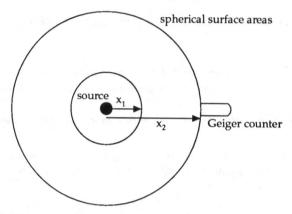

spherical surface areas

The dimensions of the source are negligible. If a Geiger counter measures 800 counts per second when it is a distance $x_1 = 40$ cm from a radioactive element, what will be the reading at a distance $x_2 = 120$ cm? At what distance will a reading of 300 counts per second be achieved?

Write down an equation for the intensity at any distance x and draw a graph to represent this relationship.

Cylindrical Rods

If the souce of radiation is in the shape of a long cylindrical rod particles will radiate outwards in a similar shape (the error at the ends is negligible for long rods).

Cylindrical surface area

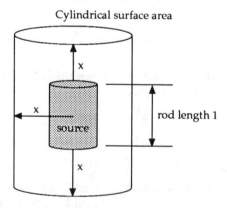

The length of a fuel rod is 200 cm. Develop a relationship between the radioactive intensity and the distance x if the product of the surface area (square centimetres) and the intensity is given by the constant 7.5×10^8.

What will be the intensity at a distance of 150 cm?

At what distance does the intensity fall to the safe level of 40 counts per second?

Information Bank Section 2   Unit 12 Quadratic curves *page 156*
Unit 22 Integration 2 *page 214*

☐Extension task

Investigage the arrangements of fuel rods that are used in nuclear reators. How do they compare with the arrangements considered in task 1.

Project D *Gas turbines*

Task 1 *Blade arrangements*

In order to convert energy from steam into electricity it passes through a set of turbine blades and rotates a shaft. The principle is the same as a windmill. The blades form a cone so that steam can pass between them easily.

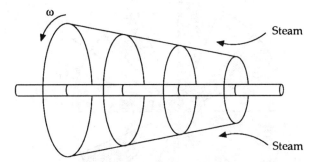

Turbine blades can be thought of as thin discs arranged along a shaft in the shape of a frustrum of a cone. The radius r of each disc is related to its distance x from the base. The basic arrangement fits within the dimensions (in metres) shown.

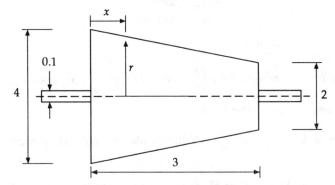

Write down an equation for the radius r in terms of distance x.

Using this equation find the area of each of 7 thin discs mounted at equal intervals on the 10cm shaft.

Develop a relationship for area in terms of distance x.

At what distance x will a disc have an area of 5 m^2

Produce a graph of area A.

Estimate the gradient (rate of change of area with distance) of the graph when $x = 1.3$.

Explain the meaning of the result.

Differentiate the function for area A and calculate a more accurate value for this rate of change when $x = 1.3$

? help information

Information Bank Section 2   Unit 6 Straight line graphs *page 125*
Unit 12 Quadratic curves *page 156*
Unit 13 Differentiation 1 *page 164*

Task 2 *Rotation*

A simplified turbine disc has radius *r* and blades as shown (they need to be twisted to produce rotation).The leading edge of a blade makes an angle of rotation θ (rads) with the horizontal centre line and is related to time *t* by the relationship;

$$\theta = 1.2t^2 + 500t$$

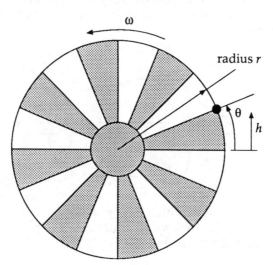

Turbine Blade Disc

How long will it take to rotate once?

Find an expression for angular velocity $\omega \left(\dfrac{d\theta}{dt} \text{ in rads/second} \right)$ of the shaft after time *t*.

Calculate the angular velocity ω after 10 seconds.

Determine the angular acceleration $\left(\dfrac{d\omega}{dt} \right)$. What would prevent a shaft continuing to accelerate at a constant rate?

The height *h* of a point at the tip of the blade can be related to the angle θ. Find this relationship and rate of change $\left(\dfrac{dh}{dt} \right)$ for a radius $r = 2$ metres.

Information Bank Section 2   Unit 12 Quadratic curves *page 156*
Unit 21 Differential 2 *page 207*

Task 3 *Shaft support*

To minimise vibration and loss of energy the turbine block needs to be held rigid, ideally it should be supported at its centre of gravity.

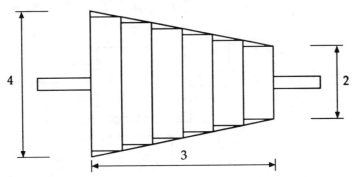

Assume that the blades approximate to solid discs of equal width and there are no gaps.

Find the centre of gravity if;

1. There are 5 blades
2. There are 10 blades
3. There are an infinite number of blades (the shape becomes a frustrum of a cone).

 Information Bank Section 2   Unit 9 Volumes and surface areas *page 140*
Unit 22 Integration 2 *page 214*
Unit 25 Centroids 5 *page 229*

☐Extension task

Repeat task 3 with different cone dimensions.

Repeat task 3 with dimensions replaced by letters as shown.

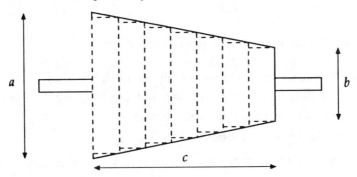

From these results what observations can you make?

Project E *Generators*

Task 1 *Production of an alternating current*

The energy from a rotating turbine shaft is converted into an electrical output when coils on an armature rotate within a magnetic field. The voltage that is induced in the coil depends on the magnetic field strength and the angular velocity ω (rads/s) of the shaft.

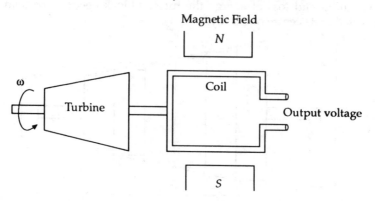

Because the voltage relates to the angle of rotation an alternating waveform is produced. The output voltage from a small generator is shown;

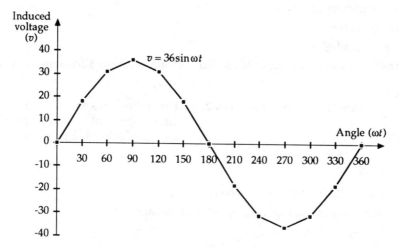

For a frequency of 20 Hz, at what time is the peak value reached?

Investigate how this waveform is affected when changes are made to the input. Draw the resulting curves and write down the corresponding equations.

1. When cutting the magnetic field a maximum induced voltage of 72 V is produced.

2. If the angular velocity ω of the input shaft is doubled.

3. If the angular velocity ω of the input shaft is halved.

Another voltage is induced which is $\pi/6$ rads out of phase with the first, and consequently has a curve as shown.

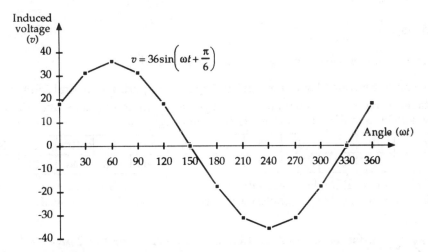

Find the resulting waveform if these voltages are added together, and also find the equation that represents the sum of these curves.

Again with a frequency of 20 Hz, find the times at which the maximum and minimum values are reached. What are these voltages.

Information Bank Section 2   Unit 20 Trigonometry 2 *page 199*
                                  Unit 19 Maximum and minimum *page 196*

Task 2 *R.M.S values*

For the waveform of task 1 determine the r.m.s value of the voltage.

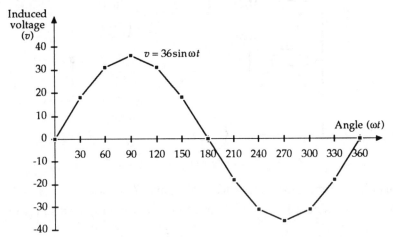

Why is it that the average (or mean) voltage produced over a full cycle is not usually very useful. Determine the mean for half a cycle and compare the value with the r.m.s.

Using: $v = V \sin \omega t$

(where V represents the maximum voltage), develop a general expression for the r.m.s value of a sinusoidal waveform. Hence, calculate the r.m.s value for the other equations from task 1.

1.   With a peak voltage of 72 V.

2.   With $\omega_2 = 2\omega$

3.   With $\omega_3 = \dfrac{\omega}{2}$

4.   For the combined waveform $v = 36\sin \omega t + 36\sin\left(\omega t + \dfrac{\pi}{6}\right)$

Some waveforms generated have an irregular shape and require a numerical solution.

Use the table of recorded instantaneous voltages to estimate the r.m.s over the period. The frequency is 20 Hz and time measurements are in milliseconds.

t (ms)	0	5	10	15	20	25	30	35	40	45	50
v	0	9	29	34	12	2	−8	−26	−40	−10	0

Which of the numerical methods available is likely to give the best approximation to the area under this particular curve? How could the accuracy of this result be improved?

Information Bank Section 2   Unit 22 Integration 2 *page 214*

Unit 23 Numerical Methods *page 222*

Task 3 *Using alternating current*

When an alternating voltage is supplied to circuit an alternating current will flow. This current may be out of phase with the voltage. The extent of this depends on the components in the circuit and how they are connected.

The circuit shown has a supply voltage of 40v a.c with frequency of 50 Hz. The resistances of each part of the circuit are shown in ohms (Ω), whilst inductance and capacitance have their own units.

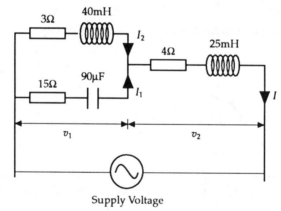

Supply Voltage

Calculate the inductive and capacitive reactances X_L and X_C in ohms.

Determine the total impedance Z for the circuit. Note that for components in parallel

$$\frac{1}{Z} = \frac{1}{Z_1} + \frac{1}{Z_2}$$

Find the current I and also the two values of current I_1 and I_2 in the parallel section.

What is the real power that is drawn by the circuit?

Information Bank Section 2   Unit 15 Complex Numbers *page 171*

Electrical resistance and the physical support of overhead cables are considered, along with the principles of a transformer. A statistical report is required on safety. Projects focus on;

Project F	Cables	Skill Areas Used:	Formulae
			Solving Equations Graphically
			Volumes and Surface Area
			Quadratic Curves
			Differentiation 1
			Series
			Vectors
			Numerical Methods

Project G	Transformers	Skill Areas Used:	Formulae
			Straight Line graphs
			Logarithms
			Solving Equations Graphically
			Exponential Relationships
			Complex Numbers
			Differentiation 2

Project H	Safety	Skill Areas Used:	Statistics

Each project is introduced with a brief explanation of how components work. Specific details are given about the application, these are required throughout the project.

Project F *Cables*

Task 1 *Support*

An overhead cable is supported over level ground between pylons of height 12 metres.

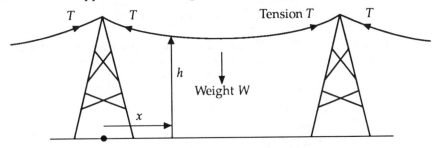

The height of the cable above the ground is given by the equation;

$$h = \frac{x^2}{600} - \frac{x}{6} + 12$$

What is the distance between the pylons? How tall would the second pylon have to be if it were 120 metres away?

Estimate the length of the cable by assuming it is in the shape of 5 straight lengths with gradients found by differentiation and using x values from the centre of each interval.

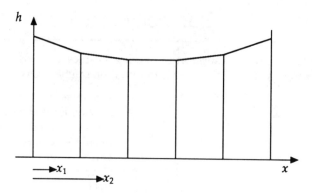

Determine a more accurate result by considering 9 intervals.

If cables are to be made from copper of diameter 1.8 cm use your best estimate for length to calculate the weight of the cable between these pylons. Find the value of tension T in this copper cable.

Information Bank Section 2	Unit 18 Vectors *pages 187*
	Unit 12 Quadratic curves *page 156*
	Unit 13 Differentiation 1 *page 164*
	Unit 23 Numerical methods *page 222*

Task 2 *Material*

Electrical current I is to be carried along a cable of length $L = 1$ km.

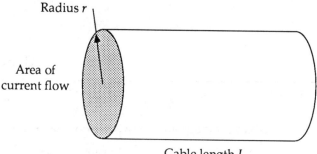

Cable length L

For a radius of 0.5 cm, find the resistance of each cable for materials given in the table.

	Resistance (Ω)
Silver	
Mild steel	
Copper	
Aluminium	

Draw a graph showing the resistance of cables with radii from 0 to 2 cm.

What radii are required for cables made from each material to have a resistance of 0.2 Ω?

Determine the weight of the cables. Comment on the practical implications of using each material.

Calculate the power required for the series of currents to be carried along a 0.2 Ω cable.

What type of series is given.

Current I	20	60	180	540	1620
Power					

Why is it useful to step down voltages, through transformers, before distribution along cables.

Information Bank Section 2   Unit 2 Formulae *page 96*
Unit 9 Volumes & Surface area *page 140*
Unit 8 Solving equations graphically *page 132*
Unit 16 Series *page 180*

☐**Extension task**

Using your own sensible pylon heights and distances, find a quadratic relationship that represents the height h if the minimum height is 60% of the pylon height.

Suggest a suitable material for overhead cables. Estimate the cable length and weight.

What is the resistance if 2 cm diameter cable is used? What current will flow if power of 50 kw is drawn?

Project G Transformers

Task 1 *Linked coils*

A transformer is produced by linking the magnetic flux of an a.c supplied coil with another coil. In this way a voltage is induced in the secondary circuit. The voltage is said to be stepped down (reduced) if the resulting voltage is less than that in the primary circuit.

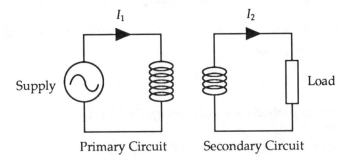

Primary Circuit   Secondary Circuit

The induced voltage is determined by the ratio of the number of turns in coils N in the circuits. We have a relationship for voltage E and current I;

$$\frac{E_1}{E_2} = \frac{N_1}{N_2} = \frac{I_2}{I_1}$$

Find the number of turns required in the secondary circuit if the voltage is to be stepped down by 25% and there are 30 turns in the primary circuit. Draw a graph to show how this transformer can be used to achieve a range of output voltages. Also show the relationship between I_1 and I_2.

A transformer is 85% efficient (some power is lost from input to output) and has coils with turns in the ratio 5:1 (input:output). What supply voltage is required so that a current of 25 amps flows at the load?

Information Bank Section 2   Unit 2 Formulae *page 96*
Unit 6 Straight line graphs *page 125*

Task 2 *Coils*

A coil of inductance $L = 0.02$ H and resistance $R = 2\ \Omega$ is connected to an a.c supply with frequency $f = 40$ Hz.

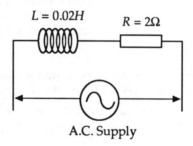

$L = 0.02H$ $R = 2\Omega$

A.C. Supply

Find the impedance Z of the circuit. If a voltage of $70/35°$ is supplied what current will flow and determine the phase angle.

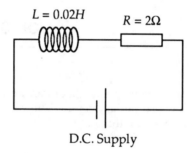

$L = 0.02H$ $R = 2\Omega$

D.C. Supply

If the same coil is connected to a d.c supply it will take time before a steady current flows.

The relationship is given by the equation;

$$I = \frac{E}{R}(1 - e^{\frac{-Rt}{L}})$$

Draw a graph of this relationship if the supply voltage E is 70 volts. Estimate the time t when the current reaches 9 amps.

Obtain a more accurate value for the time by solving the equation.

Use differentiation to find the time at which the rate of change of current ($\frac{dI}{dt}$) is 90% of the rate when $t = 0$.

Information Bank Section 2   Unit 7 Logarithms *page 128*
Unit 8 Solving equations graphically *page 132*
Unit 10 Exponential relationships *page 148*
Unit 15 Complex numbers *page 171*
Unit 21 Differentiation 2 *page 207*

☐Extension Task

If the resistance of a cable is 2 Ω find the saving in power that can be made by stepping the voltage down with a transformer before transmission. Investigate a realistic range of step down voltages.

Project H *Safety*

Task 1 *Accidents*

Industrial accidents need to be investigated so that risks can be minimised and safety precautions can be taken where necessary.

Types of Accident

A company has set aside £5000 to carry out surveys into the causes of injury. If this is to be spent in proportion to the types of injury received, how much should be spent on a head injury survey.

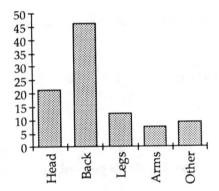

Chart showing the kind of injuries received as percentages

How could the presentation of this data have been improved.

Annual Variations

The incidence of head injuries on industrial sites from national statistics is as shown;

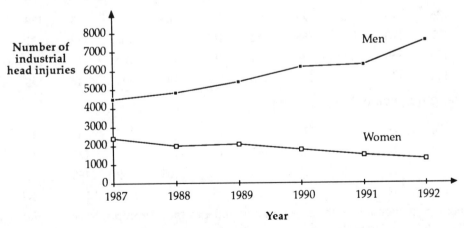

Chart showing the number of industrial head injuries

Use this chart to produce a combined line graph showing the total number of industrial head injuries over the six year period.

When was there a change in the pattern of results and what could have caused this?

Which year saw the greatest increase in head injuries?

What is the average (mean) percentage increase in the number of injuries per year? Using this figure what is likely to be the total number of head injuries in 1993?

Significance of Results

The pie chart shows the proportion of men and women working outdoors and indoors:

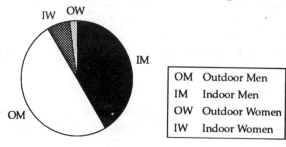

OM	Outdoor Men
IM	Indoor Men
OW	Outdoor Women
IW	Indoor Women

From this reflect on the previous results for the numbers of head injuries. Where is the problem most significant.

Information Bank Section 2   Unit 4 Statistics *page 104*

Task 2 *Helmet sizes*

In order that safety helmets may be provided, a detailed study needs to be carried out into head sizes of employees.

A sample of 40 men was selected at random and measurements of head length were taken.

Similarly, 40 women were sampled and the same system of measuring was used. The data collected is given as it was recorded.

Head lengths (men)

125	125	123	129	96	112	108	117	133	138
177	173	171	186	182	167	165	168	139	131
153	156	158	154	151	157	155	165	147	134
144	144	145	144	146	146	149	141	142	135

Head lengths (women)

154	125	123	125	126	128	123	135	132	132
144	144	145	142	143	143	146	147	139	133
113	116	156	158	125	177	169	139	138	134
112	116	101	106	153	157	166	132	137	134

Complete frequency tables for these results and produce appropriate charts and diagrams. Comment on the dispersion.

Obtain estimates for the mean and standard deviation for each set of data and make comparisons.

Draw cumulative frequency curves and again discuss the dispersion.

Helmets are available in 5 sizes suitable for head lengths as shown;

Size	A	B	C	D	E
Range	100 - 120	120 - 140	140 - 160	160 - 180	180 - 200

From the samples determine the number of people that would wear each helmet size.

Use these results together with national statistics from task 1 to provide the required sizes of helmets for a representative workforce (in proportion to national figures). For a workforce of 1000 people how many helmets of each size should be purchased for employees working outdoors.

Information Bank Section 2   Unit 4 Statistics *page 104*

☐Extension task

Find out from national statistics the number of days work lost due to injury or illness. Comment on methods of data display used.

Collect data from a small sample about their heights and complete the frequency table.

Height (ft and inches)	Frequency
4' - 4'6"	
4'6" - 5'	
5' - 5'6"	
5'6" - 6'	
6' - 6'6"	
6'6" - 7'	

Produce appropriate diagrams and calculate averages and measures of dispersion. What conclusions can be drawn from the results.

Projects here involve manufacturing components in different ways and an analysis of the processes. Modern methods of control and manipulation are also looked at.

Projects focus on;

Project I	Metal Forming	Skill Areas Used:	Trigonometry 1 Straight Line Graphs Logarithms Volumes and Surface Area Exponential Relationships Differentiation 1
Project J	Metal Cutting	Skill Areas Used:	Radians Volumes and Surface Area Integration 1 Vectors
Project K	Strength of Materials	Skill Areas Used:	Vectors Integration 2 Centroids Second Moments of Area
Project L	Computer Control	Skill Areas Used:	Calculators and Computers
Project M	Robotics	Skill Areas Used:	Trigonometry 1 Vectors

Each project is introduced with a brief explanation of how components work. Specific details are given about the application, these are required throughout the project.

Project I *Metal forming*

Task 1 *Forming*

A chess set is to be made using solid gold and silver pieces. The volume of metal needs to be calculated very precisely, and methods of forming shapes have to be considered. The shape of each piece has the design shown, but dimensions may be varied to save metal or to simplify the forming process.

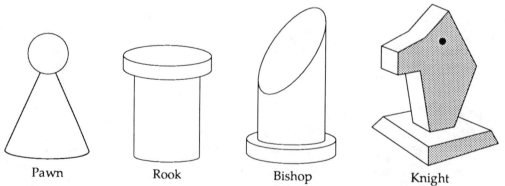

Pawn   Rook   Bishop   Knight

Pawn Design

The pawn design must use the specifications given, where values are in centimetres.

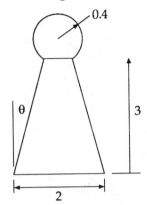

With these dimensions what range of angles θ are possible. Calculate the maximum and minimum volume of material required. Suggest a suitable angle and with this find the weight of each pawn made in gold and silver.

Rook Design

If the rook is to be 3 mm taller than the pawn, use the ratios given to calculate dimensions.

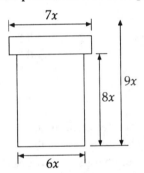

Determine the volume and hence the weight of these pieces made in each metal.

Bishop Design

The bishop dimensions are again in centimetres and the weight of this piece is to be twice that of a pawn.

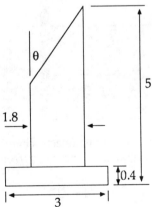

Calculate the angle θ.

Knight Design

The knights are to be made from gold and silver plate of thickness 6 mm. Dimensions are all given in millimetres.

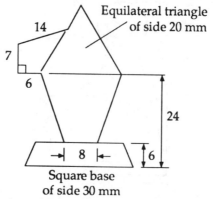

Equilateral triangle
of side 20 mm

Square base
of side 30 mm

Calculate the weight of each completed knight. What is the smallest rectangular plate area that could accommodate one knight. What rectangular area is required to make 4 knights.

The kings and queens for this exclusive chess set are to be designed as an extension task.

Without these four pieces how much will the entire set weigh?

Information Bank Section 2   Unit 9 Volumes and surface areas *page 140*
Unit 5 Trigonometry 1 *page 199*

Task 2 *Electro-plating*

A cheaper version of the same chess set designed in task 1 is also to be manufactured. The pieces are to be gold and silver plated rather than solid metal.

A system for electro-plating consists of charged electrodes (the silver or gold and the piece to be plated) immersed in a solution (electrolyte) which conducts electricity.

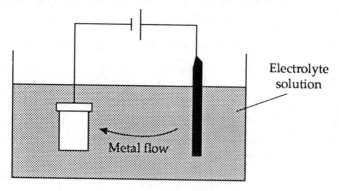

Electrolyte
solution

Metal flow

The rate of metal flow depends on a constant z (electrochemical equivalent) for the properties of the materials involved in the process, and the electric current *I*. The relationship for the mass *m* transferred in time *t* is given by;

$$M = ZIT$$

A system, with a constant flow of current I, deposits the mass m of metal shown in the table in time t. Develop an equation for mass m in each case.

Metal	Mass m (kg)	Time t (seconds)
Silver	1.5×10^{-3}	1360
Silver	4×10^{-3}	3640
Gold	1.5×10^{-3}	750
Gold	4×10^{-3}	2000

For each chess piece from task 1 calculate the surface area. Hence the mass (weight) of each metal that is required to plate the pieces to a thickness of 20×10^{-6} metres.

How long will the plating process take for the individual pieces with this electroplating system.

In another chess set electroplated rooks of each colour are plated, in both cases, with a mass of 1.2×10^{-3} kg of the precious metals. The thickness of the silver plating is 1.7×10^{-6} metres. Calculate the height of the rooks and the thickness of the gold. The dimensions are in the ratios as before.

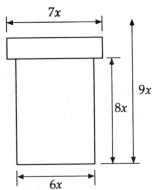

Information Bank Section 2

Unit 9 Areas and volumes *page 140*
Unit 6 Straight line graphs *page 125*
Unit 12 Quadratic curves *page 156*

Task 3 *Cooling*

Metal forming usually involves heating material so that it softens and flows easily into the shapes required. Here, the cooling of components after heating is investigated.

The rate of cooling depends on the temperature difference between the environment (usually air or water) and the component being cooled. As cooling progresses this temperature difference reduces indicating that the relationship follows an exponential decay.

The temperature difference T between a chess piece and the surrounding air was monitored as it was cooled after forming. The results are shown;

Time t (secs)	0	200	400	600	800	1000	1200
Temp T (°C)	500	335	224	150	100	60	45

Use this data to plot a cooling curve and form an equation relating the temperature T to time t if the equation is of the form;

$$T = Ae^{-bt}$$

(where A and b are constant values)

What is the rate of cooling after 8 minutes?

The same chess piece was cooled in water, the resulting cooling curve is shown below.

Form an equation as before, and use it to calculate the time that it takes to cool the component to 60°C with a water temperature of 22°C.

Develop an equation for the rate of change of temperature, and find the time when the cooling rate is –5°C per second.

Why is water a better medium in which to cool components?

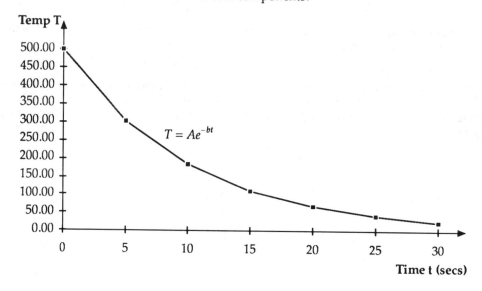

$T = Ae^{-bt}$

 Information Bank Section 2   Unit 10 Exponential relationships *page 148*
Unit 7 Logarithms *page 128*
Unit 13 Differentiation 1 *page 164*

☐ **Extension task**

Design king and queen pieces in a similar style to the rest of the set. Include all the dimensions.

Calculate both the volume and surface area of these pieces. Hence, determine the volume of gold and silver required for the solid and the budget sets.

Suggest possible methods of production.

Project J *Metal cutting*

Task 1 *Turning*

Removing material from cylindrical shapes, such as on a lathe, is a process by which the rook from a chess set could be produced.

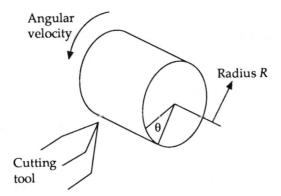

The rook is rotated an angle θ and a firmly held cutting tool is moved to a depth s to cut away the radius R of the component. The tool may also traverse the end of the component.

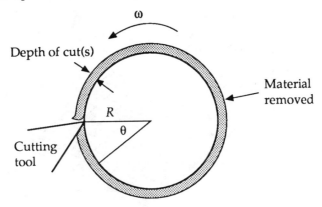

To produce these pieces a machine is set up to cut away material from a cylinder with radius $R = 1.5$ cm and height $h = 4.2$ cm. From these shapes the depth of cut s that is required is given in the diagram. Dimensions are in centimetres.

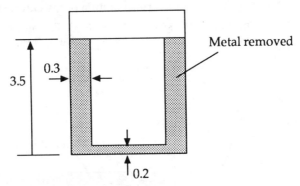

Calculate the volume of metal that has to be removed.

Reducing the radius by 0.3 cm

If the component is rotated at 15π rads/sec, what is the linear cutting velocity (the speed of the metal as it meets the tool) initially and at the final radius. What increase in the angular velocity is required in order that this cutting velocity is the same at the final radius.

If the angular acceleration is constant (angular velocity increases steadily) from 15π rads/sec up to the required value at a depth of 0.3 cm, calculate the angle θ that the rook will rotate if the process takes 3 minutes.

277

Traversing

Again with an angular velocity of 15π rads/sec, what will be the minimum cutting speed. What can be done to give a smooth cut across the end of the component.

Information Bank Section 2   Unit 9 Areas and Volumes *page 140*
                                    Unit 3 Radians *page 102*
                                    Unit 14 Integration 1 *page 168*

Task 2 *Planing*

A flat surface such as a quality metal chessboard may be planed by a rotating cutting tool moving along its length.

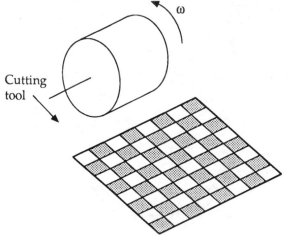

The linear velocity of the cut is more complicated here, since the velocity V of the advancing tool is in the same direction as a component of the velocity due to rotation. (See diagram).

Develop equations for both the horizontal and vertical motion of the cutting tool point.

A tool with radius $R = 9$ cm and cut depth $s = 0.8$ cm is used. For an angular velocity of 10π rads/s and an advance velocity of 2×10^{-2} m/s, determine both the initial cutting speed and as the tool leaves the material.

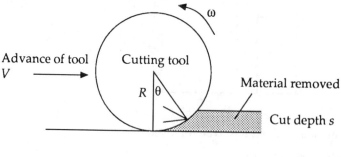

Information Bank Section 2   Unit 3 Radians *page 102*
                                    Unit 18 Vectors *page 187*

Project K *Strength of materials*

Task 1 *Structures*

Maintenance is required to a boiler which has been installed adjacent to a substantial wall. In order to gain access to the boiler the lid has to be lifted and held in position during servicing. A convenient lifting point has to be found on the lid.

An overhead structure needs to be designed to allow this procedure to be performed easily.

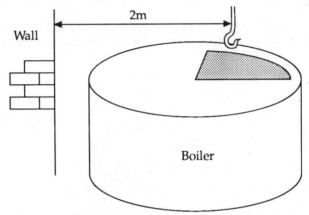

The boiler lid is made from steel plate with thickness 8 cm and is in the shape of a sector of a circle with radius 0.4 metres and angle 58°. Determine the position of a lifting point so that it will hang horizontally.

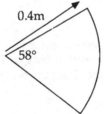

Whilst maintenance is carried out inside the boiler, the lid has to be suspended by a line which hangs 2 metres from a supporting wall.

A simple structure is to be considered as a solution to this problem. An arrangement from which the lid can be hung is to use two struts as shown, firmly anchored to the wall.

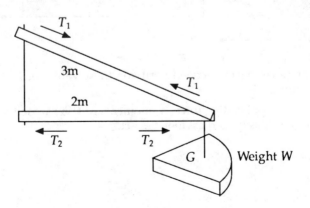

Calculate the forces T_1 and T_2 so that the system is in equilibrium. Hence determine the minimum cross sectional area that is necessary for each of the struts. The maximum permissible stress in the material is 300 MN/m² (formulae for stress are given in the formula sheet).

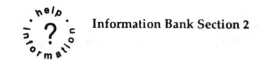

Information Bank Section 2   Unit 25 Centroids *page 229*
Unit 18 Vectors *page 187*

Task 2 *Cantilever*

As an alternative to using a structure to suspend the lid from task 1 a number of types of cantilever beams could be employed. Again they are to be firmly anchored to the wall, which is where the maximum stress will apply.

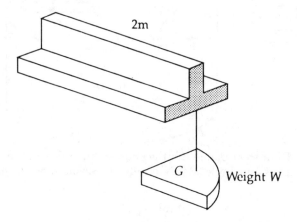

The shape of the cross section is an important factor when calculating the bending strength of a beam. Two readily available cross sections that may be used are shown. Determine the second moments of area I_{XX} and I_{YY} for each shape about the centroid.

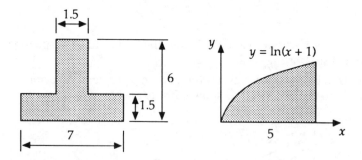

The stresses in the cantilever beams depend partly on these values of I. However, there are of cause other considerations.

When a beam is subjected to a bending force W, moments M (Wx) are felt at any point along the length. At what distance x does the largest moment act.

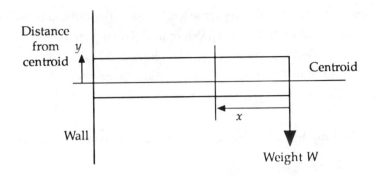

Use an appropriate formula (reference section) to determine the maximum stress that is experienced in a beam if the most suitable cross section is used.

 Information Bank Section 2   Unit 22 Integration 2 *page 214*
Unit 26 Second Moments of Area *page 239*

☐Extension task

Design a structure that could be used to support the lid of the boiler if the stress is to be limited to 300MN/m².

Calculate the maximum bending stress that would be experienced in a cross section of your own creation. Does it exceed 300MN/m².

Project L *Computer control*

Task 1 *Controlling a cutting tool*

A cutting tool is controlled by a series of switches which may be in one of two positions, on or off. Each switch relates to an aspect of the tool motion as indicated;

Switch	ON	OFF
1	Forwards	Backwards
2	(Forwards of Backwards) Fast	(Forwards of Backwards) Slow
3	Right	Left
4	(Right or Left) Fast	(Right or Left) Slow
5	Up	Down
6	(Up or Down) Fast	(Up or Down) Slow
7	Clockwise	Anticlockwise
8	(Clock or Anti) Fast	(Clock or Anti) Slow

Describe the motion of the cutting tool if the sitches are in the position shown (ON is indicated by 1 and OFF by 0).

Switch	1	2	3	4	5	6	7	8
Position	1	0	0	1	1	0	1	0

If this is binary what is its value in denary (base ten)? What is the value in octal and in hex.

Write down the binary number that would produce the following motion:

Fast, Forward	Slow to the Left
Slow Downward	Fast, Clockwise

Again convert the value into denary, octal and hex.

 Information Bank Section 2   Unit 1 Calculators and computers *page 91*

☐ **Extension task**

Design a system of switches that could control the flight of an aircraft. Show how a binary number would represent a particular type of motion.

Project M *Robotics*

Task 1 *Assembly*

Increasingly robots are used to carry out manufacturing tasks such as the assembly of devices. This involves the positioning of components, and precise instructions are required. Movements of a controlled arm have to be examined.

A robot arm moves a bolt from position *A* to position *B* as shown. A nut is then collected from position *C* and assembled with the bolt.

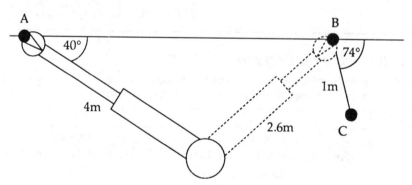

The extension of the arm is 4 m to pick up the bolt and 2.6 m to place it down. If the arm makes an angle of 40° with the direction of movement on pick up, find the distance *AB*.

Position *C* is 1 m from B at an angle of 74° to the line of *AB*. Calculate the angle of rotation and the extension required to pick up the nut.

What is the distance and angle of rotation from position *C* to position *A*.

 Information Bank Section 2   Unit 5 Trigonometry 1 *page 116*

Task 2 *Intelligent robots*

Robots and their control are constantly being improved and becoming more and more sophisticated, nevertheless they can only ever be as good as their instructions. It is therefore necessary to understand the three dimensional environment that they work in.

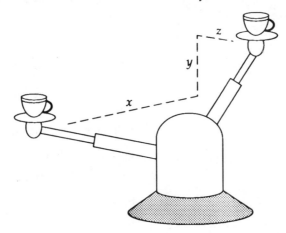

With increasing demands being placed on technology a computer controlled robot, such as the housemaid type shown, needs to think a bit more than simply x, y and z movements. There may be objects obstructing the x, y, z route, or sugar may need to be collected on the way. It is obvious to us that there is a more direct route.

Calculate and describe with angles and distances the most direct route in each of the journeys given in (x, y, z) form.

a)　(4, 6, 2)

b)　(3, 4.5, 1) followed by (0, –5, 2) and describe the direct journey back to the original position.

A 1.5 metre robot arm turns through 63° in the x, z (horizontal) plane while extending 0.4 metres and then 38° upwards in the y, z plane (vertical) whilst withdrawing the arm by 0.6 metres. Calculate the most direct route.

Information Bank Section 2　　Unit 5 Trigonometry 1 *page 116*
Unit 18 Vectors *page 187*

□Extension task

Consider a household task (eg making tea in a particular kitchen). Using some reference x, y and z axes, such as along a worktop, and obtain measurements in each direction.

Detail all the instructions to complete the task and determine the most efficient way to carry it out, with polar coordinates.

Give them to your robot.

■ Areas and Volumes

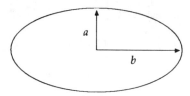

Elipse

Area = πab

Perimeter = $\pi(a + b)$

Sector

Sector Area = $\frac{\theta}{2}r^2$

Arc Length = $r\theta$

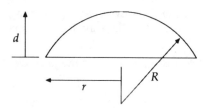

Prism

Volume = Base Area × Length

Pyramid and Cone

Volume = $\frac{1}{3}$ Base Area × Length

Sphere

Volume = $\frac{4}{3}\pi r^3$

Surface Area = $4\pi r^2$

Dome

Volume = $\frac{\pi d^2}{3}(3R - d)$

Surface Area = $2\pi Rd + \pi r^2$

■ Statistics

Mean

$$\bar{x} = \frac{\text{Sum of Values}}{\text{Number of Values}}$$

Standard Deviation

$$\sigma = \frac{\text{Sum of (Deviations)}^2}{\text{Number of Values}}$$

■ Algebra

Quadratic Formula

for an equation: $ax^2 + bx + c = 0$

$$x = \frac{-b \pm \sqrt{b^2 - 4ac}}{2a}$$

■ Series

Arithmetic Progression

General term = $a + (n - 1)d$

$$S_n = na + \frac{n(n - 1)}{2}d$$

Geometric Progression

General term = ar^{n-1}

Sum of n terms = $\frac{a(1 - r^n)}{1 - r}$

Binomial Theorem

$$(a + b)^n = a^n + na^n + na^{n-1}b + \frac{n(n - 1)}{2!}a^{n-2}b^2 + \ldots\ldots b^n$$

■ Trigonometry

Sine Rule

$$\frac{a}{\sin A} = \frac{b}{\sin B} = \frac{c}{\sin C}$$

Cosine Rule

$$a^2 = b^2 + c^2 - 2bc \cos A$$

Pythagoras Theorem

$$a^2 = b^2 + c^2$$

Trigonometrical Ratios

$$\sin x = \frac{\text{opposite}}{\text{hypotenuse}} \qquad \cos x = \frac{\text{adjacent}}{\text{hypotenuse}}$$

$$\tan x = \frac{\text{opposite}}{\text{adjacent}}$$

Trigonometrical Relationships

$$\tan x = \frac{\sin x}{\cos x}$$

$$\sin^2 x + \cos^2 x = 1$$

Compound Angle Formulae

$$\sin (A + B) = \sin A \cos B + \sin B \sin A$$

$$\sin (A - B) = \sin A \cos B - \sin B \sin A$$

$$\cos (A + B) = \cos A \cos B + \sin B \sin A$$

$$\cos (A - B) = \cos A \cos B - \sin B \sin A$$

$$\tan (A + B) = \frac{\tan A + \tan B}{1 - \tan A \tan B}$$

Double Angle Formulae

$$\sin 2A = 2 \sin A \cos A$$

$$\cos 2A = \cos^2 A - \sin^2 A$$

Sum and Difference of Angles

$$\sin (A + B) + \sin (A - B) = 2 \sin A \cos B$$

$$\sin (A + B) - \sin (A - B) = 2 \sin B \cos A$$

$$\cos (A + B) + \cos (A - B) = 2 \cos A \cos B$$

$$\cos (A + B) - \cos (A - B) = -2 \sin B \sin A$$

■ Numerical Methods

Mid-ordinate Rule

Area = Sum of mid-ordinates of strips × Strip width

Trapezium Rule

$$\text{Area} = \text{Strip width} \times \left(\tfrac{1}{2} (\text{First ordinate} + \text{last ordinate}) + \text{Sum of other ordiates} \right)$$

Simpson's Rule

$$\text{Area} = \tfrac{1}{3} \times \text{Strip width} \times \left(\text{First} + \text{Last} + 4(\text{Sum of odd ordinates}) + 2(\text{Sum of other even ordinates}) \right)$$

■ Differentiation

Function	Derivative
$y = ax^n$	$\frac{dy}{dx} = nax^{n-1}$
$y = \sin x$	$\frac{dy}{dx} = \cos x$
$y = \cos x$	$\frac{dy}{dx} = -\sin x$
$y = \tan x$	$\frac{dy}{dx} = \sec^2 x$
$y = \ln x$	$\frac{dy}{dx} = \frac{1}{x}$
$y = e^x$	$\frac{dy}{dx} = e^x$
$y = uv$	$\frac{dy}{dx} = u \frac{dv}{dx} + v \frac{du}{dx}$
$y = \frac{u}{v}$	$\frac{dy}{dx} = \frac{v \frac{du}{dx} - u \frac{dv}{dx}}{v^2}$

Product Rule

If $y = uv$ where u and v are functions of x then

$$\frac{dy}{dx} = v \frac{du}{dx} + u \frac{dv}{dx}$$

Quotient Rule

If $y = \frac{u}{v}$ where u and v are functions of x then

$$\frac{dy}{dx} = \frac{1}{v^2} \left(v \frac{du}{dx} - u \frac{dv}{dx} \right)$$

■ Integration

Function	Integral
$y = ax^n$	$\dfrac{ax^{n+1}}{n+1}$
$y = \sin x$	$-\cos x$
$y = \cos x$	$\sin x$
$y = \tan x$	$\ln \sec x$
$y = e^x$	e^x

Integrating by Parts

For a product $u\dfrac{dv}{dx}$

$$\int u\frac{dv}{dx}dx = uv - \int v\frac{du}{dx}dx$$

■ Complex Numbers

For complex numbers in polar form

a/θ and b/α

Multiplication

$a/\theta \times b/\alpha = ab/\theta + \alpha$

Division

$$\frac{a/\theta}{b/\alpha} = \frac{a}{b}/\theta - \alpha$$

■ Mechanics

Centre of Gravity

$\bar{x}$ (Total Area) $= x_1 A_1 + x_2 A_x + x_3 A_3 + \ldots\ldots$

Second Moments of Area

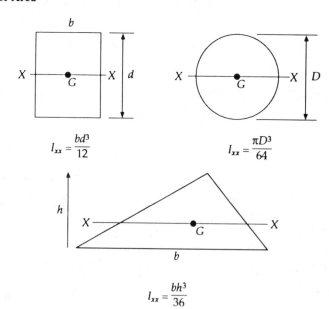

$$I_{xx} = \frac{bd^3}{12}$$

$$I_{xx} = \frac{\pi D^3}{64}$$

$$I_{xx} = \frac{bh^3}{36}$$

Parallel Axis Theorem

$I_{\text{axis}} = I_{xx} + Ah^2$

■ Vectors

Scalar Product

$a.b = |a|\,|b|\cos\theta$

Vector Product

$|a x b| = |a|\,|b|\sin\theta$

■ Polar Second Moments of Area

Circular shaft

$$J = \frac{\pi r^4}{2}$$

Moments of Inertia

Solid cylinder $\qquad\qquad I = \dfrac{MR^2}{2}$

$$I = \int mr^2\, dr$$

■ Stress

$$\text{Stress } \sigma = \frac{\text{Force}}{\text{Area}}$$

$$\frac{\sigma}{y} = \frac{M}{I}$$

■ Electrical

$V = IR$

$\text{Power} = IV = I^2 R$

$$\text{Resistance } R = \frac{\rho L}{A}$$

■ Circular Motion

$$\text{Centripetal Acceleration} = \frac{v^2}{r}$$

Appendix 2 *Data tables*

Conversion Table

Unit	Alternative
1 litre	1000 cm³
1 gallon	4.546 litres
1 mile	1609 metres
1 lb	0.4536 kg
360°	2π rads

Liquids

Liquid	Density
Water	1000
Olive oil	915

Fuel Table

Fuel	Calorific value MJ/kg
Petrol	46
Alcohol	29
Fuel oil	45
Kerosine	48
Coal	30

Physical Constants

Material	Density kg/m³	Thermal conductivity W/m	Electrical resistivity $10^{-6}\,\Omega m$
Gold	19300	300	0.023
Silver	10500	420	0.016
Mild Steel	7800	50	0.18
Cast Iron	7300	60	0.105
Copper	8930	390	0.0172
Lead	11300	35	0.21
Aluminium	2700	220	0.027

Atmospheric Pressure $P = 101.3$ kN/m²

Radiation

Radioactive material	Half life
Uranium	4.51×10^9 years
Radium	1620 years
Polonium	3 minutes
Thorium	24.1 days
Radon	3.82 days

Project A *Bodyshape*

Task 1   STEP 1 $X = 4a - 0.577\,a^2$
                          $Y = 8b - 0.429\,b^2$
               STEP 2   Graph
               STEP 3   Graph
               STEP 4 $a = 0.68 \quad b = 0.32$

Task 2.1   STEP 1   Graph
               STEP 2 $F = \dfrac{4}{3}h - \dfrac{16}{3}$
               STEP 3 $F = 155 \quad h = 37.8$

Task 2.2   STEP 1 $28°$
               STEP 2 $90°$ beyond this angle air
                          will flow below the vehicle
               STEP 3   Graph
               STEP 4   Quadratic curve
               STEP 5 $55°$

Task 2.3   STEP 1 $28°$ flow distance 17 cm
               STEP 2   17.1, 17.9, 18.7, 19.6, 20.6,
                          21.6, 23
               STEP 3   Graph
               STEP 4 $63°$

Task 3.1   STEP 1   6.26
               STEP 2 $V = 6h - h^2 - 0.107$
               STEP 3   Graph
               STEP 4 $h = 1.16$

Task 3.2   STEP 1   Volume $= 3.88$
               STEP 2   2.18, 2.57, 2.93, 3.26, 3.54,
                          3.78, 3.95, 4.02
               STEP 3   Graph
               STEP 4 $14.4°$

Task 3.3   STEP 1   3.72
               STEP 2   More intervals would
                          improve the accuracy

Project B *Fuel System*

Task 1.1   STEP 1 $t + s = 11$
                          $32t + 53s = 400$
               STEP 2 $t = 8.71 \quad s = 2.29$
               STEP 3   town 279 \quad steady 121
               STEP 4   Graph
               STEP 5 $t = 4.4 \quad s = 13.6$
               STEP 6   The range of the sports car is
                          short for town driving.

Task 1.2   STEP 1 $V = 15\,l\,w$, $V = 15\,\pi\,r^2$,
                          $V = 7.5\,cb\,\sin 60°$,
                          $V = 600h - \dfrac{5}{4}h^2$
               STEP 2 $V = 50000$ cm^3
               STEP 3 $l = \dfrac{3{,}330}{w}$, $b = \dfrac{7{,}700}{c}$
               STEP 4   Graphs
               STEP 5   Simplify Graphs

Task 1.3   STEP 1 $V = \dfrac{\pi}{3}\left(132 - 10R + 19R^2 - R^3\right)$
               STEP 2   Graph
               STEP 3 $R = 3.5$ cm

Task 1.4   STEP 1 $(1.38 \times 10^9)\,t$, $(2.3 \times 10^8)\,t^2$
               STEP 2   Graph
               STEP 3 $t = 0$ and $t = 6$
               STEP 4 $(1.45 \times 10^8)\,t^2$

               STEP 5 $t = 9.5$

Task 2.1   STEP 1   Graph
               STEP 2 $T = 13 \cos\theta$
               STEP 3 $0°, 180°, 360°$
               STEP 4 $52°, 308°, 232°, 128°$
               STEP 5   63 Nm
               STEP 6   More than 24 conductors

Task 2.2   STEP 1   5
               STEP 2   75, 250, 375, 500, 625
               STEP 3   108
               STEP 4   Graph
               STEP 5   85.2
               STEP 6 $417 - 720$

Task 2.3   STEP 1   Graph
               STEP 2   Volume $= 133 \times$ Capacity
               STEP 3   Volume 267000, 667000,
                          1600000 Capacity 398000
               STEP 4 $l = 242, b = 149, b = 841,$
                          $l = b = h = 117$
               STEP 5 $l = 4330$
               STEP 6   In order to achieve a
                          reasonable range a
                          physically large battery is
                          required.

Project C *Brakes*

Task 1.1   STEP 1   147
               STEP 2   0.714 rads
Task 1.2   STEP 1   Graph
               STEP 2   Graph
Task 1.3   STEP 1   a) 73.3   b) 71.5

               STEP 2 $V = \dfrac{w\theta}{2}\left(2Rt - t^2\right)$

Task 2.1   STEP 1 $A = \dfrac{\theta}{2}\left(17^2 - r^2\right)$
               STEP 2   0.571

STEP 3 11.7
STEP 4 Graph
STEP 5 Graph

Task 2.2 STEP 1 $A_1 = \dfrac{\pi}{12}(16^2 - r^2)$

    STEP 2 $A_2 = \dfrac{\pi}{12}(16^2 - (r-1)^2)$

    STEP 3 $r = 10.05$
    STEP 4 45.06
    STEP 5 3.33
    STEP 6 0.074 cm

Task 3.1 STEP 1 Bar charts. The MODE gives the most popular size

Task 3.2 STEP 1 & 2 Frequency table

STEP 3 Graph
STEP 4 Drums have a longer average braking distance and are less consistent.
STEP 5 Wet and heat have more effect on drum brakes. Road conditions.

Task 3.3 STEP 1 Frequency table
    STEP 2 Drum 134, Disc 127
    STEP 3 Drum 29.1, Disc 21.2
    STEP 4 Similar tendencies are indicated
    STEP 5 Comments

Project D *Cooling System*

Task 1.1 STEP 1 3690
    STEP 2 $A = 120 - 7\pi r^2$
    STEP 3 $1200 - 70\pi r^2 + 588\pi r = 4000$
    STEP 4 $r = 1.99$
    STEP 5 $r = 1.22$
    STEP 6 Larger tubes
    STEP 7 Smaller tubes

Task 1.2 STEP 1 $120h + 14.1d = 1000$
    STEP 2 $20 - h = d$
    STEP 3 $h = 6.79, \; d = 13.21$
    STEP 4 1.11 litres

Task 1.3 STEP 1&2 $240f - 4.021ft + 211.1t = 4000$

    STEP 3 $f = \dfrac{4000 - 211.1t}{240 - 4.021t}$

    STEP 4 Graph
    STEP 5 $(t = 1, f = 16)$, (4, 14), (7, 12), (8, 11), (18, 1)

Task 2.1 STEP 1 300
    STEP 2 66.31
    STEP 3 0.663

Task 2.2 STEP 1 $F = 0.04t$
    STEP 2 Graph
    STEP 3 $A = 0.2\,t^2$
    STEP 4 $0.02\,t^2 = 2.4$
    STEP 5 $t = 10.95$

Task 2.3 STEP 1 Before 66.31, After 26.46

    STEP 2 $V = \dfrac{3}{\pi r^2}$

    STEP 3 Graph
    STEP 4 Graph

Task 2.4 STEP 1 $v = \dfrac{F}{\pi r^2}$

    STEP 2 Graph
    STEP 3 Graph

STEP 4 $F = 371$

Task 2.5 STEP 1 $\dfrac{1}{-24}\begin{pmatrix} 3 & -6 \\ -5 & 2 \end{pmatrix}$

    STEP 2 $F = T^{-1}\,V$
    STEP 3 $F_1 = 0.2, \; F_2 = 1.22$ litres/sec

Task 2.6 STEP 1 $F_1 = 0.45, \; F_2 = 0.8$
    STEP 2 Velocities before 177 and 314, after 41.9 and 74.4
    STEP 3 Table
    STEP 4 Graph

Task 3.1 STEP 1 $A = \dfrac{\dfrac{dQ}{dt}L}{k(T_2 - T_1)}$

    STEP 2 Table
    STEP 3 Table
    STEP 4 Suitable Value

Task 3.2 STEP 1 Table
    STEP 2 Table
    STEP 3 Graph
    STEP 4 Table

Task 3.3 STEP 1 Graph
    STEP 2 −0.5 and −0.4
    STEP 3 Graph
    STEP 4 10 m
    STEP 5 8.85 secs

Task 3.4 STEP 1 $\dfrac{dT}{dx} = 44e^{-0.8x}$

    STEP 2 6.45
    STEP 3 $T = 70 - 55e^{-0.453t}$

    STEP 4 $\dfrac{dT}{dt} = 24.9e^{-0.453t}$

    STEP 5 2.589

Project E *Gearbox*

Task 1.1 STEP 1 $\dfrac{2}{3}\pi$

STEP 2 $\beta_1 = \dfrac{a_1}{3}$

STEP 3 $\beta_2 = \pi$

STEP 4 $\beta_2 = \dfrac{a_1}{2}$

STEP 5 $\dfrac{\alpha_1}{3} + \dfrac{\alpha_2}{2} = 25$

STEP 6 $\alpha_1 = 39, \quad \alpha_2 = 24$

Task 1.2   STEP 1 $\alpha_1 + \alpha_2 = 77$

$\dfrac{\alpha_1}{3} + \dfrac{\alpha_2}{2} = 32$

STEP 2 $\begin{pmatrix} \frac{1}{3} & \frac{1}{2} \\ 1 & 1 \end{pmatrix} \begin{pmatrix} \alpha_1 \\ \alpha_2 \end{pmatrix} = \begin{pmatrix} 12 \\ 11 \end{pmatrix}$

STEP 3   Solve

STEP 4   39, 38

Task 1.3   STEP 1 $w = 2t$

STEP 2   157

STEP 3 $\alpha = t^2 + C$

STEP 4 $C = 0$

STEP 5   3900

STEP 6   Graph

STEP 7   79

Task 1.4   STEP 1 $w = 1.5t + 314$

STEP 2   7.3

STEP 3 $\alpha = \dfrac{1.5t^2}{2} + 314t + C$

STEP 4 $C = 0$

STEP 5   370

STEP 6   Graph

STEP 7   19.1

Task 1.5   STEP 1 $\dfrac{d\alpha}{dt} = 1.4t + 2000\pi$

STEP 2   Graph

STEP 3   Graph

STEP 4 $33.3\,\pi$

Task 2.1   STEP 1 5.76×10^8

STEP 2   Graph

STEP 3   Graph

STEP 4   Graph

STEP 5   Graph

STEP 6   Graph

Task 2.2   STEP 1 2.88×10^8

STEP 2   Graph

STEP 3   Graph

STEP 4   Graph

STEP 5   Graph

Task 2.3   STEP 1 $\dfrac{dw}{dn} = \dfrac{w_1}{400} e^{\frac{n}{400}}, \ \dfrac{dw}{dn} = \dfrac{w_1}{300} e^{\frac{n}{300}},$

$\dfrac{dw}{dn} = \dfrac{w_1}{200} e^{\frac{n}{200}}$

STEP 2   0.0011, 0.0025, 0.0100

STEP 3   628 million, 513 million, 350 million

Task 3.1   STEP 1   Sketch

STEP 2   Drawing

STEP 3 $AB = 11$, $BG = 9.5$, $AG = 8.9$

STEP 4 $AB = 12$, $BG = 13.7$, $AG = 9$

STEP 5 $BG = \sqrt{225 - 216\cos BAG}$

STEP 6   Graph

STEP 7 $BG = 14$

STEP 8   Not possible

Task 3.2   STEP 1   Sketch

STEP 2 $A = 54 \sin \theta$

STEP 3 $\dfrac{dA}{d\theta} = 54 \cos \theta, \ \theta = 90°$

STEP 4   2700

Project F *Cylinder design*

Task 1.1   STEP 1   254.5

STEP 2   4.475

STEP 3 $h = 4.5 \sin \theta$

STEP 4   Graph

STEP 5   1.768

STEP 6   Graph

Task 1.2   STEP 1   157

STEP 2 $\theta = 50\,\pi t$

STEP 3 $h = 4.5 \sin 50\,\pi t$

STEP 4   5 m/s

STEP 5   785

STEP 6 -1.17

Task 1.3   STEP 1   157 and 209

STEP 2   5.81

STEP 3 $w = 157 + 5.81\,t$

STEP 4 $h = 0.045 \sin (157 + 5.81t)\,t$

STEP 5

   $0.045\,(1.57 + 11.6t)\cos(1.57 + 5.81t)\,t$

STEP 6 -3.5

STEP 7 dv/dt

STEP 8 $t = 2$

Task 2.1   STEP 1   Points

STEP 2   Graph

STEP 3 $h = 250/\pi r^2$

$S.A = 2\pi r\,(250/\pi r^2 + r)$

STEP 4 $-500r^2 + 4\pi r$

STEP 5 $r = 3.41$ min $S.A = 220$

Task 2.2   STEP 1   Volume

STEP 2 $S.A = 2x^2 + 1000/x$,

$750/0.433x + 0.866x^2$

STEP 3   6.3, 10

STEP 4   min

STEP 5   6.3, 5.77

STEP 6   Circular section

Task 3.1   STEP 1   Graph

STEP 2 $t = 0.0167$ and 0.05

STEP 3   10

STEP 4   212.4

STEP 5   441 kJ

Task 3.2   STEP 1   Graph

STEP 2 $T = \sqrt{3}\sin(\theta + 30)$

STEP 3   3

Project G *Electrics*

Task 1.1 STEP 1 Graph

STEP 2 $i = 3e^{-0.00334t}$

STEP 3 689 minutes

STEP 4 $\dfrac{di}{dt} = -0.0033e^{-0.00334t}$

STEP 5 -0.0052

STEP 6 275 minutes

Task 1.2 STEP 1 Use a greater initial current I_{max}. A larger value for the constant a (resistance etc)

STEP 2 $i = 5e^{-0.00334t}$

STEP 3 844 minutes

STEP 4 427 minutes

STEP 5 $i = 4e^{-\frac{t}{200}}$

STEP 6 2.2

Task 2.1 STEP 1 Graph

STEP 2 981.8

STEP 3 17.7

STEP 4 981.75

STEP 5 17.7

STEP 6 0.005%

STEP 7 0.2%

Task 2.2 STEP 1 Graph

STEP 2 66.8 leading, 38.7 lagging

STEP 3 $1.22 + j\,0.98$

STEP 4 800 w

Task 2.3 STEP 1 $23 - j\,9$

STEP 2 $321\ \angle 14°$

Task 2.4 STEP 1 $25.6\ \angle -38.7°,\ 7.6\ \angle 66.8°$

STEP 2 $7.8\ \angle 50°$

STEP 3 $101\ \angle 85°$

STEP 4 $13\ \angle 18.2°$

Task 2.5 STEP 1 Graph

STEP 2 Plotting

STEP 3 $v_1 + v_2 = 35.5\sin(\theta + 18.9)$

STEP 4 Computer

Project H *Suspension*

Task 1.1 STEP 1 Angles: 17.0, 19.5, 23.6, 17.9
Link lengths:
  0.20, 0.24, 0.31, 0.21

STEP 2 Arm: 10.0, 11.6, 14.0, 10.7
Link: 2.9, 4.0, 6.3, 3.3

STEP 3 Sketch

STEP 4 0.74 m

Task 1.2 STEP 1 0.077, 0.143, 0.105

STEP 2 0.92, 1.72, 1.26

STEP 3 0.2

Task 1.3 $I_G = 99cm^4,\ \ I_G = 98cm^4$

Task 2.1 STEP 1 G.P.

STEP 2 $\dfrac{a}{4} = ar^{n-1}$

STEP 3 14.2, 7.21, 3.71

STEP 4 43, 28, 15

Task 2.2 STEP 1 $f = \dfrac{\pi}{4}(25 - d^2)v$

STEP 2 4.1

STEP 3 Graph

STEP 4 0.22

STEP 5 $f = \dfrac{\pi}{4}(25 - d^2)(11 - 2.2d)$

STEP 6 $0 - 5$

STEP 7 Area

Project I *Windows*

Task 1.1 STEP 1 Sketch

STEP 2 Areas

STEPS 3, 4, 5 $x = 245$

Task 1.2 $x = 233$

Task 1.3 $x = 253$

Task 1.4 $x = 145$

Project J *Transmission*

Task 1.1 STEP 1 127

STEP 2 325 max

STEP 3 $J = 325$

STEP 4 $I_{ZZ} = 133$

Task 1.2 STEP 1 7.52 kg

STEP 2 6.15 kg

STEP 3 9.08 kg

Task 1.3 STEP 1 5.4, 5.5

STEP 2 7.23

Task 2.1 STEP 1 50πrads

STEP 2 64.5

STEP 3 10.4π

Task 2.2 STEP 1 Sketch

STEP 2 $1.5i$

STEP 3 $1.5i,\ 1.2j,\ -3i$

STEP 4 Opposite direction

Task 3.1 STEP 1 $h = 0.3 \sin 52.36t$

STEP 2 $\dfrac{dh}{dt} = \dfrac{0.3}{52.36} \cos 52.36t$

STEP 3 $v = 5 + 0.0057 \cos 52.36t$

STEP 4 Graph

STEP 5 9425 m

STEP 6 7.85

STEP 7 $h = 0.15$, height $= 0.11$

Task 3.2 STEP 1 Label shapes

STEP 2 41 kgm²

STEP 3 77.5 kgm²

Task 3.3 STEP 1 $\dfrac{1}{W} dW = 0.1 dL$

STEP 2 $W = Ae^{0.1L}$

STEP 3 $W = 270.7 e^{0.1L}$

STEP 4 18.9 cm

STEP 5 18°

Project K *Performance testing*

Task 1.1 STEP 1 Graph

STEP 2 $v = 4t$, $v = 60$,
$$v = \dfrac{2}{30}t^2 - \dfrac{20}{3}t + \dfrac{500}{3}$$

STEP 3 $7.5 + 5 + 10$

STEP 4 $4, 0, \dfrac{4}{30}t - \dfrac{20}{3}$ (mph/min)

STEP 5 35

Task 1.2 STEP 1 $\dfrac{dv}{3} - kv = dt$

STEP 2 $0.03v = 3 - Ce^{-0.03t}$

STEP 3 $0.03v = 3 - 2.7e^{-0.03t}$

STEP 4 6 hours 5 minutes

Task 1.3 STEP 1 $v = 4t + C$,
$v = 6\ln(t + 3) - 4\ln(t + 2) + C$

STEP 2 $s = 4t^2 + Ct + k$,
$s = 6(t + 3)(\ln(t + 3) - 1)$
$-4(t + 2)(\ln(t + 2) - 1) + Ct + K$

STEP 3 $s = 4t^2 + 0, s = 400, C = -3.82$,
$K = -4.23, s = 8.36$

STEP 4 Check

Task 2.1 STEP 1 $\dfrac{v^2}{r} = 0.3g$

STEP 2 7.75 m/s

STEP 3 mass (m) cancels out

STEP 4 Banked track

Task 2.2 STEP 1 Sketch

STEP 2 $R\sin\theta + 0.3R\cos\theta = \dfrac{mv^2}{20}$

STEP 3 9.61 m/s

STEP 4 $v = \sqrt{200(\cos\theta\sin\theta + 0.3\cos^2\theta)}$

STEP 5 Sketch

Task 2.3 STEP 1 $a = 2$, base $= 5$

STEP 2 $x = 2.57$

STEP 3 1.653, 1.692

STEP 4 1.024

Task 3.1 STEP 1 3500, 6062

STEP 2 $F = 1500$

STEP 3 0.25

STEP 4 $a = 4.6$ m/s²

STEP 5 $\theta = 42.2°$

Task 3.2 STEP 1 603400, 1408000

STEP 2 heat and lifting

STEP 3 14°

STEP 4 2.84

STEP 5 47.8

Task 3.3 STEP 1 $h = 125\sin\left(ks - \dfrac{\pi}{2}\right) + 125$

STEP 2 $\dfrac{dh}{ds} = 125k\cos\left(ks - \dfrac{\pi}{2}\right)$

STEP 3 $k = 0.0031$

STEP 4 $0.3875\cos\left(0.0031s + \dfrac{\pi}{2}\right)$

STEP 5 3370

STEP 6 1013

STEP 7 negative second derivative

Index

The entries in this index refer to those pages in the Section 2 Information Bank where a particular topic is explained. If you wish to find the project or task in Sections 1 or 3 that deals with a particular topic, you can use the Project/Skills tables on pages vi and 250.